Topics in
Topology

Topics in
Topology

Arlo W. Schurle

University of North Carolina at Charlotte

North Holland • New York
New York • Oxford

Elsevier North Holland, Inc.
52 Vanderbilt Avenue, New York, NY 10017

Distributors outside the United States and Canada:
Thomond Books
(A Division of Elsevier/North-Holland Scientific Publishers, Ltd.)
P.O. Box 85
Limerick, Ireland

Library of Congress Cataloging in Publication Data

Schurle, Arlo W
    Topics in topology.

    Bibliography: p.
    Includes index.
    1. Topology. I. Title.
QA611.S326   514   78-9959
ISBN 0-444-00285-5

To Dixie

Contents

Preface   ix

Acknowledgments   xi

Chapter 1 Basic Concepts of Topology: Intuitively   1

Chapter 2 Basic Concepts of Topology: Rigorously   7

2.1. Spaces and Their Basic Structure,
    Part A 7
    Part B *14*

2.2. New Spaces from Old, I: Subspaces and
Product Spaces, Part A *16*
      Part B *22*

2.3. Sequences, Part A *26*
      Part B *29*

2.4. Continuity and Homeomorphisms,
    Part A *32*
    Part B *39*

2.5. Connected Spaces, Part A *41*
      Part B *48*

2.6. Countability Properties, Part A *53*
      Part B *58*

2.7. Compact Spaces, Part A *60*
      Part B *68*

Contents

Chapter 3   More Concepts in Topology   72

3.1. Complete Metric Spaces   72
3.2. Separation Properties   78
3.3. Construction of Continuous Functions and
     Metrics   85
3.4. New Spaces from Old, II: Compactification
     and Completion   91
3.5. New Spaces from Old, III: Quotients and
     Arbitrary Products   97
3.6. An Adequate Theory of Convergence   109

Chapter 4   Examples and Pathologies   116

4.1. Cantor Sets   116
4.2. Peano Spaces   122
4.3. Embeddings   129
4.4. The Continuous Real-Valued Functions
     on [0,1]   141

Chapter 5   Winding Numbers and Their Applications   148

5.1. Definition of Winding Number and the
     Fundamental Theorem   148
5.2. Retracts and Fixed Points   153
5.3. Vector Fields   156
5.4. The Borsuk–Ulam Theorem and the Ham
     Sandwich Theorem   159
5.5. Kakutani's Theorem   164

Chapter 6   Topics in Combinatorial Topology   169

6.1. Simplicial Complexes   170
6.2. Graphs   175
6.3. Surfaces   192

Chapter 7   The Fundamental Group   223

7.1. The Homotopy Relation   224
7.2. The Fundamental Group   230
7.3. Covering Spaces and $\pi_1(S^1 x_0)$ 240

Appendix   248

A.1. Basic Set Theory   248
A.2. Euclidean Spaces   254

Epilogue   257

Bibliography   259

Index   261

Preface

Since an author's aims and his achievements may differ and since a reader may or may not agree with an author's claims for his book, it may be best to begin by stating what this book is *not* intended to do. It is not a reference book on topology, nor is it complete or detailed enough for a full-fledged thorough-going graduate course in the subject. It does not pretend to bring the reader to the forefront in any area of research. It does not attempt the impossible task of introducing the reader to all the topics in mathematics which involve topology. In fact, it fails to mention some which have topological ideas at their very core.

This book *is* intended to be a versatile introduction to that broad area of mathematics called topology. It is designed to be suitable for courses involving either students with little mathematical background other than calculus or students at the beginning graduate level who have little or no background in topology. It touches on several of the most important areas of topology and hopefully presents enough intriguing results and examples to interest the beginner in further study. Finally, it tries to help the reader understand why definitions, theorems, and proofs are the way they are by providing some motivation and strengthening the reader's intuition concerning topological ideas.

The core of the book consists of Chapters 2 and 3, which cover the basic topics in the foundations of topology. Chapter 2 has a somewhat unusual organization, in that each section comes in two parts. Part A is always restricted to the metric case, while Part B deals with the general topological case or introduces topics that are important but not as basic as those in Part A. The purpose is twofold. First, this serves to alert the reader to the differences and similarities between metric spaces and topological spaces. Second, one can construct a course by using just Parts A and then choosing further topics from the rest of the book. With the exception of the material on complete metric spaces, Chapter 3 has all of Chapter 2 as a prerequisite. These two chapters form a solid introduction to general topology.

Parts A of Chapter 2 contain all the material necessary to read and understand the remainder of the book. Chapter 4 provides several interesting examples and applications of metric-space topology. Chapter 5 does the same in a more algebraic vein and also touches on certain geometric and differential aspects of the subject. Chapter 6 can be read with little or no background from Chapter 2 but does require some study of Chapter 1. Finally, Chapter 7 requires only a little familiarity with metric-space topology but would be enhanced by knowledge of elementary group theory.

Chapter 1 provides a short preview of topology from two points of view. One is that topology is the distillation and generalization of those concepts from calculus and analysis that depend on a kind of nearness relation. From this point of view topology consists of the axiomatic development of a branch of mathematics which is worthwhile in itself and which also lies at the base of many other areas of mathematical activity. The other point of view is the popular one of topology being "rubber-sheet geometry." Many results and problems of geometric topology can be studied very profitably from this standpoint and it is the author's belief that an early introduction to it goes far toward providing motivation for the rigorous development which follows.

For a number of years the author has taught a one-semester course covering Chapter 1, Chapter 6, Parts A of Chapter 2, Chapter 5, and selections from the rest of the text in this order. The students have ranged from not very well-prepared undergraduates to secondary school teachers working on advanced degrees. It has been a very successful undertaking according to both the professor and the students. A course for better prepared students might consist of the entire Chapters 2 and 3 plus selections from the other chapters governed by the taste of the participants.

Little need be said about the book's organization. Results are numbered consecutively within each section of each chapter, so that Lemma 2.5.7 immediately follows Theorem 2.5.6 in Section 5 of Chapter 2. The end of a proof is always marked by a ■. Exercises are of course crucial to understanding, and there is an ample supply at the end of each section or part of a section. Some provide work on the concepts introduced, others expand the ideas further, and a few are even referred to later in the book. The reader is urged to read them all and do as many as he can.

Acknowledgments

A book is never written single-handedly. My thanks go first to Kenneth Bowman and all those people with Elsevier North Holland who have been associated with this project. Numerous colleagues have unwittingly served my purpose by answering miscellaneous questions and queries. In particular, Tom McMillan made a number of comments and suggestions which have been incorporated into the finished product. I am eternally grateful to Theda Williamson, Brenda Rehn, and Kim Gordon who did a superb job of translating sometimes almost indecipherable handwriting into an easily readable manuscript.

There are other people whose contributions lie deeper. Lee Sonneborn not only first helped me learn calculus but also introduced me to topology. His influence permeates both this book and my mathematical career. Charles Himmelberg led me further into the thickets of topology and made it the center of my mathematical activity.

Finally and most importantly, I thank my family and especially Dixie for being incredibly patient with both my stubborn insistence that I write this book and my obliviousness to almost everything else during the publishing process.

1

Basic concepts of topology: intuitively

If a mathematician is forced to subdivide mathematics into several subject areas, then topology/geometry will be one of them. Part of the purpose of this chapter is to discuss some of the characteristics that distinguish topology from algebra and analysis. We will also talk about a nonrigorous approach to topology which helps make some of the mathematical ideas easier to understand.

Any calculus student has been exposed to continuous functions and knows that the idea of continuity plays a fundamental role in that subject. Underlying even the idea of continuity are the notions of limit and limit point, which involve the idea of a nearness relation. Calculus students may even recognize the term closed set, which is just a set containing all its limit points. They will certainly be familiar with the idea of an open interval, which in terms of nearness is just a set which, when it contains a point x, also contains all points sufficiently near x.

Topology is exactly that area of mathematics which takes the concepts of nearness, limit, limit point, and continuity, gives them their most general meaningful rigorous definitions, and studies the consequences. Succinctly put, topology may be said to be the study of nearness. Topological concepts lie at the foundation of calculus and that branch of mathematics to which it leads, namely analysis. In fact, topology plays a role in all areas of mathematics, which only points out that the subdivision of mathematics asked for earlier is very artificial, even though sometimes useful.

Chapters 2 and 3 contain the rigorous definitions of nearness and begin to investigate the consequences of these definitions. The reader is reminded that the long history of the development of these ideas has been omitted and that just the finished product is being presented. However, he should always remember that the ideas of continuity and limits presented here are exactly the most fruitful generalizations of the ideas of continuity and limits presented in his calculus book and that the metric spaces and topological spaces, which he will meet, are just the proper settings for a study of these ideas. The branch of topology dealt with in Chapters 2 and 3 is sometimes called *general* or *point set topology*.

The reader will also become familiar with another branch of the subject called *geometric topology*. The ideas of nearness and continuity are still the foundation of geometric topology, but the study shifts toward consideration of more geometric objects, such as spheres and balls. Much of the work can be done in the plane or three-dimensional space, though as usual mathematicians try to find the most general useful setting for the subject.

One cannot really study geometric topology without a solid grounding in general topology, but we can provide the reader with a good idea of the concerns of a geometric topologist. The objects studied by a geometric topologist are properly defined in Chapter 2, but for this intuitive introduction we need only say that they include planes, triangles, disks, line segments, points, etc. We practice the same kind of idealization that is usually carried on in secondary school geometry, namely, a line is not a mark on the paper, but has no width and is represented rather well by such a mark.

What properties of such objects does a geometric topologist study? He certainly doesn't care whether object X is red or blue or if it is upside down or right side up. Another way to put this is that if object X and object Y differ only in that X is red and Y is blue, then a geometric topologist regards X and Y as equivalent objects. The question thus reduces to determining when two objects are equivalent. A topologist regards two objects as being *topologically equivalent* or *homeomorphic* if one can be made to coincide with the other by means of a motion that may include stretching, twisting, pulling, shrinking, bending, etc.—in fact, almost anything *except* cutting or tearing (unless you sew it up again exactly where it was cut or torn) and sewing together. The reader should note that all ingredients of such a motion are continuous and that such a motion takes nearby points to nearby points. Cutting and tearing are proscribed precisely because they lead to a discontinuity.

EXAMPLES.

———

————————————

A B

1. A and B are homeomorphic, since A can be stretched so as to coincide with B.

2. X can be bent so as to coincide with Y, so that X and Y are homeomorphic.

3. It seems intuitively clear that we would have to cut U in order to make it coincide with V, so that U and V are not homeomorphic. We will prove this rigorously later.

4. In this example we show why a topologist cannot distinguish between a doughnut and a coffee cup.

We can mold the "cup" part of the coffee cup into the handle, and we get

which can easily be bent into the shape of a doughnut.

We can now properly define the role of a topologist, especially one with a geometric inclination. He studies those properties of objects which are topological, that is, those properties which when possessed by an object X are also possessed by any object Y topologically equivalent to X. He

3

worries about how to build new objects from old ones and how topological properties behave under such construction projects. He is also interested in determining just when two objects are homeomorphic.

EXAMPLES.

5. Example 1 shows that length is not a topological property, since A and B are homeomorphic but do not have the same length. Note that to show that P is *not* a topological property, it is necessary and sufficient to exhibit a pair of homeomorphic figures A and B such that A has P but B does not.
6. A little study of Example 4 suggests that the property of having a hole like a doughnut is a topological property.

The reader might guess from the examples and exercises that topological properties are hard to find. He is correct only because of the intuitive approach we have taken. In fact, they are abundant but they appear after a rigorous foundation has been laid and often trace their history back to ideas in calculus rather than to the geometric approach which we have just outlined. In order to strengthen the reader's geometric/topological intuition, we investigate a topological property which is both intuitive and very geometric.

It should be clear what "being all in one piece" means with respect to a topological figure. It should also be clear that a topological motion does not disturb this property, since cutting and tearing are specifically excluded from things that such a motion can do. This attribute of "being all in one piece" is one of the most fundamental topological properties and a figure possessing it is said to be *connected*.

EXAMPLES.

7. A line segment is connected.
8. The figure Y is connected.
9. The figure ⋎ is not connected.
10. 0 0 is not connected.

Since connectedness is a topological property, it can be used to prove that certain figures are not homeomorphic. Thus the figure in Example 8 above is not homeomorphic to the figure in Example 9. However, a line segment and a circle are both connected, so this property cannot be used to show that they are not homeomorphic. See the exercises for an extension of the property of connectedness, which can often be used to prove that two connected figures are not homeomorphic.

These somewhat imprecise statements about topology, homeomorphisms, and topological properties should help the reader through the rigor to come. Even this background is enough for him to read and understand the material in Chapter 6. Other geometric questions must wait for the foundation to be built in Chapters 2 and 3.

Exercises

1. Tell whether the following pairs of figures are homeomorphic, and justify your answers.

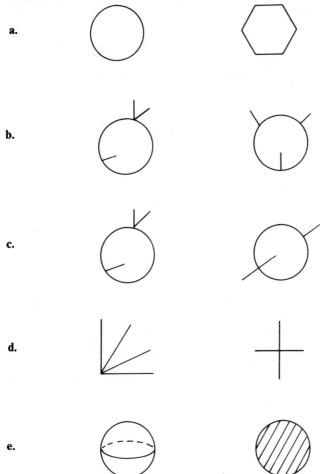

a.

b.

c.

d.

e.

f.

2. Tell whether the following properties are topological properties, and justify your answers.
   a. Area equal to 1
   b. Having an end point like point P of a line segment from P to Q
   c. Containing a right angle
   d. Capable of being drawn on a sheet of paper

3. Write a justification of the fact that for each integer n larger than 1 the following is a topological property of a figure F: F contains a point whose removal causes the remainder of F to fall into exactly n pieces.

4. Use Exercise 3 to prove that the following pairs of figures are not homeomorphic:
   a. A line segment and a circle
   b. The letter X and a line segment
   c. The letter X and the letter Y

   d.    and

2

Basic concepts of topology: rigorously

In this chapter we attack the problem of defining the figures or spaces with which a topologist works, and then investigate how to compare two such objects; that is, we define the concept of topological equivalence. Finally, we examine the most important topological properties.

2.1 The spaces and their basic structure

Part A

Chapter 1 should have provided the reader with a good intuitive understanding of the concepts of topological figure and homeomorphism. We exploit this intuition to arrive at a rigorous development of these ideas.

Our first aim is to see what kind of structure an object must possess in order that topological motions can be defined on it. Since any figure can be regarded as a set of points, we wish to impose some additional structure on a set. The set itself may as well be arbitrary, to allow as much freedom as possible (the reader unfamiliar with sets, functions, and operations on them should consult the Appendix).

The additional structure must be such that it allows us to distinguish between *stretching*, which a topological motion may do, and *tearing*, which a topological motion may not do. Intuition says that an object is *stretched* if points originally close are pulled farther apart, and this is also very close to our intuitive understanding of the *tearing* of an object. It is still not clear how we will distinguish the two ideas, but the idea of distance between points seems to be fundamental to both.

We already have available several examples of sets with a distance. The first one that comes to mind is the set of real numbers, in which the distance between the numbers a and b is $|a - b|$. The reader is probably also familiar with the distance formula for points in the plane, which states that the distance between points (x_1, y_1) and (x_2, y_2) is $[(x_1 - x_2)^2 + (y_1 - y_2)^2]^{\frac{1}{2}}$. It is this concept of distance and its related ideas that we must formalize before we can proceed.

It is not immediately clear just what properties a distance function should have. However, it is clear that distance should be nonnegative, that the distance between a point and itself should be zero, that the distance between distinct points should be positive, and finally that the distance from point x to point y should be the same as that from point y to point x. It is also reasonable that the distance from point x to point z should be no larger than the sum of the distances from x to y and from y to z. The reader should draw a picture in the plane of this last situation to see why this is called the *triangle inequality*.

It is precisely the properties of distance listed above that are the ingredients of the next definition. The question arises as to why these properties are used and not others that may come to mind. The answer is that these properties are restrictive enough to allow a great deal of mathematical theory to be built from them, but at the same time are broad enough that the theory applies in many cases of interest not only to topologists, but also to analysts, applied mathematicians, and even physicists.

Definition   A *metric* on a set X is a function d from $X \times X$ into the real numbers R, which satisfies conditions

1. $d(x, y) \geqslant 0$ for all $x, y \in X$;
2. $d(x, y) = 0$ if and only if $x = y$ for $x, y \in X$;
3. $d(x, y) = d(y, x)$ for all $x, y \in X$;
4. $d(x, z) \leqslant d(x, y) + d(y, z)$ for all $x, y, z \in X$.

A *metric space* is a pair (X, d) where X is a set and d a metric on X.

The intuition here is that the metric is the distance function discussed above, that is, $d(x, y)$ is the distance between x and y. We give a number of examples to show the wide applicability of the definition.

EXAMPLES.

1. Take X to be the real numbers R and $d(x, y) = |x - y|$.

2. Take X to be the plane R^2 and

$$d((x_1,x_2),(y_1,y_2)) = \sqrt{(x_1-y_1)^2+(x_2-y_2)^2}\ .$$

Note here that (x_1,y_1) is a single point in R^2, so that $d((x_1,x_2))$ is meaningless in this case.

3. More generally than 1. or 2., take X to be R^n and

$$d((x_1,x_2,\ldots,x_n),(y_1,y_2,\ldots,y_n))$$
$$=\sqrt{(x_1-y_1)^2+(x_2-y_2)^2+\cdots+(x_n-y_n)^2}\ .$$

Examples 1, 2, and 3 are extremely important since these spaces occur more frequently than any other. The metrics in these examples are called *Euclidean metrics*. More details are given in the Appendix.

4. Take X to be any set and define d by

$$d(x,y) = \begin{cases} 1 & x \neq y \\ 0 & x = y. \end{cases}$$

It is obvious that d satisfies conditions 1–3 of the definition. Condition 4 is clearly satisfied if $x=z$, since then $d(x,z)=0$, and if $x \neq z$, then either $x \neq y$ or $y \neq z$, so it is satisfied in this case as well. This metric is called the *discrete metric* on the set X.

5. Let $B(I)$ be the set of all bounded real-valued functions on the interval $I=\{x \in R : 0 \leq x \leq 1\}$, i.e., all functions $f:I \rightarrow R$ for which there is a constant C_f satisfying $|f(x)| \leq C_f$ for all $x \in I$. Define a function p by $p(f,g)=\text{lub}\{|f(x)-g(x)|:x \in I\}$. Since absolute values are nonnegative, $p(f,g) \geq 0$. If $f=g$ then $|f(x)-g(x)|=0$ for all x in I, so that $p(f,g)=0$, and the converse of this is just as easy. Since $|f(x)-g(x)|=|g(x)-f(x)|$, $p(f,g)=p(g,f)$. Finally,

$$\begin{aligned} |f(x) - h(x)| &= |f(x) - g(x) + g(x) - h(x)| \\ &\leq |f(x) - g(x)| + |g(x) - h(x)| \\ &\leq \text{lub}\{|f(x)-g(x)|:x \in I\} + \text{lub}\{|g(x)-h(x)|:x \in I\} \\ &= p(f,g) + p(g,h) \end{aligned}$$

for all x, so upon taking the least upper bound of the left-hand side we get the triangle inequality $p(f,h) \leq p(f,g)+p(g,h)$. Thus $(B(I),p)$ is a metric space.

The reader should not be dismayed by the abstractness and generality of the definition of metric space. Almost every property of metric spaces is well illustrated by a study of the plane, and almost without exception every proof can be found by considering the planar case. Thus the reader, if somewhat timid, is urged to keep the concrete Example 2 in mind, and should always first *think planar*.

The intuitive ideas of stretching and tearing both involve actions *close to points*, that is, points originally close are moved apart. Thus it should be useful to have a concept dealing with the set of points close to a given point.

Definition Let (X,d) be a metric space and let x be a point of X. For any positive number ε the set $\{y \in X : d(x,y) < \varepsilon\}$ is called a *basic neighborhood* of x. It will be denoted by $N(x,\varepsilon)$. If we are dealing with spaces (X,d) and (Y,d'), then for clarity we may use the notations $N_X(x,\varepsilon)$, $N_d(x,\varepsilon)$, or $N_{(X,d)}(x,\varepsilon)$ to specify precisely the space with which we are dealing.

EXAMPLES.

6. On the real line with the Euclidean metric a basic neighborhood of a point x is an open interval $(x - \varepsilon, x + \varepsilon) = \{y : x - \varepsilon < y < x + \varepsilon\}$.
7. In the plane with the Euclidean metric a basic neighborhood of the point (x_1, x_2) is a circular disk without edge whose center is (x_1, x_2) and whose radius is ε.

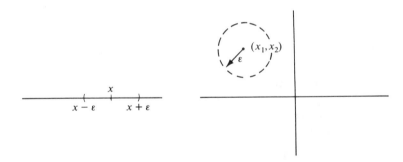

8. In a set X with the discrete metric a basic neighborhood of a point x is either $\{x\}$ (take $\varepsilon < 1$) or X itself (take $\varepsilon = 2$). There is no in between.

In view of the presumed importance of basic neighborhoods in a metric space, it seems reasonable that another important kind of set is one which contains a basic neighborhood of each of its points. If one knows which sets these are in a metric space, then one also knows which sets are their complements, and conversely. We thus have the following.

Definition Let (X,d) be a metric space. A subset O of X is said to be *open* if O contains a basic neighborhood of x whenever $x \in O$. A subset C of X is *closed* if its complement $X \setminus C$ is open.

EXAMPLES.

9. Consider R with the Euclidean metric. We show that $O = \{x \in R : x > 0\}$ is open. Let $x \in O$. Then $x > 0$, so $\varepsilon = x/2$ is positive. If $y > x$, then certainly $y \in O$. If $y < x$ and $|x - y| < \varepsilon$, then $x - y < x/2$, so that $x/2 < y$, and again $y \in O$. Hence there is a basic neighborhood of x contained in O. Since x was an arbitrary point in O, we have shown that O is open. Note that the size of the basic neighborhood of x, i.e., the ε chosen, depends on x. Since O is open, its complement, the set $\{x \in R : x \leqslant 0\}$, is closed.

10. A set may be neither open nor closed. Consider R^2 with the Euclidean metric, and let $M = \{(x_1, x_2) \in R^2 : x_1^2 + x_2^2 < 1 \text{ and } x_2 \geqslant 0\}$.

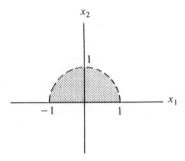

Now $(0,0) \in M$, but if ε is any positive number, $d((0,0), (0, -\varepsilon/2)) = \varepsilon/2 < \varepsilon$ and $(0, -\varepsilon/2) \notin M$. Hence, M contains no basic neighborhood of its point $(0,0)$. However, $(0,1) \in R^2 \backslash M$, but the point $(0, 1 - \varepsilon/2)$ shows that $R^2 \backslash M$ contains no basic neighborhood of $(0,1)$, so that $R^2 \backslash M$ is not open and hence M is not closed. Thus one *cannot* prove that a set is closed by proving that it is not open.

11. A set may be both open and closed. Let X be any set with the discrete metric, and let O be any subset of X. Since $\{x\}$ is a basic neighborhood of x in this case, O is certainly open. Similarly $X \backslash O$ is open, so that O is also closed.

We prove two theorems concerning open sets. They have analogs for closed sets which are obtained by taking complements.

Theorem 2.1.1 *A basic neighborhood is an open set.*

PROOF. Let (X, d) be a metric space, let $x \in X$, and let ε be positive. We must show that $N(x, \varepsilon)$ is open, so let y be in $N(x, \varepsilon)$. We need to find a basic neighborhood of y that is contained in $N(x, \varepsilon)$.

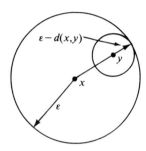

Since $d(x,y)<\varepsilon$, $\varepsilon-d(x,y)$ is positive. Let $d(y,z)$ be less than $\varepsilon-d(x,y)$. Then

$$d(x,z) \leqslant d(x,y) + d(y,z) < d(x,y) + \varepsilon - d(x,y) = \varepsilon.$$

Hence $z \in N(x,\varepsilon)$, and we have found a basic neighborhood of y contained in $N(x,\varepsilon)$. ∎

Our next theorem deals with the collection of open sets as a whole, and is crucial in the further generalization of the concept of space (or figure) that follows. The collection of open sets in a metric space (X,d) is called the *topology of* (X,d).

Theorem 2.1.2 *Let* (X,d) *be a metric space and* $\mathfrak{T}$ *be the collection of subsets of* X *which are open. Then the following statements are true*:

1. $\varnothing \in \mathfrak{T}$ *and* $X \in \mathfrak{T}$;
2. *If* O_1 *and* O_2 *are in* $\mathfrak{T}$, *then so is* $O_1 \cap O_2$;
3. *If* $\mathcal{L}$ *is a collection of sets each of which is in* $\mathfrak{T}$, *then* $\cup\{O:O \in \mathcal{L}\}$ *is a set in* $\mathfrak{T}$.

PROOF. Statement 1 is trivial, since there is nothing to check for $\varnothing$, and every basic neighborhood is a subset of X. For statement 2 we take a point x in $O_1 \cap O_2$. Then there are positive numbers $\varepsilon_1, \varepsilon_2$ such that $N(x,\varepsilon_1) \subset O_1$ and $N(x,\varepsilon_2) \subset O_2$. Clearly $N(x,\min\{\varepsilon_1,\varepsilon_2\}) \subset O_1 \cap O_2$. The proof of statement 3 is left as an exercise. ∎

Theorem 2.1.3 *Let* (X,d) *be a metric space, and let* $\mathcal{C}$ *be the collection of subsets of* X *which are closed. Then the following statements are true*:

1. $\varnothing \in \mathcal{C}$ *and* $X \in \mathcal{C}$;
2. *If* C_1 *and* C_2 *are in* $\mathcal{C}$, *then so is* $C_1 \cup C_2$;
3. *If* $\mathcal{L}$ *is a collection of sets each of which is in* $\mathcal{C}$, *then* $\cap\{C:C \in \mathcal{L}\}$ *is a set in* $\mathcal{C}$.

PROOF.   We leave the proof as an exercise with a nod to DeMorgan.   ∎

There are many other basic notions which can be defined easily by using the fundamental ideas presented so far, but we present only two and urge the reader to consult elsewhere for others.

Definition   Let (X,d) be a metric space, let A be a subset of X, and let x be a point of X. We say that x is a *limit point* of A if each basic neighborhood of x contains a point of A other than x. We then define the *closure* of A to be the set $\mathrm{Cl}(A) = A \cup \{x : x$ is a limit point of $A\}$.

Loosely speaking we can say that x is a limit point of A if there are points of A other than x as near as we like to x. Also, the use of the term "closure" suggests a relationship with closed sets. We will investigate this after some examples.

EXAMPLE.

12. Let $A = \{x \in R : 0 < x \leqslant 1\} \cup \{2\}$, and let R have the Euclidean metric. Since $d(0, \varepsilon/2) = \varepsilon/2 < \varepsilon$, every basic neighborhood of 0 contains a point of A other than 0 (recall that ε is positive), and so 0 is a limit point of A. A similar argument shows that all points between 0 and 1 inclusive are limit points of A. However, no point of A other than 2 lies within $\frac{1}{2}$ of 2, so that 2 is not a limit point of A. Similarly one can show that no point greater than 1 or less than 0 can be a limit point of A. Thus $\mathrm{Cl}(A) = \{x \in R : 0 \leqslant x \leqslant 1\} \cup \{2\}$.

Theorem 2.1.4   *Let (X,d) be a metric space, and let A be a subset of X. Then*

1. *$\mathrm{Cl}(A)$ is a closed set;*
2. *$\mathrm{Cl}(\mathrm{Cl}(A)) = \mathrm{Cl}(A)$;*
3. *$\mathrm{Cl}(A) = \cap \{F : A \subset F \subset X$ and F is closed$\}$.*

PROOF.

1. We must show that $X \setminus \mathrm{Cl}(A)$ is open. Suppose y is a point of $X \setminus \mathrm{Cl}(A)$ which has no basic neighborhood contained in $X \setminus \mathrm{Cl}(A)$. Then each basic neighborhood $N(y, \varepsilon)$ of y contains a point z of $\mathrm{Cl}(A)$. If z is a limit point of A, then since $N(y, \varepsilon)$ is open it contains a basic neighborhood of z, which in turn must contain a point of A. Hence every basic neighborhood of y contains a point of A, necessarily different from y since $y \notin A$. Hence y is a limit point of A, so that y must be in $\mathrm{Cl}(A)$. This contradiction establishes that such a y cannot exist, and hence that $X \setminus \mathrm{Cl}(A)$ is open.

2. Since $\text{Cl}(A)$ is closed according to (1), every point in $X \backslash \text{Cl}(A)$ has a basic neighborhood which misses $\text{Cl}(A)$, so that $\text{Cl}(A)$ has no limit points not already in $\text{Cl}(A)$. Then by definition $\text{Cl}(\text{Cl}(A)) = \text{Cl}(A)$.

3. Since $\text{Cl}(A)$ is closed and contains A, $\text{Cl}(A)$ is one of the F's, and so $\text{Cl}(A) \supset \cap \{F : A \subset F \subset X$ and F is closed$\}$. Conversely, suppose there is a closed set F containing A but not the point y. Since $X \backslash F$ is open, y has a basic neighborhood missing F and hence A, so $y \notin \text{Cl}(A)$. Thus $\cap \{F : A \subset F \subset X$ and F is closed$\} \supset \text{Cl}(A)$.

Exercises

1. Tell whether the following sets are closed and what their closure is (the Euclidean metric is always assumed for R and R^n unless explicitly stated otherwise):
   a. $\{x \in R : 0 < x < 1\}$ as a subset of R
   b. $\{x \in R : x < 0\}$ as a subset of R
   c. $\{x \in R : 0 \leqslant x \leqslant 1\} \cup \{2,3,4,5,\ldots\}$ as a subset of R
   d. $\{1/n : n = 1,2,3,\ldots\}$ as a subset of R
   e. $\{(x_1,x_2) \in R^2 : x_1^2 + x_2^2 < 1\}$ as a subset of R^2
   f. $\{(x_1,x_2) \in R^2 : 0 \leqslant x_1 \leqslant 1, \, 0 \leqslant x_2 \leqslant 1\}$ as a subset of R^2.

2. Justify your answers in Exercise 1.

3. Complete the proof of Theorem 2.1.2.

4. Prove Theorem 2.1.3.

5. Tell what the limit points of the sets in Exercise 1 are.

6. Justify your answers in Exercise 5.

7. Let A be a subset of X, and let d be the discrete metric on X. What are the limit points of A?

8. a. Prove that if d is a metric on a set X, then so is $\rho(x,y) = 3\,d(x,y)$.
   b. Show that the metric spaces (X,d) and (X,ρ) have the same open sets.

9. a. Prove that $\rho((x_1,x_2), (y_1,y_2)) = \max\{|x_1 - y_1|, |x_2 - y_2|\}$ is a metric on R^2.
   b. Draw a picture of a basic neighborhood in the metric space (R^2,ρ).
   c. Show that the metric spaces $(R^2$, Euclidean metric$)$ and (R^2,ρ) have the same open sets.

10. Do Exercise 9 when ρ is replaced by λ, where $\lambda((x_1,x_2), (y_1,y_2)) = |x_1 - y_1| + |x_2 - y_2|$.

Part B

It is possible to generalize the concept of figure even more than is done in Part A of this section. To show how this generalization should proceed, we prove a theorem about limit points.

Theorem 2.1.5 *Let (X,d) be a metric space and A a subset of X. A point x is a limit point of A if and only if each open set containing x also contains a point of A other than x.*

PROOF. Since basic neighborhoods are open sets, the *if* part of this theorem is trivial. To prove the *only if* part, we suppose that x is a limit point of A and that O is an open set containing x. Then O contains a basic neighborhood of x, which in turn contains a point of A other than x, so that O does, too. ∎

Looking back on the concepts defined in Part A, we see that each of them (with the exception of the original ones dealing with metric and metric spaces) can be defined in terms of open sets only. We will see that this also holds true for concepts yet to come, so that our generalization is indeed that. We base it on Theorem 2.1.2.

Definition A *topology* on a set X is a collection $\mathfrak{T}$ of subsets of X which satisfies the following conditions:

1. $\varnothing \in \mathfrak{T}$ and $X \in \mathfrak{T}$;
2. If O_1 and O_2 are in $\mathfrak{T}$, then so is $O_1 \cap O_2$;
3. If $\mathcal{C}$ is a collection of sets each of which is in $\mathfrak{T}$, then $\cup \{O : O \in \mathcal{C}\}$ is also in $\mathfrak{T}$.

The members of $\mathfrak{T}$ are called *open sets*, and their complements in X are called *closed sets*. A *topological space* is a pair $(X, \mathfrak{T})$ where X is a set and $\mathfrak{T}$ is a topology on X.

Theorem 2.1.5 tells us how to define *limit point* in a topological space, and then the definition of *closure* goes over word for word to the topological case. The following definition shows how to replace *basic neighborhood*, and then Theorems 2.1.3 and 2.1.4 have easy proofs in the topological case. We leave them as exercises.

Definition Let $(X, \mathfrak{T})$ be a topological space and let x be a point of X. A *neighborhood* of x is any open set which contains x.

We conclude this section with some examples.

EXAMPLES.

1. Theorem 2.1.2 says that the open sets in a metric space form a topology, so in this way every metric space becomes a topological space. This topology is said to be *induced* by the metric, and the metric is said to be *compatible* with this topology.
2. Consider the set R of real numbers, and let $\mathfrak{T}$ consist of $\varnothing$ together with all sets whose complements are finite.

15

Clearly $\varnothing$ and R are in $\mathcal{T}$. If $O_1 = R \setminus F_1$ and $O_2 = R \setminus F_2$ are in $\mathcal{T}$, where F_1, F_2 are finite sets, then $R \setminus (O_1 \cap O_2) = F_1 \cup F_2$ is finite, so that $O_1 \cap O_2$ is in $\mathcal{T}$. Certainly $O_1 \cap \varnothing$ is in $\mathcal{T}$. Finally, since the complement of a union is the intersection of the complements, any union of sets in $\mathcal{T}$ is also in $\mathcal{T}$. This topology is called the *cofinite* topology.

3. Again consider the set R of real numbers, but this time let $\mathcal{S}$ be the collection of all sets which are unions of half-open intervals of the form $[a,b) = \{x \in R : a \leqslant x < b\}$ together with $\varnothing$. Clearly R and $\varnothing$ are in $\mathcal{S}$. If x is a point of $O_1 \cap O_2$, where O_1, O_2 are in $\mathcal{S}$, then there are numbers a_1, b_1, a_2, b_2 such that $x \in [a_1, b_1) \subset O_1$ and $x \in [a_2, b_2) \subset O_2$. Then $x \in [\max\{a_1, a_2\}, \min\{b_1, b_2\}) \subset O_1 \cap O_2$, so that $O_1 \cap O_2$ is a union of such intervals and hence is in $\mathcal{S}$. Since unions of unions are unions, the union of sets in $\mathcal{S}$ is again a set in $\mathcal{S}$. This topology for R is called the *half-open interval topology*, and R with this topology is called the *Sorgenfrey line*, after the mathematician who first used it.

4. It is easy to verify that for any set X both the set of all subsets of X and $\{\varnothing, X\}$ are topologies on X. The former is called the *discrete topology* and the latter the *indiscrete topology* on X.

Exercises

1. Prove that $\{\varnothing, \{a,b,c\}, \{a\}\}$ is a topology on the set $\{a,b,c\}$.

2. List all possible topologies on the set $\{a,b,c\}$.

3. Give an example of two different metrics on the same set X which induce the same topology.

4. Show that the intersection of two topologies on a set X is again a topology on X. Is this true for unions?

5. Show that the topology of Example 3 is not that induced by the Euclidean metric on R.

6. Show that $\{\varnothing\} \cup \{R\} \cup \{(a, +\infty) : a \in R\}$ is a topology on R, where $(a, +\infty) = \{x \in R : a < x\}$.

7. Redo parts 1(a–d) of Exercise 1 on page 14, but use
   a. The co-finite topology on R
   b. The half-open interval topology on R and
   c. The topology of Exercise 6 on R.

2.2 New spaces from old, I: subspaces and product spaces

Part A

Examples are a basic commodity among mathematicians, who use them both to show the limitations of theorems and to show how widely applicable the theorems are. Without examples mathematics would tend to be lifeless and sterile. In this section we investigate two fundamental ways of constructing new examples, that is, new metric spaces.

The first method can be illustrated by the relationship of the interval $I = \{x \in R : 0 \leqslant x \leqslant 1\}$ to the entire set of real numbers R. We often wish to restrict our attention to only those points in I, for example, in specifying the domain or range of a function. The interval I has a distance structure which is inherited from R, and this is the idea we now make precise.

Definition Let (X, d) be a metric space. A *subspace* of (X, d) is a metric space (Y, d'), where Y is a subset of X and $d'(y_1, y_2) = d(y_1, y_2)$ for y_1, y_2 points of Y.

It is easy to check that d' is actually a metric on Y. Also note that we could express d' as $d \mid Y \times Y$.

EXAMPLES.

1. The above discussion shows that we can regard I as a subspace of R. We often suppress mention of the metric and we often use the same symbol for the metric in both a space and its subspaces.
2. Let $Y = \{(x_1, x_2) \in R^2 : x_1^2 + x_2^2 = 1\}$. By restricting the metric on R^2 to Y we see that the circle is a subspace of R^2. For reasons which will be apparent later, the usual notation for the circle is S^1.
3. Let $Z = \{(x_1, 0) \in R^2 : x_1 \text{ is real}\}$. This subspace is just the real axis in the plane. It is not identical to R, since it consists of ordered pairs and R does not, but we will see that it can be identified with R with no resulting loss.
4. In Section 2.7 we will show that each continuous real-valued function on $I = [0, 1]$ is bounded; thus $C([0, 1]) = \{f : [0, 1] \to R : f \text{ is continuous}\}$ can be regarded as a subspace of the space $B(I)$ of bounded real-valued functions on I.

Subspaces should be thought of as subsets of metric spaces which are regarded as metric spaces in their own right, where the metric is the *inherited* one. Subspaces thus have open sets, closed sets, limit points of sets, and closures of sets, and in each case the points not in the subspace are essentially ignored. To distinguish between these ideas as applied to (X, d) and (Y, d'), we use the terminology X-open, Y-open, X-closed, Y-closed, X-limit, Y-limit, X-closure, and Y-closure. Thus for a subset A of Y, the Y-closure of A is its closure when regarded as a subset of the metric space (Y, d'), and the X-closure of A is its closure when regarded as a subset of the metric space (X, d). We now investigate the relationship between these concepts in the big space (X, d) and in a subspace (Y, d'), and then give some examples.

17

Theorem 2.2.1 *Let* (Y, d') *be a subspace of the metric space* (X, d), *and let* B *be a subset of* Y. *Then*

1. B *is* Y-*open if and only if there is an* X-*open set* B^1 *such that* $B = B^1 \cap Y$.
2. B *is* Y-*closed if and only if there is an* X-*closed set* B^1 *such that* $B = B^1 \cap Y$.
3. *A point* y *of* Y *is a* Y-*limit point of* B *if and only if it is an* X-*limit point of* B.
4. *The* Y-*closure of* B *is the intersection of* Y *with the* X-*closure of* B.

PROOF.
1. Suppose that B is Y-open. Then for each y in B there is a positive number ε_y such that $N_Y(y, \varepsilon_y) = \{z \in Y : d'(y, z) < \varepsilon_y\} \subset B$. For each such y consider $N_X(y, \varepsilon_y) = \{z \in X : d(y, z) < \varepsilon_y\}$, and let $B^1 = \cup \{N_X(y, \varepsilon_y) : y \in B\}$. Then as a union of X-open sets, B^1 is X-open, and since $y \in N_X(y, \varepsilon_y)$ for each $y \in B$, $B \subset B^1 \cap Y$. Finally, if $z_0 \in B^1 \cap Y$, then for some y in B, z_0 is in $N_X(y, \varepsilon_y) \cap Y$ and hence in $N_Y(y, \varepsilon_y) \subset B$. Here we have used the fact that d' is the restriction of d to $Y \times Y$. Thus $B = B^1 \cap Y$.

   Conversely, suppose that B^1 is X-open and $B = B^1 \cap Y$. Then for each y in B there is a positive number ε_y such that $N_X(y, \varepsilon_y) \subset B^1$, so clearly $\{z \in Y : d'(y, z) < \varepsilon_y\} \subset B^1 \cap Y = B$. Hence B is Y-open.
2. This proof is left as an exercise.
3. Let y be a point of Y and a limit point of B. It is evident from the techniques used in the proof of (1) that each basic X-neighborhood of y contains a point of B other than y. Hence y must be an X-limit point of B. The converse is just as easy and is left as an exercise.
4. Using the definition of closure and (3), we see that the

$$Y\text{-closure of } B = B \cup \{y \in Y : y \text{ is a } Y\text{-limit point of } B\}$$
$$= B \cup \{y \in Y : y \text{ is an } X\text{-limit point of } B\}$$
$$= B \cup (\{y \in X : y \text{ is an } X\text{-limit point of } B\} \cap Y)$$
$$= (B \cup \{y \in X : y \text{ is an } X\text{-limit point of } B\}) \cap Y$$
$$= (X\text{-closure of } B) \cap Y.$$

∎

EXAMPLES.

5. Consider the closed interval $[0, 1]$ as a subspace of R with the usual metric. Since $(\frac{1}{2}, 1] = (\frac{1}{2}, 2) \cap [0, 1]$, $(\frac{1}{2}, 1]$ is open in $[0, 1]$.
6. Consider the open interval $(0, 1)$ as a subspace of R with the usual metric. Since $[\frac{1}{2}, 1) = [\frac{1}{2}, 1] \cap (0, 1)$, $[\frac{1}{2}, 1)$ is a closed subset of $(0, 1)$. Also, the closure of $[\frac{1}{2}, 1)$ in $(0, 1)$ is $(0, 1) \cap [\frac{1}{2}, 1] = [\frac{1}{2}, 1)$.

These examples illustrate that care must be taken when dealing with subspaces, especially in deciding which points are relevant and which are not. The reader is urged to construct other examples for himself.

We now turn to another powerful method of constructing new spaces from old ones. This is best illustrated by the relationship between the line and the plane. The reader should know that the plane is usually regarded as the Cartesian product of R with itself, that is, as $R \times R = \{(x_1, x_2) : x_1, x_2 \in R\}$. Further, if we denote the Euclidean metric on R by ρ and that on R^2 by d, then

$$d((x_1, x_2), (y_1, y_2)) = \sqrt{(\rho(x_1, y_1))^2 + (\rho(x_2, y_2))^2} \ .$$

Finally, the accompanying illustration shows the relationship between basic neighborhoods in R^2 and Cartesian products of basic neighborhoods in R. It is these ideas which we now investigate.

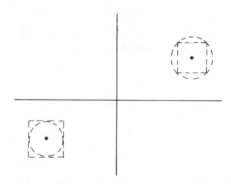

Definition Let $(X_1, d_1), (X_2, d_2), \ldots, (X_n, d_n)$ be any collection of metric spaces. The product of these metric spaces is the metric space (X, ρ), where $X = X_1 \times X_2 \times \cdots \times X_n$ and

$$\rho((x_1, x_2, \ldots, x_n), (y_1, y_2, \ldots, y_n))$$
$$= \sqrt{(d_1(x_1, y_1))^2 + (d_2(x_2, y_2))^2 + \cdots (d_n(x_n, y_n))^2}$$
$$= \sqrt{\sum_{i=1}^{n} (d_i(x_i, y_i))^2} \ .$$

(X, ρ) is called a *product space* and $(X_1, d_1), (X_2, d_2), \ldots, (X_n, d_n)$ are its *factors*.

We must verify that the function ρ in the definition is actually a metric. The verifications of the elementary properties are not hard and are left as exercises. To verify the triangle inequality, we recall that if $a_1, a_2, \ldots,$

$a_n, b_1, b_2, \ldots, b_n$ are any real numbers, then (see the Appendix)

$$\sqrt{\sum_{i=1}^{n} (a_i + b_i)^2} \leqslant \sqrt{\sum_{i=1}^{n} a_i^2} + \sqrt{\sum_{i=1}^{n} b_i^2}.$$

Then

$$\rho((x_1, x_2, \ldots, x_n), (z_1, z_2, \ldots, z_n)) = \sqrt{\sum_{i=1}^{n} (d_i(x_i, z_i))^2}$$

$$\leqslant \sqrt{\sum_{i=1}^{n} (d_i(x_i, y_i) + d_i(y_i, z_i))^2}$$

$$\leqslant \sqrt{\sum_{i=1}^{n} (d_i(x_i, y_i))^2} + \sqrt{\sum_{i=1}^{n} (d_i(y_i, z_i))^2}$$

$$= \rho((x_1, x_2, \ldots, x_n), (y_1, y_2, \ldots, y_n))$$
$$+ \rho((y_1, y_2, \ldots, y_n), (z_1, z_2, \ldots, z_n)).$$

Unless stated otherwise, we will always assume that the Cartesian product of metric spaces carries this product metric ρ.

EXAMPLES.

7. It is clear that n-dimensional Euclidean space R^n can be regarded as the n-fold product of R with itself.
8. The square together with its interior can be regarded as the product of $[0, 1]$ with itself; the cube can be regarded as $[0, 1] \times [0, 1] \times [0, 1]$.
9. If at each point of a circle we attach another circle, we get the inner tube shown. This space is called the *torus*, and is the product of S^1 with itself. This is a useful way of thinking of a product of X and Y, namely, as the result of attaching a copy of Y to each point of X.

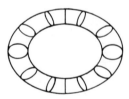

Theorem 2.2.2 *Let* $(X_1, d_1), (X_2, d_2), \ldots, (X_n, d_n)$ *be metric spaces, and let* (X, ρ) *be their product.*

1. *If* U_i *is open in* X_i *for* $i = 1, 2, \ldots, n$, *then* $U_1 \times U_2 \times \cdots \times U_n$ *is open in* X.

2. *If $(x_1, x_2, \ldots, x_n)$ is a point of an open set U in X, then there are open sets $U_1, U_2, \ldots, U_n$ in $X_1, X_2, \ldots, X_n$, respectively, such that $(x_1, x_2, \ldots, x_n) \in U_1 \times U_2 \times \cdots \times U_n \subset U$.*

PROOF.

1. Let $(x_1, x_2, \ldots, x_n)$ be a point of $U_1 \times U_2 \times \cdots \times U_n$. Then for each $i = 1, 2, \ldots, n$ there is a positive number ε_i such that $N_{X_i}(x_i, \varepsilon_i) \subset U_i$. Let ε be the smallest of $\varepsilon_1, \varepsilon_2, \ldots, \varepsilon_n$. If $(y_1, y_2, \ldots, y_n) \in N_X((x_1, x_2, \ldots, x_n), \varepsilon)$, then for $i = 1, 2, \ldots, n$

$$\varepsilon_i \geqslant \varepsilon > \rho((x_1, x_2, \ldots, x_n), (y_1, y_2, \ldots, y_n)) = \sqrt{\sum_{i=1}^{n} (d_i(x_i, y_i))^2} \geqslant d_i(x_i, y_i),$$

so that $y_i \in N_{X_i}(x_i, \varepsilon_i) \subset U_i$. Thus $(y_1, y_2, \ldots, y_n) \in U_1 \times U_2 \times \cdots \times U_n$, so that $N_X((x_1, x_2, \ldots, x_n), \varepsilon) \subset U_1 \times U_2 \times \cdots \times U_n$, and the latter set is open in X.

2. Since $(x_1, x_2, \ldots, x_n)$ is a point of the open set U in X, there is a positive number ε such that $N((x_1, x_2, \ldots, x_n), \varepsilon) \subset U$. Let $U_i = N_{X_i}(x_i, \varepsilon/\sqrt{n})$ for $i = 1, 2, \ldots, n$. If $(z_1, z_2, \ldots, z_n) \in U_1 \times U_2 \times \cdots \times U_n$, then

$$\rho((x_1, x_2, \ldots, x_n), (z_1, z_2, \ldots, z_n)) = \sqrt{\sum_{i=1}^{n} (d_i(x_i, z_i))^2} < \sqrt{\sum_{i=1}^{n} \frac{\varepsilon^2}{n}}$$

$$= \sqrt{\varepsilon^2} = \varepsilon.$$

Hence $U_1, U_2, \ldots, U_n$ are the desired sets. ∎

This theorem is the basic one relating the open sets in a product space with the open sets in the factor spaces. An easy consequence is that the open sets in the factor spaces completely determine the open sets in the product space, since the latter are precisely unions of Cartesian products of the former. We leave further investigation of product spaces for the exercises and later chapters.

Exercises

1. In each of the following tell whether the given set is open or closed and give its closure (the Euclidean metric and subspace metric are used unless stated otherwise):
   a. $(1, 2)$ as a subset of $[0, 2]$
   b. $(1, 2)$ as a subset of $[0, 2)$
   c. $[1, 2]$ as a subset of $[0, 2]$
   d. $(1, 2]$ as a subset of $[0, 2]$
   e. $\{(x_1, x_2) : x_1^2 + x_2^2 \leqslant 1, x_2 > 0\}$ as a subset of $\{(y_1, y_2) : y_1^2 + y_2^2 \leqslant 1\}$
   f. $\{(x_1, x_2) : x_1^2 + x_2^2 = 1, -1 < x_1 < 1\}$ as a subset of S^1.

2. Prove part 2 of Theorem 2.2.1.

3. Complete the proof of part 3 of Theorem 2.2.1.

4. Give a complete proof of the fact that the function ρ in the definition of product space is actually a metric.

5. Prove that if $C_1, C_2, \ldots, C_n$ are closed subsets of $X_1, X_2, \ldots, X_n$, respectively, then $C_1 \times C_2 \times \cdots \times C_n$ is closed in $X_1 \times X_2 \times \cdots \times X_n$. Hint: The complement of a product is rarely the product of the complements.

Part B

In this section we will generalize the concepts of subspace and product space to the setting of topological spaces, and give an important example of a metric space that is an infinite product, namely, the *Hilbert cube*.

We consider subspaces first. Theorem 2.2.1 tells us how to define a subspace of a topological space and also tells us that a (metric) subspace of a metric space has the subspace topology.

Definition Let $(X, \mathfrak{T})$ be a topological space and Y a subset of X. The *subspace topology* on Y is $\mathfrak{U} = \{O \cap Y : O \in \mathfrak{T}\}$, and $(Y, \mathfrak{U})$ is called a *subspace* of $(X, \mathfrak{T})$.

It is easy to check that $\mathfrak{U}$ is actually a topology on Y. Also, since "basic neighborhood of Y" can be replaced by "neighborhood of y," the proofs of parts (2), (3), and (4) of Theorem 2.2.1 apply to yield the following theorem. The same notation is used as is used in Part A of this section: for example, Y-closed and X-closed.

Theorem 2.2.3 *Let* $(Y, \mathfrak{U})$ *be a subspace of* $(X, \mathfrak{T})$, *and let B be a subset of Y. Then*

1. *B is Y-closed if and only if there is an X-closed set B^1 such that $B = B^1 \cap Y$;*
2. *A point y of Y is a Y-limit point of B if and only if it is an X-limit point of B;*
3. *The Y-closure of B is the intersection of Y with the X-closure of B.*

EXAMPLES.

1. Theorem 2.2.1 implies that all the *metric* examples of subspaces are also *topological* examples.

2. The set of integers Z has the discrete topology as a subspace of R with the usual topology and also with the half-open interval topology. Here $\{n\} = Z \cap (n - \frac{1}{2}, n + \frac{1}{2}) = Z \cap [n - \frac{1}{2}, n + \frac{1}{2})$, so that in each case *single-ton* sets, that is, sets containing a single point, are open and hence any set is open.

3. Let $S = \{0\} \cup \{-1/n : n = 1, 2, \ldots\}$. The set S does not have the discrete topology as a subspace of R with the usual topology, since any open set containing 0 must also contain $-1/n$ for large enough n. However, as a subspace of R with the half-open interval topology, S does have the discrete topology, since $\{-1/n\} = S \cap [-1/n, -1/(n+1))$ and also $\{0\} = S \cap [0, 1)$.

We now turn to the concept of product space. In this case Theorem 2.2.2 gives the clue for the definition and also says that the (metric) product of metric spaces carries the product topology.

Definition Let $(X_1, \mathfrak{I}_1), (X_2, \mathfrak{I}_2), \ldots, (X_n, \mathfrak{I}_n)$ be topological spaces and $X = X_1 \times X_2 \times \cdots \times X_n$. The *product topology* $\mathfrak{U}$ on X consists of all sets which are unions of sets of the form $U_1 \times U_2 \times \cdots \times U_n$, where U_i is open in X_i for each $i = 1, 2, \ldots, n$. Then $(X, \mathfrak{U})$ is called a *product space* and $(X_1, \mathfrak{I}_1), (X_2, \mathfrak{I}_2), \ldots, (X_n, \mathfrak{I}_n)$ are its *factors*.

We verify that $\mathfrak{U}$ is actually a topology on X. Since $\varnothing = \varnothing \times \varnothing \times \cdots \times \varnothing$ and $X = X_1 \times X_2 \times \cdots \times X_n$, both $\varnothing$ and X are in $\mathfrak{U}$. Since unions of unions are unions, $\mathfrak{U}$ contains any union of sets in $\mathfrak{U}$. Finally, suppose that $(x_1, x_2, \ldots, x_n)$ is a point of $O \cap P$, where O, P are in $\mathfrak{U}$. Then there are open sets $U_1, U_2, \ldots, U_n$ in $X_1, X_2, \ldots, X_n$ such that $(x_1, x_2, \ldots, x_n) \in U_1 \times U_2 \times \cdots \times U_n \subset O$ and similarly open sets $V_1, V_2, \ldots, V_n$ such that $(x_1, x_2, \ldots, x_n) \in V_1 \times V_2 \times \cdots \times V_n \subset P$. Let $W_i = U_i \cap V_i$ for $i = 1, 2, \ldots, n$. Then it is easy to check that $(x_1, x_2, \ldots, x_n) \in W_1 \times W_2 \times \cdots \times W_n \subset O \cap P$. Hence $O \cap P$ is a union of sets of the proper form and so belongs to $\mathfrak{U}$.

EXAMPLES.

4. Theorem 2.2.2 implies that all *metric* examples of product spaces are also *topological* examples.

5. Let $(X, \mathfrak{U})$ be the product of the Sorgenfrey line with itself. Then sets of the form $\{(x_1, x_2) : a \leqslant x_1 < b, \ c \leqslant x_2 < d\}$ are open in $(X, \mathfrak{U})$. Thus any subset of the line $\mathscr{L}$ with equation $x_2 = -x_1$ is closed. A proof can be constructed from the following picture.

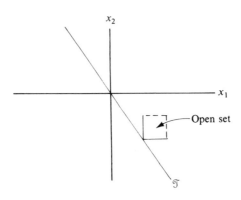

6. If each of $(X_1, \mathcal{T}_1), (X_1, \mathcal{T}_2), \ldots, (X_n, \mathcal{T}_n)$ is discrete, then so is the product space $(X, \mathcal{U})$, since $\{(x_1, x_2, \ldots, x_n)\} = \{x_1\} \times \{x_2\} \times \cdots \times \{x_n\}$ is an open set for any choice of $x_1, x_2, \ldots, x_n$.

We close this section with an example of a metric product space with a countably infinite number of factors. This example is exceedingly important in many areas of topology. We must assume some familiarity with infinite series, and we also slide over a completely rigorous definition of Cartesian product. Thus we regard the Cartesian product of countably many sets $X_1, X_2, \ldots$ as the set of all *infinite-tuples* $(x_1, x_2, \ldots)$ such that $x_i \in X_i$ for each $i = 1, 2, \ldots$.

Let $X_i = [0, 1/i] = \{x \in R : 0 \leqslant x \leqslant 1/i\}$ for $i = 1, 2, \ldots$ and give each X_i the usual subspace metric, that is, the absolute value metric. Let $X = X_1 \times X_2 \times \cdots$. Define a metric ρ on X by

$$\rho((x_1, x_2, \ldots), (y_1, y_2, \ldots)) = \sqrt{\sum_{i=1}^{\infty} |x_i - y_i|^2} \ .$$

Now $|x_i - y_i|^2 \leqslant 1/i^2$, so the infinite series converges and ρ is well defined. The function ρ is clearly nonnegative; certainly $\rho((x_1, x_2, \ldots), (y_1, y_2, \ldots)) = \rho((y_1, y_2, \ldots), (x_1, x_2, \ldots))$, and $\rho((x_1, x_2, \ldots), (y_1, y_2, \ldots)) = 0$ if and only if $|x_i - y_i| = 0$ for each $i = 1, 2, \ldots$, which in turn is true if and only if $x_i = y_i$ for each $i = 1, 2, \ldots$, that is, $(x_1, x_2, \ldots) = (y_1, y_2, \ldots)$.

It remains to check the triangle inequality. Results from the Appendix imply that

$$\sqrt{\sum_{i=1}^{n} |x_i - z_i|^2} = \sqrt{\sum_{i=1}^{n} |x_i - y_i + y_i - z_i|^2}$$
$$\leqslant \sqrt{\sum_{i=1}^{n} |x_i - y_i|^2} + \sqrt{\sum_{i=1}^{n} |y_i - z_i|^2}.$$

This last term is then no greater than

$$\sqrt{\sum_{i=1}^{\infty} |x_i - y_i|^2} + \sqrt{\sum_{i=1}^{\infty} |y_i - z_i|^2} \ .$$

The integer n is arbitrary, so we obtain $\rho((x_1, x_2, \ldots), (z_1, z_2, \ldots)) \leqslant \rho((x_1, x_2, \ldots), (y_1, y_2, \ldots)) + \rho((y_1, y_2, \ldots), (z_1, z_2, \ldots))$.

The space we have obtained is called the *Hilbert cube* and is usually denoted by I^{ω} or I^{∞}. It is very important for many purposes, some of which we will encounter later. For now we will be content with just one theorem.

Theorem 2.2.4 *The open sets in I^{∞} are precisely the unions of sets of the form $U_1 \times U_2 \times \cdots \times U_n \times X_{n+1} \times X_{n+2} \cdots$, where $U_1, U_2, \ldots, U_n$ are open in $X_1, X_2, \ldots, X_n$ and n may be any positive integer.*

PROOF. The proof that sets of the given form are open in I^{∞} closely parallels the proof of part 1 of Theorem 2.2.2 and is left as an exercise. Now suppose that $(x_1, x_2, \ldots)$ is a point of the set U which is open in I^{∞}. Then there is a positive number ε such that $N_{I^{\infty}}((x_1, x_2, \ldots), \varepsilon) \subset U$. There is an integer n such that $\sum_{i=n+1}^{\infty} 1/i^2 < \varepsilon^2/2$. Now suppose that $(z_1, z_2, \ldots)$ is in

$$W = N_{X_1}\left(x_1, \frac{\varepsilon}{\sqrt{2n}}\right) \times N_{X_2}\left(x_2, \frac{\varepsilon}{\sqrt{2n}}\right) \times \cdots \times N_{X_n}\left(x_n, \frac{\varepsilon}{\sqrt{2n}}\right)$$
$$\times X_{n+1} \times X_{n+2} \times \cdots .$$

Then

$$\rho((x_1, x_2, \ldots), (z_1, z_2, \ldots)) = \sqrt{\sum_{i=1}^{\infty} |x_i - z_i|^2}$$
$$< \sqrt{\frac{\varepsilon^2}{2n} + \frac{\varepsilon^2}{2n} + \cdots + \frac{\varepsilon^2}{2n} + \sum_{i=n+1}^{\infty} \frac{1}{i^2}}$$
$$< \sqrt{\frac{\varepsilon^2}{2} + \frac{\varepsilon^2}{2}} = \varepsilon.$$

Thus $(x_1, x_2, \ldots) \in W \subset U$, so U must be a union of sets of the proper form. ∎

Exercises

1. Prove that the subspace topology is really a topology.

2. Give a complete proof of Theorem 2.2.3.

3. Tell whether the following spaces have the discrete topology and justify your answers:
   a. $\{0\} \cup \left\{ \dfrac{1}{n} : n = 1, 2, \dots \right\}$ as a subspace of the Sorgenfrey line
   b. A subspace of any space with the discrete topology
   c. A finite subspace of a metric space
   d. A finite subspace of R with the cofinite topology
   e. The integers as a subspace of R with the cofinite topology.

4. Verify Example 5 concerning the product of the Sorgenfrey line with itself.

5. Prove that the product of indiscrete spaces is indiscrete.

6. Prove that if U is an open subset of the product of $(X, \mathfrak{I})$ and $(Y, \mathfrak{U})$, then $\{ x : (x, y) \in U \text{ for some } y \}$ is open in X.

7. Complete the proof of Theorem 2.2.4.

2.3. Sequences

Part A

There are many approaches to the study of the topology of metric spaces. We have chosen one in which the fundamental ideas are *basic neighborhood* and *open set*. This approach has the advantage that it leads immediately to the proper generalization of metric space, which we have been studying in Part B of each section. In this section we introduce another approach, namely, the study of *sequences* and their *limits*. Even though in general sequences do not have all the "right" properties, they are still one of the most important tools of a topologist. Further, the behavior of sequences is one of the most pervasive topics in all of mathematics.

Definition A *sequence* in a set X is a function s from the set of positive integers into X.

A sequence s in X can be regarded as an infinite list of elements of X, namely, $s(1), s(2), s(3), \dots$. Notation often used for $s(i)$ is s_i, and so one can write $s_1, s_2, s_3, \dots$. We will frequently use $[s_i]$ to denote a sequence. Be careful to distinguish this from $\{ s_i : i = 1, 2, \dots \}$, which is the set of elements of X which appear in the sequence $[s_i]$.

EXAMPLES.

1. $[1/i]$ is the sequence given by $s(i) = 1/i$, and the first three elements in the list are $1, \frac{1}{2}$, and $\frac{1}{3}$.

2. The first few elements in the list for the sequence $[(-1)^i]$ are $-1, 1, -1, 1, \ldots$. In this case $\{s_i : i = 1, 2, \ldots\} = \{-1, 1\}$.
3. There is a sequence $[f_i]$ defined by $f_1 = 0$, $f_2 = 1$, and $f_i = f_{i-1} + f_{i-2}$ for $i \geq 3$. The first few elements in the list are $0, 1, 1, 2, 3, 5, 8, 13, \ldots$, and this is called the *Fibonacci sequence*.

These examples illustrate some of the advantages of sequences, namely, that one can get a "feel" for them by writing out the first few terms, and that they can be defined step by step as in Example 3.

If $[s_i]$ is a sequence in a metric space (X, d), then one can define what it means for the sequence to get and stay closer and closer to a given element of X. Thus, the sequence in Example 1 above gets and stays close to 0, but there is no number to which the sequences in Examples 2 and 3 get and stay close.

Definition   Let $[s_i]$ be a sequence in a metric space (X, d). The sequence $[s_i]$ *converges* to the point y of X if for each positive number ε there is an integer P such that $d(s_i, y) < \varepsilon$ for $i \geq P$. If $[s_i]$ converges to y, then we also say that $[s_i]$ has *limit* y and we write $s_i \to y$ as $i \to \infty$ or $\lim_{i \to \infty} s_i = y$.

The proof that a sequence $[s_i]$ converges to y can be viewed as a game in which the opponent gives you a positive real number ε and you must find the integer P to satisfy the definition. The integer P may depend on the ε given but on nothing else. The following theorems begin the study of the relationship between convergent sequences and previously defined topological ideas.

Theorem 2.3.1   *Let $[s_i]$ be a sequence in a metric space (X, d). Then $[s_i]$ converges to the point y of X if and only if for each basic neighborhood $N(y, \varepsilon)$ there is an integer P such that $s_i \in N(y, \varepsilon)$ for all $i \geq P$.*

PROOF.   This is a trivial application of the definition of basic neighborhood and is left as an exercise.   ∎

Theorem 2.3.2   *Let $[s_i]$ be a sequence in the metric space (X, d). Then $[s_i]$ converges to the point y of X if and only if for each open set U containing y there is an integer P such that $s_i \in U$ for all $i \geq P$.*

PROOF.   This is an application of the relationships between basic neighborhoods and open sets, and is left as an exercise.   ∎

Theorem 2.3.3   *Let C be a subset of the metric space (X, d). A point y of X is a limit point of C if and only if there is a sequence in $C \setminus \{y\}$ that converges to y.*

PROOF. Suppose $[s_n]$ is a sequence in $C \backslash \{y\}$ which converges to y. For any positive ε there is an integer P such that $s_i \in N(y, \varepsilon)$ for all $i \geqslant P$ by Theorem 2.3.1. Hence each basic neighborhood $N(y, \varepsilon)$ contains a point of C other than y, namely, s_P, so that y is a limit point of C.

To prove the converse we consider the basic neighborhood $N(y, 1/n)$ where n is a positive integer. Since y is a limit point of C, the neighborhood $N(y, 1/n)$ contains a point s_n of C other than y, that is $s_n \in C \backslash \{y\}$. This defines a sequence $[s_n]$, and we must show that it converges to y. For any positive ε there is a positive integer P such that $1/P < \varepsilon$. Then for $i \geqslant P$, $s_i \in N(y, 1/i) \subset N(y, 1/P) \subset N(y, \varepsilon)$. ∎

The proof of Theorem 2.3.3 contains a basic idea which is present in much of the theory of sequences. It is that the basic neighborhoods $N(y, 1), N(y, 1/2), N(y, 1/3), \ldots$ are fully representative of the entire collection of basic neighborhoods of y, in the sense that every basic neighborhood of y contains $N(y, 1/n)$ for some n. This in turn depends on a fundamental property of real numbers called the *Archimedean property*, which states that for a given real number α there is an integer n larger than α. Thus for any positive ε there is an integer P larger than $1/\varepsilon$, so that $1/P$ is less than ε. This reasoning appears again and again in proofs involving sequences.

We close this section with another theorem and some examples. Sequences and their limits will appear frequently in the sequel, so the reader is urged to become thoroughly familiar with them.

Theorem 2.3.4 *Let C be a subset of the metric space (X, d). The subset C is closed if and only if the point y is in C whenever there is a sequence $[s_n]$ in C converging to y.*

PROOF. Suppose that C is closed and that y is a point of X but not of C. Then $X \backslash C$ is an open set containing y, so any sequence $[s_n]$ converging to y must eventually be in $X \backslash C$, that is, s_i must be in $X \backslash C$ for large enough i. Hence $[s_n]$ cannot be a sequence in C, so that any sequence in C which converges must converge to a point of C.

To prove the converse we note that by Theorem 2.3.3 each limit point of C is the limit of a sequence in C and so by hypothesis must be in C. Thus C contains all its limit points, and so is its own closure. Since closures are closed, C must be closed. ∎

EXAMPLES.

4. Let R have the usual Euclidean metric. We show that $[1/n]$ converges to 0. Let ε be positive. There is an integer P for which $1/P < \varepsilon$, so that if $n \geqslant P$, then $0 < 1/n \leqslant 1/P < \varepsilon$. Hence $d(0, 1/n) < \varepsilon$ for $n \geqslant P$.

5. Let R have the discrete metric. Then $[1/n]$ does not converge to 0. In this case $d(1/n,0)=1$ for each n, so there is no integer P that will work when $\varepsilon = 1/2$.

Exercises

1. Tell whether the following sequences converge and justify your answer. In each case assume that R has its usual metric.

   a. $\left[(-1)^n + \dfrac{1}{n} \right]$

   b. $\left[\dfrac{(-1)^n}{n} \right]$

   c. $\left[2 + \dfrac{1}{n} \right]$

   d. $[2^n]$

   e. $[a^n]$, where $0 \leqslant a \leqslant 1$

   f. $[(-a)^n]$, where $0 \leqslant a \leqslant 1$

2. Prove that the limit of a sequence is unique, if it exists.

3. Suppose that $[s_n]$ is a sequence in $X \setminus N(y,r)$, where (X,d) is a metric space and y is in X. Suppose also that $s_n \to s$ as $n \to \infty$. Prove that $d(y,s) \geqslant r$.

4. Let $(X_1,d_1),(X_2,d_2),\ldots,(X_n,d_n)$ be metric spaces and let (X,ρ) be their product. Let $[\bar{s}_i] = [(s_i^1,s_i^2,\ldots,s_i^n)]$ be a sequence in X. Prove that $[\bar{s}_i]$ converges to $\bar{s} = (s^1,s^2,\ldots,s^n)$ if and only if $[s_i^1]$ converges to s^1, $[s_i^2]$ converges to $s^2,\ldots,$ and $[s_i^n]$ converges to s^n. Hint: Carefully write out $\rho(\bar{s}_i,\bar{s})$.

5. Prove that if $[s_i]$ is a sequence in a metric space (X,d) which converges to s, then there is a number M such that $d(s_i,s) \leqslant M$ for all $i = 1,2,\ldots$.

6. Prove that if $[s_i]$ is a sequence in a metric space (X,d) and $d(s_n,s) < \dfrac{1}{n}$ for all $n = 1,2,\ldots,$ then $[s_i]$ converges to s.

Part B

Recalling that in a topological space a neighborhood of a point y is any open set containing y, we see that Theorem 2.3.2 is the clue to the following definition. Further, Theorem 2.3.2 implies that this definition agrees with the one already given for metric spaces.

Definition Let $[s_n]$ be a sequence in a topological space $(X,\mathfrak{I})$. The sequence $[s_n]$ *converges* to the point y of X if for each neighborhood N of y there is an integer P such that $s_n \in N$ for $n \geqslant P$. If $[s_n]$ converges to y, then we also say that $[s_n]$ has *limit* y and we write $s_n \to y$ as $n \to \infty$ or $\lim_{n \to \infty} s_n = y$.

The relationship between convergent sequences and other topological notions is not nearly as nice in general topological spaces as it is in metric spaces. The following examples illustrate some of the pathologies.

EXAMPLES.

1. Let $(X, \mathcal{T})$ be an indiscrete topological space, $[s_n]$ a sequence in X, and y *any* point of X. Since X is the only neighborhood of y and $s_n \in X$ for $n \geqslant 1$, the sequence $[s_n]$ converges to y. Thus limits of sequences need not be unique, as is the case in metric spaces (Exercise 2 of the preceding set).

2. Let R have the cofinite topology and let $s_n = n$ for $n = 1, 2, \ldots$. Let x be *any* point of R and N a neighborhood of x. Then $R \setminus N$ is finite and so contains s_n for at most finitely many n, say, $n_1, n_2, \ldots, n_z$. If P is larger than $\max\{n_1, n_2, \ldots, n_z\}$, then certainly $s_n \in N$ for $n \geqslant P$. Hence $s_n \to x$ as $n \to \infty$.

3. We define the cocountable topology on R as follows (see the Appendix for information on countable sets). A set σ is open in the cocountable topology if either $\sigma = \varnothing$ or $R \setminus \sigma$ is countable. We leave it as an exercise to show that this is indeed a topology on R. Suppose $[s_n]$ is a sequence in R that converges to y in this topology. The set $\{s_n : n = 1, 2, \ldots\}$ is countable, so that $N = \{y\} \cup (R \setminus \{s_n : n = 1, 2, \ldots\})$ is a neighborhood of y. Hence there is an integer P such that $s_n \in N$ for $n \geqslant P$. Since s_n is certainly not in $R \setminus \{s_n : n = 1, 2, \ldots\}$, it must be that $s_n = y$ for $n \geqslant P$. Hence the only convergent sequences in this space are those which are eventually constant.

   Continuing this example, we consider the subset $(0, 1)$ of R. If σ is a nonempty open set, then $R \setminus \sigma$ is countable, and since $(0, 1)$ is uncountable, $R \setminus \sigma$ cannot contain $(0, 1)$. Thus every nonempty open set meets $(0, 1)$, so that every point of R is a limit point of $(0, 1)$. However, the above argument shows that no sequence in $(0, 1)$ converges to any point not in $(0, 1)$, so that Theorem 2.3.3 does not hold in the general case.

We need some property of spaces that will overcome the pathology indicated in Example 3. The clue lies in the remarks following the proof of Theorem 2.3.3, which also show that a metric space satisfies the following definition.

Definition A topological space $(X, \mathcal{T})$ is *first countable* if each point x of X has a sequence of neighborhoods $\{N_{x,i} : i = 1, 2, \ldots\}$ such that each neighborhood of x contains one of the neighborhoods $N_{x,i}$.

The neighborhoods $N_{x,i}$ in this definition should be thought of as corresponding to the basic neighborhoods $N(x, 1/i)$ in a metric space. The following theorem shows that this analogy can be carried even farther.

Theorem 2.3.5 *Let* $(X, \mathfrak{T})$ *be a first countable topological space. Then each point* x *of* X *has a sequence of neighborhoods* $\{M_{x,i} : i = 1, 2, \ldots\}$ *such that* $M_{x,i} \supset M_{x,i+1}$ *for* $i = 1, 2, \ldots$ *and each neighborhood of* x *contains one of the neighborhoods* $M_{x,i}$.

PROOF. Let $\{N_{x,i} : i = 1, 2, \ldots\}$ be the sequence of neighborhoods given in the definition of first countable space. Define $M_{x,1}$ to be $N_{x,1}$, and $M_{x,i} = N_{x,1} \cap N_{x,2} \cap \cdots \cap N_{x,i}$ for $i = 2, 3, \ldots$. Clearly $M_{x,i} \supset M_{x,i+1}$ for $i = 1, 2, \ldots$. Further, each neighborhood of x contains $N_{x,i}$ for some i and hence $M_{x,i}$ for that i. ∎

Sequences in a first countable space behave just as nicely as they do in a metric space. The following two theorems bear this out. Further properties of sequences will be developed in later sections.

Theorem 2.3.6 *Let* C *be a subset of the first countable space* $(X, \mathfrak{T})$. *A point* y *of* X *is a limit point of* C *if and only if there is a sequence in* $C \setminus \{y\}$ *that converges to* y.

PROOF. If $[s_n]$ is a sequence in $C \setminus \{y\}$ that converges to y, then each neighborhood of y contains s_n for large enough n; that is, each neighborhood of y contains points of $C \setminus \{y\}$: thus y is a limit point of C.

Conversely, suppose that y is a limit point of C. Let $\{M_{y,i} : i = 1, 2, \ldots\}$ be the sequence of neighborhoods of y delivered by Theorem 2.3.5. In each $M_{y,i}$ there is a point s_i of $C \setminus \{y\}$, so we get the sequence $[s_i]$ in $C \setminus \{y\}$. If U is a neighborhood of y, then there is an integer P such that $M_{y,P} \subset U$. If $i \geqslant P$, then $s_i \in M_{y,i} \subset M_{y,P} \subset U$, so that $s_n \to y$ as $n \to \infty$. ∎

Theorem 2.3.7 *Let* C *be a subset of the first countable space* $(X, \mathfrak{T})$. *The subset* C *is closed if and only if the point* y *is in* C *whenever there is a sequence in* C *converging to* y.

PROOF. The proof is identical to that of Theorem 2.3.4. ∎

Exercises

1. Verify that the cocountable topology on R is indeed a topology.

2. Prove that the Sorgenfrey line is a first countable space.

3. Prove that R with the cocountable topology is not a first countable space.

4. Tell whether the following sequences converge in the Sorgenfrey line and justify your answer.

    a. $\left[(-1)^n + \dfrac{1}{n}\right]$

    b. $\left[\dfrac{(-1)^n}{n}\right]$

    c. $\left[2 + \dfrac{1}{n}\right]$

    d. $[a^n]$, where $0 \leqslant a \leqslant 1$

    e. $[(-a)^n]$, where $0 \leqslant a \leqslant 1$.

5. Let $(X_1, \mathcal{T}_1), (X_2, \mathcal{T}_2), \ldots, (X_k, \mathcal{T}_k)$ be topological spaces, and let $(X, \mathcal{T})$ be their product. Let $[\bar{s}_n] = [(s_{1,n} s_{2,n}, \ldots, s_{k,n})]$ be a sequence in X. Prove that $[\bar{s}_n]$ converges to $\bar{s} = (s_1, s_2, \ldots, s_k)$ if and only if $[s_{1,n}]$ converges to s_1, $[s_{2,n}]$ converges to $s_2, \ldots,$ and $[s_{k,n}]$ converges to s_k.

6. State and prove a theorem like that in Exercise 5 for the Hilbert cube.

7. Prove that if $(X, \mathcal{T})$ is a first countable space, then $U \subset X$ is open if and only if there is an integer P such that $s_n \in U$ for $n \geqslant P$ whenever $\lim_{n \to \infty} s_n = x$, where $x \in U$.

2.4 Continuity and homeomorphisms

Part A

In this section we wish to build on the reader's intuition and arrive at a rigorous definition of topological equivalence or homeomorphism. The preceding sections have shown what additional structure is needed on a set in order to make it a metric or topological space. It is now necessary to find a way of comparing two such spaces, and as in most other mathematical situations the basic tool used is the function. For information on functions and their properties, see the Appendix.

It is reasonable to expect that a function must have some additional properties in order that it can be used to compare spaces, just as a set must have additional properties in order to be a space. We begin our investigation of these properties by examining a specific case.

Consider the line segment I consisting of all real numbers between 0 and 1 inclusive. We will define two functions on I, only one of which corresponds to a topological motion or homeomorphism. Recalling from Chapter 1 that stretching is allowed as part of a topological motion, we expect the function $f(x) = 10,000,000x$ to be a homeomorphism. Since tearing is not allowed as part of a topological motion, the function

$$g(x) = \begin{cases} x & 0 \leqslant x \leqslant \frac{1}{2} \\ x + \frac{1}{3} & \frac{1}{2} < x \leqslant 1 \end{cases}$$

should *not* be a homeomorphism. The problem is to express the difference mathematically.

A first guess might be that a homeomorphism should preserve all distances, but reflection shows that this is much too restrictive, since it would not allow stretching or shrinking. The basic question is how to prevent (mathematically) the tearing that is done by the function g, without preventing the enormous amount of stretching done by the function f.

One way to express the fact that g tears the line segment apart at $\frac{1}{2}$ is to say that g moves points which are originally close to $\frac{1}{2}$ to points which are not close to where g puts $\frac{1}{2}$. More precisely, no matter how close x is to $\frac{1}{2}$, $g(x)$ is at least distance $\frac{1}{3}$ from $g(\frac{1}{2}) = \frac{1}{2}$ when x is larger than $\frac{1}{2}$.

Let us examine f in this light. If we want $f(x)$ to be within $\frac{1}{3}$ of $f(\frac{1}{2})$, we need only take x within $1/30,000,000$ of $\frac{1}{2}$, since then

$$\left| f(x) - f\left(\frac{1}{2}\right) \right| = |10,000,000x - 5,000,000| = 10,000,000 \left| x - \frac{1}{2} \right|$$

$$< 10,000,000 \cdot \frac{1}{30,000,000} = \frac{1}{3}.$$

A similar argument works when we replace $\frac{1}{3}$ by $\frac{1}{4}$, $\frac{1}{8}$, $1/786395$, or in general any positive number. The last replacement for $\frac{1}{3}$, i.e., any positive number, is crucial since we could have made g represent as tiny a tear as we wish, but nevertheless a tear, by replacing $\frac{1}{3}$ by any positive number in the definition of g. We arrive at the following definition.

Definition Let (X, d) and (Y, ρ) be metric spaces and let f be a function from X to Y. We say that f is *continuous at the point* x_0 of X if for every positive number ε there is a positive number α such that $\rho(f(x_0), f(x)) < \varepsilon$ whenever $d(x_0, x) < \alpha$. If f is continuous at each point of X, then we say that f is *continuous on* X. Also, to emphasize the metrics used we often write $f : (X, d) \to (Y, \rho)$.

EXAMPLES.

1. We show that $f(x) = 10,000,000x$ is continuous as a function from (R, d) to (R, d), where d is the usual metric. Let x_0 be a point of R and let ε be positive. We need to find an α such that $|f(x) - f(x_0)| < \varepsilon$ whenever

$|x - x_0| < \alpha$. Now $|f(x) - f(x_0)| = |10,000,000x - 10,000,000x_0| = 10,000,000|x - x_0|$, so it is clear that $\alpha = \varepsilon/10,000,000$ works. Note that to check continuity, we must find an α in terms of ε which works *for each ε*.

2. We show that

$$g(x) = \begin{cases} x & x \leqslant \dfrac{1}{2} \\ x + \dfrac{1}{3} & x > \dfrac{1}{2} \end{cases}$$

is not continuous at $1/2$. Let $\varepsilon = 1/3$. For any positive α,

$$\left| \frac{1}{2} - \left(\frac{1}{2} + \frac{\alpha}{2} \right) \right| = \frac{\alpha}{2} < \alpha,$$

whereas

$$\left| g\left(\frac{1}{2} \right) - g\left(\frac{1}{2} + \alpha \right) \right| = \left| \frac{1}{2} - \left(\frac{1}{2} + \frac{1}{3} \right) \right| = \frac{1}{3}.$$

Thus no α works when $\varepsilon = 1/3$. Note that to show that g is not continuous, we must find a *single* ε for which *no* α works.

3. It is easy to use the technique above to show that $f(x) = ax + b$ is continuous as a function from R to R (usual metrics) when a and b are any real numbers.

4. Let (X, d) be a discrete metric space and (Y, ρ) any metric space. Let f be any function from X to Y. Let $x_0 \in X$, and let ε be positive. If $d(x_0, x) < 1/2$, then $x_0 = x$, so that $\rho(f(x_0), f(x)) = \rho(f(x_0), f(x_0)) = 0$. Hence f is continuous on X.

5. Let $B([0, 1])$ be the space of bounded real-valued functions on $[0, 1]$ with the metric introduced in Example 5 on p. 9. Define $\phi_0 : B([0, 1]) \to R$ by $\phi_0(f) = f(0)$. If ε is any positive number, then $\rho(f, g) < \varepsilon$ implies that $|\phi_0(f) - \phi_0(g)| = |f(0) - g(0)| < \varepsilon$, so that ϕ_0 is continuous on $B([0, 1])$.

There are many other formulations of continuity, some of which are expressed in the following theorem. Topologists are almost always concerned with functions which are continuous everywhere, so we restrict ourselves to that case. Experience will teach us which of the formulations of continuity is best to use in a given instance.

Theorem 2.4.1 *Let (X, d) and (Y, ρ) be metric spaces and f a function from X to Y. The following statements are equivalent:*

1. *f is continuous on X;*
2. *For each point x_0 of X and each basic neighborhood V of $f(x_0)$ in Y,*

there is a basic neighborhood U of x_0 in X such that $f(U) \subset V$;

3. $f^{-1}(O)$ *is open in X whenever O is open in Y;*
4. $f^{-1}(C)$ *is closed in X whenever C is closed in Y;*
5. *If $[x_n]$ is a sequence in X converging to a point x_0 in X, then $[f(x_n)]$ converges to $f(x_0)$ in Y.*

PROOF.

(1)$\Rightarrow$(2). V must be of the form $N(f(x_0), \varepsilon)$ for some positive ε. By (1) there is a positive α such that $\rho(f(x_0), f(x)) < \varepsilon$ whenever $d(x_0, x) < \alpha$. Then certainly $f(N(x_0, \alpha)) \subset V$.

(2)$\Rightarrow$(3). Let x_0 be a point of $f^{-1}(O)$. Then there is a basic neighborhood V of $f(x_0)$ contained in O. By (2) x_0 has a basic neighborhood U such that $f(U) \subset V \subset O$, so that $U \subset f^{-1}(O)$. Hence $f^{-1}(O)$ contains a basic neighborhood of each of its points and so is open.

(3)$\rightleftarrows$(4). If C is closed in Y, then $Y \backslash C$ is open. By (3), $f^{-1}(Y \backslash C)$ is open, so that $f^{-1}(C) = X \backslash (X \backslash f^{-1}(C)) = X \backslash f^{-1}(Y \backslash C)$ is closed. The converse is just as easy.

(3)$\Rightarrow$(5). Let O be an open set in Y containing $f(x_0)$. Then $f^{-1}(O)$ is an open set in X containing x_0, so there is an integer P such that $x_n \in f^{-1}(O)$ when $n \geqslant P$. But then $f(x_n) \in O$ when $n \geqslant P$, so that $[f(x_n)]$ converges to $f(x_0)$. Here we have used Theorem 2.3.2.

(5)$\Rightarrow$(1). Suppose that f is not continuous at x_0. Then there is some positive ε for which no α works. We must create a sequence, so consider the fact that $1/n$ never works for α. This means that there is an x_n with $d(x_0, x_n) < 1/n$ but $\rho(f(x_0), f(x_n)) \geqslant \varepsilon$. Then $[x_n]$ is a sequence in X which converges to x_0, but $[f(x_n)]$ never gets within ε of $f(x_0)$ and so certainly does not converge to $f(x_0)$. This contradiction establishes that (5)$\Rightarrow$(1).

We have shown that (1)$\Rightarrow$(2)$\Rightarrow$(3)$\rightleftarrows$(4) and that (3)$\Rightarrow$(5)$\Rightarrow$(1), which shows that all five statements are equivalent. ∎

Before we turn our attention back to homeomorphisms, we prove three more very useful theorems regarding continuity. In fact, Theorem 2.4.4 is probably the most important single fact regarding product spaces.

Theorem 2.4.2 *Let f be a continuous function from the metric space (X,d) to the metric space (Y,ρ), and let (A,d') be a subspace of (X,d). Then the restriction of f to A is continuous.*

PROOF. Since open sets behave nicely in subspaces, we use part (3) of Theorem 2.4.1. Let O be open in Y. Then $(f|A)^{-1}(O) = f^{-1}(O) \cap A$ is open in A since $f^{-1}(O)$ is open in X. ∎

Theorem 2.4.3 *Let f be a continuous function from the metric space (X,d) to the metric space (Y,ρ), and let g be a continuous function from (Y,ρ) to the metric space (Z,θ). Then $g \circ f$ is continuous from (X,d) to (Z,θ).*

PROOF. We again use part (3) of Theorem 2.4.1, this time because compositions and inverses of functions are nicely behaved. Let O be open in (Z,θ). Then $g^{-1}(O)$ is open in Y, so that $f^{-1}(g^{-1}(O))$ is open in X. But $(g \circ f)^{-1}(O) = f^{-1}(g^{-1}(O))$. ∎

Theorem 2.4.4 *Let Y be the product of spaces $Y_1, Y_2, \ldots, Y_n$, and define $\pi_i : Y \to Y_i$ by $\pi_i((y_1, y_2, \ldots, y_n)) = y_i$.*

1. *π_i is continuous for $i = 1, 2, \ldots, n$.*
2. *A function f from a space X into Y is continuous if and only if $\pi_i \circ f$ is continuous for each $i = 1, 2, \ldots, n$.*

PROOF.

1. Let O be open in Y_i. Then $\pi_i^{-1}(O) = Y_1 \times Y_2 \times \cdots \times Y_{i-1} \times O \times Y_{i+1} \times \cdots \times Y_n$ which is open by Theorem 2.2.2.
2. If f is continuous, then so is $\pi_i \circ f$ by part (1) and Theorem 2.4.3. Conversely, suppose that $\pi_i \circ f$ is continuous for each $i = 1, 2, \ldots, n$. Let O be an open set in Y and suppose $x_0 \in f^{-1}(O)$. Then $f(x_0) \in O$, so there are sets $O_1, O_2, \ldots, O_n$ open in $Y_1, Y_2, \ldots, Y_n$, respectively, such that $f(x_0) \in O_1 \times O_2 \times \cdots \times O_n \subset O$. Then $\pi_i(f(x_0)) \in O_i$, so there is an open set U_i in X such that $x_0 \in U_i$ and $\pi_i(f(U_i)) \subset O_i$. Let $U = U_1 \cap U_2 \cap \cdots \cap U_n$. Since $\pi_i(f(U)) \subset O_i$ for each i, $f(U) \subset O_1 \times O_2 \times \cdots \times O_n$, so that $x_0 \in U \subset f^{-1}(O)$. Hence $f^{-1}(O)$ contains an open set about each of its points and so is open, so that f is continuous. ∎

Continuity is the property that corresponds to the *nontearing* part of the idea of a topological motion. The *nonsewing* part is partially expressed by requiring that the function f not identify distinct points, that is, that f be one-to-one. However, the following example illustrates a more subtle kind of sewing.

EXAMPLE.

6. Let $X = [-2, -1) \cup [1, 2]$ and $Y = [-1, 1]$, both with the usual metric inherited from R. Define $f : X \to Y$ by

$$f(x) = \begin{cases} x + 1 & x \in [-2, -1) \\ x - 1 & x \in [1, 2]. \end{cases}$$

It is easy to show that f is continuous and one-to-one. Intuitively, however, X is not connected whereas Y is, so that f cannot be a homeomorphism. One easily checks that

$$f^{-1}(y) = \begin{cases} y-1 & y \in [-1,0) \\ y+1 & y \in [0,1], \end{cases}$$

so that f^{-1} is not continuous at 0. Since topological motions should be reversible, we must make the continuity of f^{-1} a requirement.

Definition A *homeomorphism* from the space X to the space Y is a one-to-one continuous function from X onto Y whose inverse is continuous. X is then said to be *homeomorphic* or *topologically equivalent* to Y. Finally, a property P of spaces is a *topological property* if Y has P whenever X has P and Y is homeomorphic to X.

EXAMPLES.

7. We show that any closed interval in R is homeomorphic to $[0,1]$. Consider $[a,b] = \{x : a \leqslant x \leqslant b\}$, where $a < b$. We already know that linear functions are continuous, so let $f(x) = x/(b-a) - a/(b-a)$. Now f is continuous, and if $a \leqslant x \leqslant b$, then $a/(b-a) \leqslant x/(b-a) \leqslant b/(b-a)$ and $0 = a/(b-a) - a/(b-a) \leqslant x/(b-a) - a/(b-a) \leqslant b/(b-a) - a/(b-a) = 1$, so that f takes $[a,b]$ into $[0,1]$. If we set $y = x/(b-a) - a/(b-a)$ and solve for x, we get $x = (b-a)y + a$, so that $f^{-1}(y) = (b-a)y + a$. One now easily shows that f is onto, and f^{-1} is again linear and so continuous. This example confirms that length is not a topological property.

8. We show that R is homeomorphic to $(-1,1)$. Here we need a function whose values are always between -1 and 1, so we try $f(x) = x/(1 + |x|)$. Continuity of f follows from results in the next exercises. If $x < 0$ and $x/(1 + |x|) = y$, then solving $x/(1-x) = y$ for x we obtain $x = y/(1+y)$. Similarly, if $x \geqslant 0$ and $x/(1 + |x|) = y$, we obtain $x = y/(1-y)$. In either case the formula is expressed by $x = y/(1 - |y|)$, so that $f^{-1}(y) = y/(1 - |y|)$. We have thus simultaneously shown that f is one-to-one and onto. Further, f^{-1} is continuous just as f is.

It would be nice to generalize Example 1 and state that any two closed intervals are homeomorphic. This is in fact the case and is a result of the following theorem, which is quite useful in questions of homeomorphism.

Theorem 2.4.5

1. *Any space is homeomorphic to itself.*
2. *If X is homeomorphic to Y, then Y is homeomorphic to X.*

3. *If X is homeomorphic to Y and Y is homeomorphic to Z, then X is homeomorphic to Z.*

PROOF.

1. It is easy to check that the identity function is a homeomorphism.
2. If $f: X \to Y$ is a homeomorphism, then so is $f^{-1}: Y \to X$, since $(f^{-1})^{-1} = f$.
3. Let $f: X \to Y$ and $g: Y \to Z$ be homeomorphisms. By Theorem 2.4.3 $f \circ g$ and $(f \circ g)^{-1} = g^{-1} \circ f^{-1}$ are both continuous. Since composition preserves "one-to-one-ness" and "onto-ness," $f \circ g$ is a homeomorphism from X to Z. ∎

Questions of homeomorphism and topological properties, especially the latter, will occupy us for the remainder of this book. We will develop a number of topological properties which can be used to distinguish different spaces. However, questions of this sort are exceedingly difficult, so the reader is warned that all but the simplest cases are beyond the scope of this book.

Exercises

1. Prove that $f(x) = ax + b$ is continuous from R to R, where a and b are any real numbers.

2. Let (X, d) be a discrete metric space. Which functions from R to X are continuous?

3. Define $\phi_a : B([0, 1]) \to R$ by $\phi_a(f) = f(a)$, where $0 \leqslant a \leqslant 1$. Prove in detail that ϕ_a is continuous.

4. Let c be a real number and define $T_c : B([0, 1]) \to B([0, 1])$ by $T_c(f) = cf$. Prove that T_c is a homeomorphism if $c \neq 0$.

5. Let f and g be continuous functions from a metric space (X, d) into R. Prove that the following functions are continuous:
   a. $f + g$
   b. cf, where c is a real number
   c. $f \cdot g$
   d. f/g, when $g(x)$ is never 0
   e. $|f|$

6. Repeat Exercise 5, parts (a), (b), (c) when R is replaced by R^n. (Hint: recall Theorem 2.4.4.)

7. Use Exercise 5 to prove that polynomials are continuous.

8. Prove that any two intervals of the form (a, b), $(a, +\infty)$, or $(-\infty, b)$ are homeomorphic.

9. Let $X = \{1/n : n = 1,2,\ldots\} \cup \{0\}$ and let $f : X \to Y$ be given by $f(1/n) = y_n$, $f(0) = y_0$. Prove that f is continuous if and only if $[y_n]$ converges to y_0.

10. Let f be a continuous function from the space X to the space Y, and suppose that $f(X) \subset B$. Prove that $f : X \to B$ is continuous, where B is regarded as a subspace of Y.

11. Let (X,d) be the product of $(X_1,d_1), (X_2,d_2), \ldots$, and (X_n,d_n).
   a. Prove that if O is open in X and $\pi_i : X \to X_i$ is defined by $\pi_i(x_1,x_2,\ldots,x_n) = x_i$, then $\pi_i(O)$ is open in X_i.
   b. Prove that if $x_1,x_2,\ldots,x_n$ are points of $X_1,X_2,\ldots,X_n$, respectively, and $\psi : X_i \to X$ is defined by $\psi(z) = (x_1,x_2,\ldots,x_{i-1},z,x_{i+1},\ldots,x_n)$, then ψ is a homeomorphism from X_i to $\psi(X_i)$.

Part B

In this section we extend the concepts of continuity, homeomorphism, and topological property to the general case. Part 2 of Theorem 2.4.1 shows how to proceed, and also shows that the following definition agrees with that given for the metric case.

Definition Let $(X,\mathcal{T})$ and $(Y,\mathcal{U})$ be topological spaces. A function $f : X \to Y$ is *continuous at the point* x_0 of X if for each neighborhood V of $f(x_0)$ in Y there is a neighborhood U of x_0 in X such that $f(U) \subset V$. If f is continuous at each point of X, then we say that f is *continuous on* X. Also, to emphasize the topologies used we often write $f : (X,\mathcal{T}) \to (Y,\mathcal{U})$.

One might now expect Theorem 2.4.1 to be true in the topological case. However, part 5 of that theorem is suspect because of the sometimes bad behavior of sequences. What does result is the following:

Theorem 2.4.6 *Let $(X,\mathcal{T})$ and $(Y,\mathcal{U})$ be topological spaces and f a function from X to Y. Then statements (1), (2), and (3) are equivalent, and each implies statement (4).*

1. *f is continuous on X;*
2. *$f^{-1}(O)$ is open in X whenever O is open in Y;*
3. *$f^{-1}(C)$ is closed in X whenever C is closed in Y;*
4. *If $[x_n]$ is a sequence in X converging to a point x_0 in X, then $[f(x_n)]$ converges to $f(x_0)$ in Y.*

PROOF. Since by definition part (1) of Theorem 2.4.6 is essentially identical to part (2) of Theorem 2.4.1, the proofs of $(1) \Rightarrow (2) \rightleftarrows (3)$ are identical to the proofs of $(2) \Rightarrow (3) \rightleftarrows (4)$ of Theorem 2.4.1. Further, $(2) \Rightarrow (4)$ in this theorem just as $(3) \Rightarrow (5)$ in Theorem 2.4.1. We leave the proof that $(2) \Rightarrow (1)$ as an exercise. ∎

The remaining theorems and definitions of Part A go over without change to the general case. We end this section with some illuminating examples.

EXAMPLES.

1. Let $(Y, \mathfrak{U})$ be an indiscrete space, $(X, \mathfrak{T})$ any space, and $f: X \to Y$ any function. The only open sets in Y are Y and $\varnothing$, and $f^{-1}(Y) = X$, $f^{-1}(\varnothing) = \varnothing$, so that f is continuous.
2. Let $(R, \mathfrak{S})$ be the Sorgenfrey line and define

$$f(x) = \begin{cases} 0 & x < 0 \\ 1 & 0 \leqslant x. \end{cases}$$

Consider f as a function from $(R, \mathfrak{S})$ to $(R, \mathfrak{S})$. We show that f is continuous at 0. Let V be any neighborhood of $f(0) = 1$. Then $[0, 1)$ is a neighborhood of 0, and $f([0, 1)) = \{1\} \subset V$. Since we used only the fact that a neighborhood of 1 contains 1, the function f is continuous at 0 even as a function from $(R, \mathfrak{S})$ to $(R, \mathfrak{D})$, where $\mathfrak{D}$ is the discrete topology.
3. Let $(R, \mathfrak{E})$ denote R with the topology induced by the Euclidean metric, and let $\mathfrak{T}$ be the cofinite topology on R. Define $f: (R, \mathfrak{T}) \to (R, \mathfrak{E})$ by $f(x) = x$. Since $[0, 1]$ is closed in $(R, \mathfrak{E})$, but only R and finite sets are closed in $(R, \mathfrak{T})$, the function f is not continuous. This example shows strikingly that continuity depends not only on the function but also on the topologies involved.
4. Let $(R, \mathfrak{E})$ be the same as in Example 3, and let $\mathfrak{U}$ be the cocountable topology on R. Recall that the only convergent sequences in $(R, \mathfrak{U})$ are those which are eventually constant. Define $f: (R, \mathfrak{U}) \to (R, \mathfrak{E})$ by $f(x) = x$ for each x. If $x_n \to x_0$ as $n \to \infty$ in $(R, \mathfrak{U})$, then there is an integer P such that $x_n = x_0$ for $n \geqslant P$, so certainly $[f(x_n)]$ converges to $f(x_0)$ in $(R, \mathfrak{E})$. However, f is not continuous, since $[0, 1]$ is closed in $(R, \mathfrak{E})$ but only R and countable sets are closed in $(R, \mathfrak{U})$.

Example 4 shows again that sequences do not work well in nonfirst countable spaces. A theorem should immediately suggest itself, and we state it next. The proof is left as an exercise.

Theorem 2.4.7 *Let $(X, \mathfrak{T})$ be a first countable topological space and $(Y, \mathfrak{U})$ any topological space. A function $f: (X, \mathfrak{T}) \to (Y, \mathfrak{U})$ is continuous if and only if $[f(x_n)]$ converges to $f(x_0)$ in $(Y, \mathfrak{U})$ whenever $[x_n]$ converges to x_0 in $(X, \mathfrak{T})$.*

Exercises

1. Tell whether the following functions are continuous and justify your answers. $(R, \mathcal{E})$, $(R, \mathcal{T})$, $(R, \mathcal{S})$, and $(R, \mathcal{U})$ have the same meaning as in the examples in this section.

   a. $f:(R, \mathcal{T}) \to (R, \mathcal{E})$ given by $f(x) = \begin{cases} 0 & x \leqslant 0 \\ 1 & x > 0 \end{cases}$

   b. $f:(R, \mathcal{S}) \to (R, \mathcal{E})$ given by $f(x) = \begin{cases} 0 & x \leqslant 0 \\ 1 & x > 0 \end{cases}$

   c. $f:(R, \mathcal{U}) \to (R, \mathcal{T})$ given by $f(x) = x$.

   d. $f:(R, \mathcal{S}) \to (R, \mathcal{T})$ given by $f(x) = x$.

   e. $f:(R, \mathcal{T}) \to (R, \mathcal{U})$ given by $f(x) = x^2$.

2. Prove Theorem 2.4.7.

3. Prove that being first countable is a topological property.

4. Let $\bar{\mathcal{S}}$ be the topology on R consisting of R, $\varnothing$, and unions of sets of the form $(a, b]$. Prove that $(R, \bar{\mathcal{S}})$ and $(R, \mathcal{S})$ are homeomorphic.

5. Prove that if $f:(X, \mathcal{T}) \to (Y, \mathcal{U})$ is a homeomorphism and C is closed in $(X, \mathcal{T})$, then $f(C)$ is closed in $(Y, \mathcal{U})$.

6. Prove that no two of $(R, \mathcal{T})$, $(R, \mathcal{E})$, and $(R, \mathcal{U})$ are homeomorphic.

7. Which indiscrete spaces are homeomorphic? Which discrete spaces are homeomorphic?

8. State and prove the topological case of the results of Exercise 11 on p. 39.

9. Let $X = \{1, 2, 3\}$, $\mathcal{T} = \{\varnothing, X, \{1\}, \{1, 2\}\}$, $\mathcal{U} = \{\varnothing, Y, \{a\}, \{b\}, \{a, b\}\}$, $Y = \{a, b, c\}$.

   a. List all the continuous functions from $(X, \mathcal{T})$ to $(Y, \mathcal{U})$.

   b. List all the continuous functions from $(Y, \mathcal{U})$ to $(X, \mathcal{T})$.

10. Complete the proof of Theorem 2.4.6.

2.5 Connected spaces

Part A

In this section we begin our study of topological properties by making rigorous the intuitive idea of being connected, that is, being in one piece. This idea was introduced in Chapter 1, and together with some refinements was used to distinguish between several familiar spaces. We must now make mathematically correct and precise statements of these notions, and then make sure that these mathematical statements actually correspond to our intuition.

It turns out to be easier to think about the property that is the opposite of connectedness, namely, the property of being in two or more pieces. A little thought shows that the only sets which cannot be broken into two pieces are the empty set and a set consisting of exactly one element. If X is any set containing distinct elements a and b, then we can write $X = (\{a\}) \cup (X \setminus \{a\})$, neither of which is empty. Hence the property of connectedness must take account of the distance or nearness structure on the space.

Let us compare $I = [0, 1]$, which is connected (intuitively, at this stage), with $X = [0, 1] \cup [2, 3]$, which is not. X has two "natural" pieces, namely $[0, 1]$ and $[2, 3]$. I has no such natural pieces, but can be broken into two disjoint subsets in many different ways, e.g., $I = [0, \frac{1}{2}) \cup [\frac{1}{2}, 1]$. We must somehow express the difference. If we think about topological concepts, it should quickly come to mind that $[0, 1]$ and $[2, 3]$ are both closed in X, whereas no easy splitting of I into disjoint non-empty sets yields two closed subsets. This leads to the following definition.

Definition   A space X is *connected* if it is not the union of two non-empty disjoint closed subsets. The space X is *disconnected* if it is not connected. A subset A of a space X is *connected* if it is connected as a subspace of X.

It is difficult to give examples of connected spaces before some tools are developed. However, it is clear that $[0, 1] \cup [2, 3]$ is disconnected, and the reader can easily construct lots of such examples. We now prove a theorem giving some equivalent formulations of connectedness. Others will be left for the exercises.

Theorem 2.5.1   *The following are equivalent for a space X:*

1. *X is connected;*
2. *X is not the union of two non-empty disjoint open sets;*
3. *X and $\varnothing$ are the only subsets of X which are both open and closed.*

PROOF.

(1)$\Rightarrow$(2). Many proofs involving connectedness proceed by contradiction, and this one is no exception. Suppose $X = A \cup B$, where A and B are disjoint non-empty open sets. Then $A = X - B$ is closed as is $B = X - A$, so that X is not connected. This contradiction finishes this part of the proof.

(2)$\Rightarrow$(3). Suppose C is an open-and-closed subset of X which is neither X nor $\varnothing$. Then $D = X \setminus C$ is also open and non-empty, so that X is the union of the non-empty disjoint open sets C and D. Again we are done.

(3)$\Rightarrow$(1). Suppose X is not connected. Then $X = K \cup L$, where K and L are disjoint non-empty closed sets. Since $K = X \setminus L$, the set K is also open, and is neither X nor $\varnothing$. ∎

We now return to the familiar space $I = [0, 1]$. It should be connected, but the process of making concepts rigorous often leads to strange consequences (see Chapter 4). The next theorem lays any such fears to rest in this case. We first make explicit the property of the real numbers upon which the proof rests. See the Appendix for more information.

Completeness property of the real numbers *If K is a non-empty subset of the real numbers which has an upper bound, then K has a least upper bound.*

Theorem 2.5.2 *The closed unit interval $[0, 1]$ with the usual metric is connected.*

PROOF. Suppose $[0, 1]$ is not connected. Then it is the union of two non-empty disjoint closed sets K and L. We may rename these sets if necessary so that 1 is not in K. Since $K \subset [0, 1]$, the set K has an upper bound and hence a least upper bound t. If $t = 0$, then since $K \neq \varnothing$, $K = \{0\}$ and $t \in K$. If $t > 0$, then since t is the least upper bound of K each interval $(t - \varepsilon, t]$ contains a point of K, and since K is closed, t must be in K. Thus $t \neq 1$, and $(t, 1] \subset L$. But then t is certainly a limit point of L, and since L is closed, t must be in L. This contradicts the fact that K and L are disjoint. ∎

It would now be nice to conclude that any closed bounded interval is connected since it is homeomorphic to $[0, 1]$. However, we have not yet shown that connectedness is a topological property. This omission is remedied by the following theorem, which shows much more and is a very useful fact about connectedness.

Theorem 2.5.3 *Let X be a connected space, Y any space, and f a continuous function from X onto Y. Then Y is connected.* ∎

PROOF. Suppose Y is not connected. Then Y has an open-and-closed subset T which is neither Y nor $\varnothing$. Since f is onto, $f^{-1}(T)$ is neither X nor $\varnothing$. Since f is continuous, Theorem 2.4.1 implies that $f^{-1}(T)$ is both open and closed. This contradicts the fact that X is connected. ∎

Corollary 2.5.4 *Connectedness is a topological property.*

PROOF. Since a homeomorphism is certainly continuous and onto, if X and Y are homeomorphic and X is connected, Y must be connected also. ∎

The next theorem is usually quoted in calculus courses, and we see it here in its full generality. It is a very useful computational tool, as the example to follow shows.

Theorem 2.5.5 **(Intermediate Value Theorem)** *Let f be a continuous function from a connected space X to the real numbers. Let x_1 and x_2 be points of X and suppose that $f(x_1) < c < f(x_2)$. Then there is a point y of X such that $f(y) = c$.*

PROOF. Suppose there is no such point y of X. Then $f^{-1}((-\infty, c)) = f^{-1}((-\infty, c])$, so that $K = f^{-1}((-\infty, c))$ is both open and closed in X. Since $f(x_1) < c$, the set K is not empty; since $f(x_2) > c$, the set K is not all of X. This contradicts the fact that X is connected. ∎

EXAMPLE.

1. A root-finding procedure. Suppose we wish to find a root of $f(x) = x^5 - x^4 - 2x + 1$, that is, we wish to solve $f(x) = 0$. The Intermediate Value Theorem says that if $f(x_1) < 0 < f(x_2)$, then f has a root between x_1 and x_2. Now $f(0) = 1$ and $f(1) = -1$, so f has a root between 0 and 1. Since $f(\frac{1}{2}) = -\frac{1}{16}$, the function f has a root between 0 and $\frac{1}{2}$. Since $f(0.4) = 0.20768$, f has a root between 0.4 and 0.5. This procedure can be carried on inductively to locate a root of f to any desired degree of accuracy. In this case a calculator or lots of arithmetic will show that f has a root between 0.4856 and 0.4857. Further, it is clear that the procedure can be applied to any continuous computable function.

We still have very few tools to use to prove that a given space is connected. Such proofs often use the connectedness of subsets to prove the connectedness of an entire space, so we now introduce some terminology which is useful in dealing with connected subsets, and then prove some helpful theorems.

Definition Two subsets K and L of a space X are *mutually separated* if $\text{Cl}(K) \cap L = K \cap \text{Cl}(L) = \varnothing$.

EXAMPLE.

2. $[0, \frac{1}{2})$ and $(\frac{1}{2}, 1]$ are mutually separated, since $\text{Cl}([0, \frac{1}{2})) \cap (\frac{1}{2}, 1] = [0, \frac{1}{2}] \cap (\frac{1}{2}, 1] = \varnothing$ and $[0, \frac{1}{2}) \cap \text{Cl}((\frac{1}{2}, 1]) = [0, \frac{1}{2}) \cap [\frac{1}{2}, 1] = \varnothing$.

Theorem 2.5.6 *A subset A of a space X is connected if and only if A is not the union of two non-empty mutually separated subsets of X.*

PROOF. Suppose $A = K \cup L$, where K and L are non-empty mutually separated subsets of X. Then $\mathrm{Cl}_A(K) = \mathrm{Cl}_X(K) \cap A = \mathrm{Cl}_X(K) \cap (K \cup L) = (\mathrm{Cl}_X(K) \cap K) \cup (\mathrm{Cl}_X(K) \cap L) = K \cup \varnothing = K$, so that K is closed in A. Similarly L is closed in A, so that A is not connected.

Suppose A is not connected. Then $A = M \cup N$, where M and N are non-empty disjoint closed subsets of A. Since M is closed in A and $N \subset A$, $\mathrm{Cl}_X(M) \cap N = \mathrm{Cl}_X(M) \cap (A \cap N) = (\mathrm{Cl}_X(M) \cap A) \cap N = \mathrm{Cl}_A(M) \cap N = M \cap N = \varnothing$. Similarly $M \cap \mathrm{Cl}(N) = \varnothing$, so that A is the union of two non-empty mutually separated sets. ∎

Lemma 2.5.7 *Let A be a connected subset of X which is contained in the union of two mutually separated sets K and L. Then either $A \subset K$ or $A \subset L$.*

PROOF. Since $A \subset K \cup L$, $A = (A \cap K) \cup (A \cap L)$. Since K and L are mutually separated, $\mathrm{Cl}((A \cap K)) \cap (A \cap L) \subset \mathrm{Cl}(K) \cap L = \varnothing$, and similarly $(A \cap K) \cap (\mathrm{Cl}(A \cap L) = \varnothing$. Thus A is the union of the mutually separated sets $A \cap K$ and $A \cap L$, so that either $A \cap K = \varnothing$ or $A \cap L = \varnothing$ since A is connected. In the former case $A \subset L$, and in the latter case $A \subset K$. ∎

The next theorem says that the result of sewing together connected spaces is a connected space and Theorem 2.5.9 says that adding limit points does not destroy connectedness. Both are useful in constructing new connected spaces, as can be seen in the examples.

Theorem 2.5.8 *Let $\{A_\alpha : \alpha \in \mathcal{C}\}$ be a collection of connected subsets of a space X, each of which contains the point x_0. Then $A = \cup \{A_\alpha : \alpha \in \mathcal{C}\}$ is connected.*

PROOF. Suppose that A is the union of the mutually separated sets K and L, and that $x_0 \in K$. Since $A_\alpha \subset A$, Lemma 2.5.7 implies that $A_\alpha \subset K$ or $A_\alpha \subset L$. But $x_0 \in K$, so that $A_\alpha \subset K$. This is true for each α, so $A = \cup \{A_\alpha : \alpha \in \mathcal{C}\} \subset K$, and hence $L = \varnothing$. Thus A is not the union of two non-empty mutually separated sets and so it is connected. ∎

Theorem 2.5.9 *Let A be a connected subset of a space X, and let B be such that $A \subset B \subset \mathrm{Cl}(A)$. Then B is connected.*

PROOF. Suppose B is the union of mutually separated sets K and L. Since $A \subset B$ and A is connected, we can assume that $A \subset K$. Then $\mathrm{Cl}(A) \subset \mathrm{Cl}(K)$, so that $L = B \cap L \subset \mathrm{Cl}(A) \cap L \subset \mathrm{Cl}(K) \cap L = \varnothing$. Then B is connected by Theorem 2.5.6. ∎

EXAMPLES.

3. We have seen that $[0, \frac{1}{2})$ and $(\frac{1}{2}, 1]$ are mutually separated, so that $X = [0, \frac{1}{2}) \cup (\frac{1}{2}, 1]$ is not connected. X is therefore not homeomorphic to $[0, 1]$.

4. Since $[-n, n]$ is homeomorphic to $[0, 1]$, $[-n, n]$ is connected for each $n = 1, 2, \ldots$. Since $R = \cup \{[-n, n] : n = 1, 2, \ldots\}$ and $0 \in [-n, n]$ for each n, Theorem 2.5.8 applies to show that R is connected. Since (a, b) and R are homeomorphic, (a, b) is connected. Since $\mathrm{Cl}((a, b)) = [a, b]$, Theorem 2.5.9 applies to show that $(a, b]$ is connected.

5. Let p and q be distinct points of R^n. The line segment from p to q is $[p, q] = \{tp + (1 - t)q : 0 \leqslant t \leqslant 1\}$. It is an exercise to show that $[p, q]$ is homeomorphic to $[0, 1]$ and hence is connected. Since $R^n = \cup \{[\theta, q] : q \in R^n\}$, where $\theta = (0, 0, \ldots, 0)$, R^n is connected by Theorem 2.5.8.

6. Let $p = (1, 0, \ldots, 0)$ and $q = (0, 1, 0, \ldots, 0)$ be points of R^n, $n > 1$. If z is any point of R^n other than θ, then either $[p, z]$ or $[q, z]$ does not contain θ, and it is easy to show that $[p, q]$ does not contain θ. Let L_z be the one of $[p, z]$ or $[p, q] \cup [q, z]$ that misses θ. In either case L_z is connected, contains p and z, and misses θ. Hence $R^n \setminus \{\theta\} = \cup \{L_z : z \in R^n, z \neq \theta\}$ is connected.

7. The standard n-sphere S^n is defined to be $\{x \in R^{n+1} : |x| = 1\}$. For example, S^1 is the circle and S^2 the usual two-dimensional sphere. It is not hard to show that $f : R^{n+1} \setminus \{\theta\} \to S^n$ defined by $f(x) = x/|x|$ is continuous and onto. By Example 6 and Theorem 2.5.3, S^n is connected for $n \geqslant 1$.

8. Consider the space $B([0, 1])$ of bounded real-valued functions on $[0, 1]$ and its subspace $C([0, 1])$ of continuous bounded real-valued functions on $[0, 1]$. If f and g are distinct points in either of these spaces, then let $[f, g] = \{tf + (1 - t)g : 0 \leqslant t \leqslant 1\}$. Again one can show that $[f, g]$ is homeomorphic to $[0, 1]$, and techniques like those in Example 5 can be used to show that $B([0, 1])$ and $C([0, 1])$ are connected.

We conclude this section with some results and examples which make rigorous some of the exercises in Chapter 1. Note that $[0, 1]$ and S^1 are both connected, so that connectedness alone does not distinguish between these two (intuitively nonhomeomorphic) spaces. However, removal of the point $\frac{1}{2}$ disconnects $[0, 1]$, whereas S^1 contains no point whose removal disconnects S^1. It is these ideas which lie behind the following definition and theorems.

Definition Let X be a connected space. A subset S of X is said to *separate* X if $X \setminus S$ is not connected, and we then also say that S is a *cutting* of X. If $S = \{x\}$ is a cutting of X, then x is said to be *cut point* of X. If $X \setminus \{x\}$ is connected, then x is a *noncut point* of X.

Theorem 2.5.10

1. *If A is any space, X is a space with a cutting homeomorphic to A, and X is homeomorphic to Y, then Y has a cutting homeomorphic to A.*
2. *If X and Y are homeomorphic, then X and Y have the same number of cut points.*
3. *If X and Y are homeomorphic, then X and Y have the same number of noncut points.*

PROOF. We only indicate how the proofs go and leave details for the exercises. Suppose $h : X \to Y$ is a homeomorphism. For (1), if B is the cutting of X homeomorphic to A, then $h(B)$ can be shown to be a cutting of Y homeomorphic to A. For (2) and (3) we note that one can show that h is a one-to-one onto function from the set of cut points of X to the set of cut points of Y, and similarly for the sets of noncut points. ∎

EXAMPLES.

9. Since $[0,1] \setminus \{0\} = (0,1]$ is connected, 0 is a noncut point of $[0,1]$. However, if $0 < p < 1$, then $(0,1) \setminus \{p\} = (0,p) \cup (p,1)$ is not connected, so no point of $(0,1)$ is a noncut point. Hence, $[0,1]$ and $(0,1)$ are not homeomorphic by part (3) of Theorem 2.5.10.
10. The point $\frac{1}{2}$ is a cut point of $[0,1]$, but the circle S^1 has no cut point. Hence $[0,1]$ and S^1 are not homeomorphic.
11. The triod **Y** has exactly three noncut points where as the 4-od **X** has exactly four. Hence they are not homeomorphic.

Exercises

1. Prove in detail that $[0,1] \cup [2,3]$ is not connected, and give two more examples of disconnected spaces.

2. Which discrete spaces are connected? Prove your answer.

3. A subset J of the real numbers is an interval if c is in J whenever $a < c < b$ and a, b are in J. Prove that a subset of R is connected if and only if it is an interval.

4. **a.** Prove that every polynomial function is bounded on $[0,1]$.
   b. By (a) we may regard the set $P([0,1])$ of polynomials restricted to $[0,1]$ as a subset of $B([0,1])$. Prove that $P([0,1])$ is connected.

5. Give all details of the proof of Theorem 2.5.10.

6. **a.** Prove that if p and q are distinct points of R^n, then $[p,q]$ is homeomorphic to $[0,1]$.
   b. Prove that if f and g are distinct points in $B([0,1])$, then $[f,g]$ is homeomorphic to $[0,1]$.

7. Prove that if $n>1$ then no countable subset of R^n is a cutting of R^n.

8. Suppose that A and B are connected subsets of a space X. Show by example that $A \cap B$ and $A \cup B$ need not be connected.

9. Prove that R and R^n are not homeomorphic when $n>1$.

10. Prove that the following pairs of subsets of R^2 are not homeomorphic:
    a. E and H,
    b. B and 1,
    c. P and D,
    d. R and P,
    e. H and T,
    f. H and X. Warning: this may need some new tools.

11. Prove that X is connected if and only if there is no continuous function from X onto the discrete space $\{0,1\}$.

12. Find roots to three-place accuracy for the following functions:
    a. $f(x)=x^4+x^3+x-1$;
    b. $g(x)=x^2-\cos x$;
    c. $h(x)=x^4-x-1$.

13. If $x \in R^n$ and $x \neq \theta$, then define $R(x)=\{tx:t>0\}$. If C is any subset of R^n not containing θ, then prove that $R^n \setminus \cup \{R(x):x \in C\}$ is connected.

14. Use a result like that in Exercise 13 to prove that S^n has no cut points.

Part B

An examination of Part A of this section shows that all the definitions, theorems and proofs are phrased in terms of open sets, closed sets, and limit points. Nothing depends on either sequences or a metric. Hence Part A is completely valid without change for the general topological case. The purpose of this section is to delve more deeply into the theory of connectedness.

We are led into our first topic by noticing that connectedness alone does not distinguish between the space $X=[0,1]\cup[2,3]$ and the space $Y=[0,1]\cup[2,3]\cup[4,5]$. Neither of these spaces is connected; the distinguishing feature seems to be that X has two pieces whereas Y has three. *Piece* here means something like *largest connected subset*. It is this idea that is the heart of the next definition.

Definition Let x be a point of a space X. The *component* of X containing x is $\cup \{K:K$ is a connected subset of X containing $x\}$. A *component* of X is a component of X containing x for some point x of X.

The following theorem lists some important properties of components of a space, and Theorem 2.5.12 shows the usefulness of the idea.

Theorem 2.5.11 *Let X be a space.*

1. *Any component of X is connected and is not properly contained in any connected subset of X.*
2. *Distinct components of X are disjoint.*
3. *Any component of X is closed in X.*

PROOF.   Let C be the component of X containing x. Theorem 2.5.8 implies that C is connected. If $C \subset D$ and D is connected, then D is a connected subset of X containing x. Hence D is one of the K's in the definition of C, so that $D \subset C$. Thus C is not properly contained in any connected subset of X.

Suppose that C and D are components of X such that $C \neq D$. If $C \cap D \neq \varnothing$, then $C \cup D$ is connected by Theorem 2.5.8. But then C is a proper subset of the connected set $C \cup D$. This contradiction shows that $C \cap D = \varnothing$ if $C \neq D$.

Finally, consider $\mathrm{Cl}(C)$. Theorem 2.5.9 implies that $\mathrm{Cl}(C)$ is connected. It certainly contains C but cannot properly contain it, so $C = \mathrm{Cl}(C)$. Hence C is closed. ∎

Theorem 2.5.12 *The number of components of a space is a topological property of the space.*

PROOF.   Let X and Y be spaces and $f : X \to Y$ a homeomorphism. We will be done if we show that $f(C)$ is a component of Y when C is a component of X, for then $C \to f(C)$ is a one-to-one onto function from the set of components of X to the set of components of Y. Since f is continuous, $f(C)$ is connected, and hence contained in some component D of Y (see the exercises). Since f^{-1} is continuous, $f^{-1}(D)$ is connected and it also contains C, so that $f^{-1}(D) = C$. Thus $f(C) = D$. ∎

Before we see some examples, we prove a theorem which is very useful in determining the components of a space.

Theorem 2.5.13 *If K and L are mutually separated sets whose union is a space X and C is a component of X, then either $C \subset K$ or $C \subset L$.*

PROOF. C is a connected subset of $X = K \cup L$, so this theorem follows from Lemma 2.5.7. ∎

EXAMPLES.

1. Consider the spaces $X = [0,1] \cup [2,3]$ and $Y = [0,1] \cup [2,3] \cup [4,5]$ which started this discussion. $[0,1]$ and $[2,3]$ are mutually separated connected subsets of X, and so are the components of X by Theorem 2.5.13. Further, $[0,1]$ is a connected subset of Y and $[0,1]$ is mutually separated

from $[2,3] \cup [4,5]$, so $[0,1]$ is a component of Y. Similarly, $[2,3]$ and $[4,5]$ are components of Y. Theorem 2.5.12 then says that X and Y are not homeomorphic.

2. Consider the subspace Q of R consisting of all rational numbers. If p and q are any two distinct points of Q, then there is an irrational number t between them. It is easy to show that $(-\infty, t) \cap Q$ and $(t, +\infty) \cap Q$ are mutually separated, so that p and q cannot belong to the same component of Q. Hence the components of Q consist of single points.

3. One might guess that any two distinct components of a space X lie in distinct mutually separated sets whose union is X. This example shows that this guess is incorrect.

   Let $X = \{(0,0)\} \cup \{(0,1)\} \cup (\cup_{n=1}^{\infty} \{(x,y) : x = 1/n \text{ and } 0 \leqslant y \leqslant 1\})$, and regard X as a subspace of R^2. It is easy to verify that each line segment of X is a component of X.

None of these segments contains $(0,0)$ or $(0,1)$, so the component containing $(0,0)$ is a subset of $\{(0,0),(0,1)\}$ and so must be $\{(0,0)\}$. Similarly, $\{(0,1)\}$ is a component of X. Now let K and L be mutually separated sets whose union is X, and suppose that $(0,0) \in K$. The sets K and L are both closed and hence both open in X, so K is a neighborhood of $(0,0)$. Certainly the sequence $[(1/n,0)]$ converges to $(0,0)$, so there is a P such that $(1/n,0) \in K$ for $n \geqslant P$. But then the segment with one end point $(1/n,0)$ lies in K for $n \geqslant P$, so $(1/n,1) \in K$ for $n \geqslant P$. Since K is closed and the sequence $[(1/n,1)]$ converges to $(0,1)$, the set K must contain $(0,1)$. Hence $(0,1)$ and $(0,0)$ always lie in the same one of any pair of mutually separated subsets whose union is X.

Examples 2 and 3 both show that components of a space need not be open, though they are always closed. This fact allows a good deal of pathology to occur, and it is partly because of this that the following concept is needed. It is typical of a process which occurs frequently in topology which could be called the *localization* of a topological property. Given such a property P, one could require that each point of a space have arbitrarily small neighborhoods which have property P. This often leads to important and very useful ideas, and taking P to be *connectedness* is no exception.

Definition   A space X is *locally connected* if for each point x_0 of X and each neighborhood N of x_0 there is a neighborhood U of x_0 which is connected and lies in N.

It turns out that this is not the only way to localize connectedness. However, other definitions are equivalent to this one when they hold at each point of a space, but differ when they hold at some but not all points. The reader is warned to watch out for this slight nastiness when reading other more detailed texts.

Again, a theorem will make it easier to consider examples. Also, Theorem 2.5.14 shows that local connectedness prevents the pathologies present in Examples 2 and 3.

Theorem 2.5.14   *Let X be a locally connected space. Then any component of X is open in X.*

PROOF.   Let x be a point of a component C of X. Since X is a neighborhood of x, there is a connected neighborhood U of x. Then $x \in U \subset C$, so C contains a neighborhood of each of its points and so is open in X.   ∎

EXAMPLES.

4. Let X be a discrete space. Since each point x of X has $\{x\}$ for a neighborhood, X is locally connected. If X has two or more points, then X is not connected, so that locally connected spaces need not be connected.
5. Recall that if p and q are distinct points of R^n, then $[p, q]$ is the line segment joining p and q. Since $N(x_0, \varepsilon) = \cup \{[x_0, z] : z \in N(x_0, \varepsilon)\}$, the set $N(x_0, \varepsilon)$ is connected, so that R^n is locally connected. Similarly, if $x_0 \in I^n \subset R^n$, then $N(x_0, \varepsilon) \cap I^n$ is a connected neighborhood of x_0 in I^n, so that I^n is locally connected.
6. The topologist's sine curve is $S = \{(x, \sin 1/x) : 0 < x \leqslant 1\} \cup \{(0, y) : -1 \leqslant y \leqslant 1\}$ regarded as a subspace of R^2. Let $K = \{(x, \sin 1/x) : 0 < x \leqslant 1\}$. K is the continuous image of $(0, 1]$ under the map $x \rightarrow (x, \sin 1/x)$ and so K is connected. Clearly $S = \mathrm{Cl}(K)$, so that S is connected. Any neighborhood of $(0, 0)$ in S contains a neighborhood of the form $N_s((0, 0), \varepsilon)$, which looks like

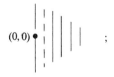

Thus no sufficiently small neighborhood of $(0,0)$ in S is connected, so that S is connected but not locally connected.

7. Recall that (R, S) denotes the Sorgenfrey line. The set $[0, +\infty)$ is both open and closed in (R, S), so that the Sorgenfrey line is not connected. Even worse, $[x_0, x_0 + \varepsilon)$ is open and closed in (R, S) for each positive ε, so that no two distinct points can lie in the same component. Thus components of (R, S) are singleton sets, and since these are not open, (R, S) is not locally connected.

We conclude this section with an investigation of a type of function which is very important in topology, and for which we will have use in Chapter 4. These functions lie somewhere between continuous functions and homeomorphisms, in that they preserve more properties than continuous functions do, but need not be homeomorphisms. An example of this is the property of local connectedness, which is not preserved by arbitrary continuous functions but is by quotient maps, which we now define.

Definition   A function f from a space X to a space Y is a *quotient map* if it is continuous, onto, and has the property that O is open in Y if $f^{-1}(O)$ is open in X.

EXAMPLES.

8. Homeomorphisms f are certainly quotient maps, because if $f^{-1}(O)$ is open, then so is $O = (f^{-1})^{-1}(f^{-1}(O))$ since f^{-1} is continuous. It will be shown later that any map from I onto any subset of R^n is a quotient map.

Theorem 2.5.15   *Let X be a locally connected space and f a quotient map from X onto a space Y. Then Y is locally connected.*

PROOF.   Let N be a neighborhood of the point y_0 of Y, and let C be the component of N containing y_0. Let $z \in f^{-1}(C) \subset f^{-1}(N)$. Since f is continuous, $f^{-1}(N)$ is a neighborhood of z, so there is a connected neighborhood U of z lying in $f^{-1}(N)$. Then $f(U)$ is connected and meets C, so $f(U) \subset C$, and hence $U \subset f^{-1}(C)$. Since $f^{-1}(C)$ contains a neighborhood of each of its points, $f^{-1}(C)$ is open. Since f is a quotient map, C is open. C certainly contains y and is contained in N, so that Y is locally connected. ∎

Corollary 2.5.16   *Local connectedness is a topological property.*

Exercises

1. Verify the details of Example 2.

2. Verify all the details of Example 3.

3. Localize the property of being first countable and prove that a locally first countable space is first countable. Thus localization does not produce a new property in this case.

4. Tell what the components of the following spaces are and verify your assertions.
   a. $[0, \frac{1}{2}) \cup (\frac{1}{2}, 1] \cup [2, 3]$
   b. The subspace of R consisting of the irrational numbers.
   c. $\{(x,y) : x = 0 \text{ or } 1/n \text{ for } n = 1, 2, 3, \ldots \text{ and } 0 \leqslant y \leqslant 1\}$
   d. The Sorgenfrey plane.
   e. The reals with the cofinite topology.

5. Use properties of sine and cosine to prove that $f : [0, 2\pi] \to S^1$ defined by $f(x) = (\cos x, \sin x)$ is a quotient map.

6. Prove that open subsets of locally connected spaces are locally connected as subspaces.

7. Give an example to show that continuous onto functions need not preserve local connectedness. Hint: any function on a discrete space is continuous.

8. Tell which of the spaces in Exercise 4 are locally connected and verify your assertions.

9. Prove that if $X_1, X_2, \ldots, X_n$ are connected spaces and X is their product, then X is connected. Hint:

$$(\{x_1\} \times \{x_2\} \times \cdots \times X_i \times \cdots \times \{x_n\})$$
$$\cap (\{x_1\} \times \{x_2\} \times \cdots \times X_j \times \cdots \times \{x_n\}) = \{(x_1, x_2, \ldots, x_n)\}.$$

10. Prove that a connected subset of a space X is contained in a unique component of X.

2.6 Countability properties

Part A

In this section we begin our study of topological properties which are linked to the question of "How many?" (See the Appendix for the necessary set theory background. The reader is warned that questions of countability will play a large role.) For example, many open sets, especially the large ones, are more or less irrelevant when dealing with problems of continuity and closure. The question arises as to how many open sets are really necessary to completely describe the topological properties of a space. We have already encountered an example of this in the fact that $\{N(x, 1/n) : n = 1, 2, \ldots\}$ is a sufficient collection of neighborhoods of x in a metric space. Properties such as this are not as intuitive or geometric as connectedness, but they play an extremely important role in many mathematical applications of topology.

Our first definition is motivated by the "thickness" of the rationals in the reals. One learns early in one's mathematical life that between every pair of distinct real numbers lies a rational number. Further, the set of rationals is countable. Countability is very useful, since it allows us to make constructions sequentially. The betweenness property of the rationals can be restated by saying that the closure of the set of rationals is the set of all real numbers.

Definition Let X be a space. A subset D of X is *dense* in X if $\mathrm{Cl}(D) = X$. X is *separable* if X has a countable dense subset.

Theorem 2.6.1 *Let X be a space. A subset D of X is dense in X if and only if every non-empty open subset of X meets D.*

PROOF. Suppose that D is dense in X and let U be a non-empty open subset of X. If $D \cap U = \varnothing$, then D is contained in the closed set $X \setminus U$, so that $\mathrm{Cl}(D) \subset X \setminus U$. But then $\mathrm{Cl}(D) \neq X$, and this contradiction establishes half of the theorem. For the converse, we note that $X \setminus \mathrm{Cl}(D)$ is open and misses D, and so must be empty. Hence $\mathrm{Cl}(D) = X$ and D is dense. ■

EXAMPLES.

1. Since every non-empty open subset of R contains an open interval (a,b), and (a,b) in turn contains a rational, the set Q of rationals is dense in R. Since Q is countable, R is separable.
2. Let X be a discrete space. Since $\{x\}$ is an open subset of X for each $x \in X$, the only dense subset of X is X itself. Thus X is separable if and only if X is countable.
3. Consider the space $B([0,1])$ and its subspace $C([0,1])$. We show that $B([0,1])$ is not separable and then with the aid of results from Section 2.7 we show that $C([0,1])$ is separable. A consequence is that on the basis of Theorem 2.6.2 these spaces are not homeomorphic.

    Suppose $D = \{ f_n : n = 1, 2, \dots \} \subset B([0,1])$. We define a function g such that $N(g, 1/2) \cap D = \varnothing$, so that D cannot be dense. Let

$$g\left(\frac{1}{n}\right) = \begin{cases} 0 & \text{if } \left| f_n\left(\frac{1}{n}\right) \right| \geq 1 \\ 2 & \text{if } \left| f_n\left(\frac{1}{n}\right) \right| < 1 \end{cases}$$

and $g(x) = 0$ when $x \notin \{1/n : n = 1, 2, \dots\}$. Certainly $g \in B([0,1])$, and $\rho(g, f_n) = \mathrm{lub}\{ |g(x) - f_n(x)| : x \in [0,1]\} \geq 1$, so that no f_n is in $N(g, 1/2)$.

The proof that $C([0,1])$ is separable is harder. Let Q denote the set of rationals, and for $\bar{s} = (s_0, s_1, \ldots, s_n) \in Q^{n+1}$ define a function $f_{\bar{s}}$ by letting $f_{\bar{s}}(k/n) = s_k$ for $k = 0, 1, \ldots, n$ and extending $f_{\bar{s}}$ linearly to the rest of $[0,1]$. Since Q^{n+1} is countable, this yields a countable set of continuous functions $f_{\bar{s}}$ for each n which in turn yields the countable set $D = \{f_{\bar{s}} : \bar{s} \in Q^{n+1}, n = 1, 2, \ldots\}$. We show that D is dense in $C([0,1])$.

Let g be in $C([0,1])$ and let ε be positive. Theorem 2.7.9 implies that there is an integer n such that $|g(x) - g(y)| < \varepsilon/6$ when $|x - y| < 1/n$. There are rational numbers $s_0, s_1, \ldots, s_n$ such that $|s_k - g(k/n)| < \varepsilon/6$ for $k = 0, 1, \ldots, n$. Let $\bar{s} = (s_0, s_1, \ldots, s_n)$. Now

$$
\begin{aligned}
|s_{k-1} - s_k| &= \left| s_{k-1} - g\left(\frac{k-1}{n}\right) + g\left(\frac{k-1}{n}\right) - g\left(\frac{k}{n}\right) + g\left(\frac{k}{n}\right) - s_k \right| \\
&\leq \left| s_{k-1} - g\left(\frac{k-1}{n}\right) \right| + \left| g\left(\frac{k-1}{n}\right) - g\left(\frac{k}{n}\right) \right| + \left| g\left(\frac{k}{n}\right) - s_k \right| \\
&< \frac{\varepsilon}{6} + \frac{\varepsilon}{6} + \frac{\varepsilon}{6} = \frac{\varepsilon}{2},
\end{aligned}
$$

so that if $x \in [(k-1)/n, k/n]$, then $|f_{\bar{s}}(x) - f_{\bar{s}}(k/n)| < \varepsilon/2$. For this same x we have

$$
\begin{aligned}
|f_{\bar{s}}(x) - g(x)| &= \left| f_{\bar{s}}(x) - f_{\bar{s}}\left(\frac{k}{n}\right) + f_{\bar{s}}\left(\frac{k}{n}\right) - g\left(\frac{k}{n}\right) + g\left(\frac{k}{n}\right) - g(x) \right| \\
&\leq \left| f_{\bar{s}}(x) - f_{\bar{s}}\left(\frac{k}{n}\right) \right| + \left| f_{\bar{s}}\left(\frac{k}{n}\right) - g\left(\frac{k}{n}\right) \right| + \left| g\left(\frac{k}{n}\right) - g(x) \right| \\
&< \frac{\varepsilon}{2} + \frac{\varepsilon}{6} + \frac{\varepsilon}{6} < \varepsilon.
\end{aligned}
$$

Thus $\rho(f_{\bar{s}}, g) < \varepsilon$, so that D meets every non-empty open subset of $C([0,1])$.

We now state and prove two facts regarding separability, one of which implies as usual that separability is a topological concept. The other allows us to conclude on the basis of Example 1 that R^n is separable.

Theorem 2.6.2

1. *Continuous images of separable spaces are separable.*
2. *Let $X_1, X_2, \ldots, X_n$ be separable spaces and let X be their product. Then X is separable.*

PROOF.

1. Let X be a separable space and f a continuous function from X onto the space Y. Let D be a countable dense subset of X and U a non-empty open subset of Y. Then $f^{-1}(U)$ is open in X and is not empty, so

55

$f^{-1}(U) \cap D \neq \emptyset$. Hence $U \cap f(D) \neq \emptyset$, and $f(D)$ is a countable dense subset of Y.

2. Let $D_1, D_2, \ldots, D_n$ be countable dense subsets of $X_1, X_2, \ldots, X_n$ and let $D = D_1 \times D_2 \times \cdots \times D_n$. D is a countable subset of X, and it remains only to show that it is dense. A non-empty open subset U of X contains a non-empty set $U_1 \times U_2 \times \cdots \times U_n$, where U_i is open in X_i. Thus there is a $d_i \in U_i \cap D_i$, so $(d_1, d_2, \ldots, d_n) \in (U_1 \times U_2 \times \cdots \times U_n) \cap D \subset U \cap D$. ∎

We now turn to a countability property which is closely related to separability but which is stronger in the general case. The motivating example is the fact that any open subset of R is a union of open intervals with rational endpoints. This does not generalize even to R^2, but notice that if a and b are rational, then $(a,b) = N(\frac{1}{2}(a+b), \frac{1}{2}(b-a))$ and both $\frac{1}{2}(a+b)$ and $\frac{1}{2}(b-a)$ are rational. Thus we should consider the collection of sets $N(x,r)$, where x belongs to a countable dense subset and r is rational. This collection of open sets is countable, and we are led to the following definition.

Definition A space X is *second countable* if there is a countable collection $\mathcal{B} = \{U_i : i = 1, 2, \ldots\}$ of open sets such that every open subset of X is a union of some subcollection of $\mathcal{B}$. Such a collection $\mathcal{B}$ is said to be a *countable base* for the space X. We remark that the empty set is the union of the empty subcollection of $\mathcal{B}$, so that we may and always will assume that $\mathcal{B}$ consists of non-empty sets.

EXAMPLES.

4. Earlier remarks show that R is second countable. Subsequent results coupled with the fact that R^n is separable will imply that R^n is second countable.

Our next theorem shows the relationship between separability and second countability for metric spaces. The general case is examined in Part B of this section.

Theorem 2.6.3 *Let X be a metric space. X is separable if and only if it is second countable.*

PROOF. Let $\mathcal{B} = \{U_i : i = 1, 2, \ldots\}$ be a countable base for X. Choose a point x_i in U_i for $i = 1, 2, \ldots$ and let $D = \{x_i : i = 1, 2, \ldots\}$. If O is a non-empty open subset of X, then there is some U_i with $U_i \subset O$, so that $x_i \in O$. Thus D is a countable dense subset of X, so that X is separable.

Conversely, let $D = \{x_i : i = 1, 2, \ldots\}$ be a countable dense subset of X. Let $\mathcal{B} = \{N(x_i, r) : x_i \in D$ and r is positive and rational$\}$. $\mathcal{B}$ is a countable collection of open subsets of X, and we can finish by showing that any open subset O of X is a union of elements of $\mathcal{B}$. Let $x \in O$. There is a positive ε such that $N(x, \varepsilon) \subset O$, and since D is dense there is a point x_i in D with $d(x, x_i) < \varepsilon/2$. There is a rational number r with $d(x, x_i) < r < \varepsilon/2$. It is an exercise to use the triangle inequality to show that $x \in N(x_i, r) \subset O$. If we denote $N(x_i, r)$ by U_x, then $O = \cup \{U_x : x \in O\}$. ∎

Theorem 2.6.2 now can be applied to second countable metric spaces, so that spaces of this type behave quite nicely. In fact, we are now able to show that separability of metric spaces is hereditary in the sense of the following theorem and corollary.

Theorem 2.6.4 *Subspaces of second countable spaces are second countable.*

PROOF. Let $\mathcal{B}$ be a countable base for a space X and let A be a subspace of X. Let $\mathcal{B}_A = \{U \cap A : U \in \mathcal{B}\}$. If O is open in A, then there is an open subset V of X such that $O = V \cap A$. Since V is a union of elements of $\mathcal{B}$, $V \cap A$ is a union of elements of $\mathcal{B}_A$, so that $\mathcal{B}_A$ is a countable base for A. ∎

Corollary 2.6.5 *Subspaces of separable metric spaces are separable.*

We will see in Part B of this section that neither Theorem 2.6.3 nor Corollary 2.6.5 holds in the general case. We conclude this section with a theorem which will be crucial in later proofs involving compactness. Before we look at the Lindelöf Covering Theorem, we introduce some terminology which will be useful both in its statement and in later work.

Definition Let X be a space. An *open cover* of X is a collection $\mathcal{C}$ of open subsets whose union is X. An *open subcover* of X is a subcollection $\mathcal{C}'$ of $\mathcal{C}$ which is also an open cover of X. We always assume that open covers consist of non-empty sets.

Theorem 2.6.6 (**Lindelöf Covering Theorem**) *Let X be a second countable space. Then every open cover $\mathcal{C}$ of X has a countable open subcover $\mathcal{C}'$.*

PROOF. We must use a countable base $\mathcal{B}$ of X to produce the countable open subcover $\mathcal{C}'$. To do this, for each element U of $\mathcal{B}$ choose an element V_U of $\mathcal{C}$ which contains U whenever this is possible. Then the collection $\mathcal{C}'$ of V_U's is countable, and we must show that the union of the V_U's is X. If

$x \in X$, then since the union of the sets in $\mathcal{C}$ is X, there is an element W of $\mathcal{C}$ containing x. Since $\mathcal{B}$ is a countable base, there is an element U of B satisfying $x \in U \subset W$. Thus it is possible to make the choice described above for U, so that $x \in U \subset V_U \in \mathcal{C}'$. ◪

Exercises

1. Prove in detail that any subspace of R^n is separable.

2. Complete the proof of Theorem 2.6.3.

3. Prove that separability is a topological property.

4. Let X be a separable space and $\mathcal{P}$ a collection of pairwise disjoint open subsets of X. Prove that $\mathcal{P}$ is countable.

5. Let A be a subset of a space X. A point x of X is a *condensation point* of A if each neighborhood of x contains uncountably many points of A. Prove that an uncountable subset A of a second countable space contains uncountably many condensation points of A. Hint: let $Y = \{x \in A : x$ is not a condensation point of $A\}$. Apply Theorem 2.6.6 to a suitable collection of open subsets of Y.

Part B

We are again in the fortunate position of having all the definitions and most of the theorems of Part A available without change in the topological case. The only exceptions are Theorem 2.6.3 and Corollary 2.6.5. Also, Theorem 2.6.2 does not apply to second countable topological spaces as it does to metric spaces, so we must determine just what does happen in the general case.

Most of this section will be devoted to examples showing the limitations encountered in the general case, but before we proceed, we abstract and investigate the property expressed in Theorem 2.6.6.

Definition A space X is a *Lindelöf space* if each open cover of X has a countable open subcover.

Results from Part A imply that each second countable space is a Lindelöf space, and hence each separable metric space is a Lindelöf space. In particular, all subspaces of R^n or $C([0, 1])$ are Lindelöf spaces. On the other hand, uncountable discrete spaces are not Lindelöf.

Lindelöf is the first covering property we have seen, but it will by no means be the last. Properties of this type permeate topology, as can be seen from an examination of more detailed works on the subject. We will not go far into this area, but only prove a theorem which is typical of such covering properties.

Theorem 2.6.7 *A closed subspace of a Lindelöf space is Lindelöf.*

PROOF. Let A be a closed subspace of the Lindelöf space X and let $\{U_\alpha : \alpha \in J\}$ be an open cover of A. There are open subsets V_α of X such that $U_\alpha = V_\alpha \cap A$. Then $\{V_\alpha : \alpha \in J\} \cup \{X - A\}$ is an open cover of X which has a countable subcover $\{V_{\alpha_i} : i = 1, 2, \ldots\} \cup \{X - A\}$. Then clearly $\{U_{\alpha_i} : i = 1, 2, \ldots\}$ is a countable open subcover of $\{U_\alpha : \alpha \in J\}$. ∎

EXAMPLES.

1. Recall that $\mathcal{T}$ denotes the cofinite topology on R. Let $\mathcal{B}$ be any countable collection of non-empty open subsets of $(R, \mathcal{T})$. Then $R \setminus B$ is finite for each B in $\mathcal{B}$, so $\cup \{R \setminus B : B \in \mathcal{B}\}$ is countable. Hence there is a point z in $R \setminus (\cup \{R \setminus B : B \in \mathcal{B}\}) = \cap \{B : B \in \mathcal{B}\}$. Then $R \setminus \{z\}$ is an open subset of $(R, \mathcal{T})$ which cannot be a union of elements of $\mathcal{B}$, so that $(R, \mathcal{T})$ is not second countable. The function $f(x) = x$ from $(R, \mathcal{E})$ to $(R, \mathcal{T})$ is continuous, so we conclude that continuous images of second countable spaces need not be second countable, in contrast to Theorem 2.6.2.

2. Recall that $(R, \mathcal{S})$ is the Sorgenfrey line. Since any neighborhood of x in $(R, \mathcal{S})$ must contain a neighborhood of the form $[x, x + 1/n)$ for some positive integer n, $(R, \mathcal{S})$ is first countable. The exercises outline a proof of the fact that $(R, \mathcal{S})$ is Lindelöf. Finally, any non-empty open subset of $(R, \mathcal{S})$ contains a set of the form $[y, y + \varepsilon)$ which in turn contains a rational, so $(R, \mathcal{S})$ is separable.

   Let $\mathcal{B}$ be a collection of open subsets of $(R, \mathcal{S})$. If every open subset of $(R, \mathcal{S})$ is to be a union of elements of $\mathcal{B}$, then $\mathcal{B}$ must contain a set U_x which satisfies $x \in U_x \subset [x, x + 1)$ for each $x \in R$. If $x < y$, then $x \in U_x$ but $x \notin U_y$, so that $U_x \neq U_y$. Hence $\mathcal{B}$ must be uncountable since R is.

   We conclude that $(R, \mathcal{S})$ is first countable, separable and Lindelöf but not second countable. However, the proof of half of Theorem 2.6.3 shows that second countable spaces are always separable.

3. Let $(R^2, \mathcal{S}')$ denote the *Sorgenfrey plane*, that is, the product of $(R, \mathcal{S})$ with itself. Let $A = \{(x, -x) : x \in R\} \subset R^2$. Since $[x, x + 1) \times [-x, -x + 1)$ is open in $(R^2, \mathcal{S}')$ and intersects A in $\{(x, -x)\}$, A has the discrete topology as a subspace of R^2. Since A is uncountable, it is certainly not separable nor Lindelöf and it is not hard to show that A is closed.

   Since any non-empty open subset of $(R^2, \mathcal{S}')$ contains a set of the form $[x, x + \varepsilon) \times [y, y + \delta)$ which in turn contains a point (p, q) with p and q rational, $(R^2, \mathcal{S}')$ is separable. Hence separable spaces may have nonseparable closed subspaces. Further, since A is closed but not Lindelöf, Theorem 2.6.7 implies that $(R^2, \mathcal{S}')$ is not Lindelöf, so that the product of Lindelöf spaces need not be Lindelöf.

Exercises

1. Prove that the subset A of (R^2, S') in Example 3 is closed.

2. Prove that a second countable space is first countable.

3. Prove that the product of second countable spaces $X_1, X_2, \ldots, X_n$ is second countable.

4. Prove that the continuous image of a Lindelöf space is Lindelöf.

5. Tell whether the following spaces are Lindelöf, second countable, or separable and justify your answers.
   a. R with the cofinite topology
   b. R with the cocountable topology
   c. R with the topology $\{R, \varnothing\} \cup \{(a, +\infty) : a \in R\}$
   d. R with the topology $\{U : 0 \in U$ or $R \setminus \{1, 2\} \subset U\} \cup \{\varnothing\}$.

6. Prove that open subspaces of separable spaces are separable.

7. Throughout this exercise we suppose that $\sigma = \{[a_\alpha, b_\alpha) : \alpha \in J\}$ is a collection of half-open intervals whose union is R.
   a. Prove that there is a countable subcollection $\{[a_{\alpha_i}, b_{\alpha_i}) : i = 1, 2, \ldots\}$ of σ whose union contains $\cup\{(a_\alpha, b_\alpha) : \alpha \in J\}$.
   b. Prove that $R \setminus \cup\{(a_\alpha, b_\alpha) : \alpha \in J\}$ is countable. Hint: suppose a_1 and a_2 are elements of $R \setminus \cup\{(a_\alpha, b_\alpha) : \alpha \in J\}$. Then $[a_1, b_1) \cap [a_2, b_2) = \varnothing$. Use Exercise 4, page 58.
   c. Prove that some countable subcollection of A has union R.

2.7 Compact spaces

Part A

In this section we study the topological property which may well be the most important of all, namely compactness. It is a cover-and-counting kind of property similar to the one introduced in the Lindelöf Covering Theorem (Theorem 2.6.6) but much more powerful and also capable of being translated into properties which are useful in other areas of mathematics. Its consequences are fundamental even in the first calculus courses, as we shall eventually see.

Before we plunge into a study of compactness, we give a preview of some reasons for its importance. Though we will not develop a proof of the result, it turns out that compact metric spaces are exactly those on which every continuous real-valued function has a maximum value. This is a property which any calculus student should readily appreciate. Further, compact subsets of R^n are precisely those that are closed and bounded, and some readers may already be aware of the fact that sequences behave as nicely as possible in such spaces. We have already hinted at several possible definitions, but after much evolution the following one has turned out to be correct.

Definition A space X is *compact* if every open cover of X has a finite subcover. As usual, a subset K of a space X is compact if it is compact as a subspace.

Note that compactness is precisely the strengthening of the Lindelöf property of Theorem 2.6.6 obtained by replacing *countable* by *finite*. We also remark that as in the case of connectedness, some theorems will be necessary before we can give good examples. Further, part 3 of Theorem 2.7.1 implies as usual that compactness is a topological property.

Theorem 2.7.1

1. *Closed subsets of compact spaces are compact.*
2. *If X is the product of compact spaces $X_1, X_2, \ldots, X_n$, then X is compact.*
3. *Continuous images of compact spaces are compact.*

PROOF.

1. Let K be a closed subset of a compact space X, and let $\mathcal{U} = \{ U_\alpha : \alpha \in J \}$ be an open cover of K. X has open sets V_α such that $U_\alpha = V_\alpha \cap K$, and $\{ V_\alpha : \alpha \in J \} \cup \{ X \setminus K \}$ is an open cover of X. Hence we get a finite open subcover $\{ V_{\alpha_1}, V_{\alpha_2}, \ldots, V_{\alpha_n}, X \setminus K \}$, and clearly $\{ U_{\alpha_1}, U_{\alpha_2}, \ldots, U_{\alpha_n} \}$ is a finite open subcover of $\mathcal{U}$.
2. It is enough to prove that the product $X \times Y$ of compact spaces X and Y is compact, for induction can then be used to get the general result. So let $\mathcal{U} = \{ U_\alpha : \alpha \in J \}$ be an open cover of $X \times Y$. We must transfer attention to the individual spaces X and Y, so we note that for each point (x,y) of $X \times Y$ there are open sets $U_{(x,y)}$, $V_{(x,y)}$ in X, Y, respectively, such that $(x,y) \in U_{(x,y)} \times V_{(x,y)} \subset U_\alpha$ for some $\alpha \in J$.

   Fix a point x in X for the time being. $\{ V_{(x,y)} : y \in Y \}$ is then an open cover of Y, and so has a finite subcover $\{ V_{(x,y_{x,i})} : i = 1, 2, \ldots, r_x \}$. If $U_x = \cap \{ U(x, y_{x,i}) : i = 1, 2, \ldots, r_x \}$, then U_x is an open set in X containing x such that $U_x \times V_{(x, y_{x,i})} \subset U_\alpha$ for some $\alpha \in J$ and all $i = 1, 2, \ldots, r_x$.

   Now $\{ U_x : x \in X \}$ is an open cover of X, and so has a finite subcover $\{ U_{x_j} : j = 1, 2, \ldots, s \}$. It is not hard to check that $\{ U_{x_j} \times V_{(x_j, y_{x_j, i})} : i = 1, 2, \ldots, r_{x_j}, j = 1, 2, \ldots, s \}$ is an open cover of $X \times Y$, each member of which is contained in some member of $\mathcal{U}$. Choosing such members of $\mathcal{U}$ yields a finite open subcover of $\mathcal{U}$.
3. Let X be a compact space and f a continuous function from X onto a space Y. Let $\mathcal{U} = \{ U_\alpha : \alpha \in A \}$ be an open cover of Y. Then

$\{f^{-1}(U_\alpha):\alpha\in A\}$ is an open cover of X and so has a finite subcover $\{f^{-1}(U_{\alpha_1}),f^{-1}(U_{\alpha_2}),\ldots,f^{-1}(U_{\alpha_n})\}$. Since f is onto, $\{U_{\alpha_1},U_{\alpha_2},\ldots,U_{\alpha_n}\}$ is a finite subcover of $\mathfrak{U}$. ■

Part 2 of Theorem 2.7.1 has an extremely important generalization to the case of arbitrary products which is called the *Tychonoff theorem*. We postpone its statement and proof, and instead take an important step toward determining precisely which subsets of R^n are compact. First we need some terminology.

Definition A subset B of a metric space (X,d) is *bounded* if there is a point x_0 and a number M such that $B\subset N(x_0,M)$.

Theorem 2.7.2 *Let K be a compact subset of a metric space (X,d). Then K is closed and bounded.*

PROOF. Let $x_0\in X$. Then $\{N(x_0,r)\cap K:r>0\}$ is an open cover of K and so has a finite subcover $\{N(x_0,r_1),N(x_0,r_2),\ldots,N(x_0,r_s)\}$. Let $M=\max\{r_1,r_2,\ldots,r_s\}$. Then $N(x_0,r_i)\subset N(x_0,M)$ for $i=1,2,\ldots,s$, so that $K\subset N(x_0,M)$.

To prove that K is closed we use a technique that is quite common in proofs involving compactness. Let x be a point of X not in K. We will be done if we find an open set containing x and missing K, and to do this we must use the finite subcovering property of K.

Let p be a point of K. Then $p\neq x$, so $U_p=N(p,\frac{1}{2}d(p,x))$ and $V_p=N(x,\frac{1}{2}d(p,x))$ are disjoint. $\{U_p\cap K:p\in K\}$ is an open cover of K, and so has a finite subcover $\{U_{p_1}\cap K,U_{p_2}\cap K,\ldots,U_{p_n}\cap K\}$. Let $V=V_{p_1}\cap V_{p_2}\cap\ldots\cap V_{p_n}$. Then $V\cap U_{p_i}=\varnothing$ for $i=1,2,\ldots,n$, and $K\subset U_{p_1}\cup U_{p_2}\cup\ldots\cup U_{p_n}$, so that V is an open set containing x and missing K. Note that finiteness is necessary because an infinite intersection of open sets need not be open. ■

We are already in the position of being able to prove one of the fundamental theorems of elementary calculus. In fact, a close examination of the first theorems of differential calculus will show that almost all have the following as their basis.

Theorem 2.7.3 *A real-valued continuous function f on a compact space X has a maximum value and a minimum value, i.e., there are points x_0, x_1 of X such that $f(x_0)\leqslant f(x)\leqslant f(x_1)$ for each $x\in X$.*

PROOF. Theorem 2.7.1 implies that $f(X)$ is a compact subset of R, and so $f(X)$ is closed and bounded by Theorem 2.7.2. Then $\text{lub}f(X)$ and $\text{glb}f(X)$

exist, and it is not hard to show that they belong to $f(X)$. Letting x_0 and x_1 be points such that $\text{lub} f(X) = f(x_1)$ and $\text{glb} f(X) = f(x_0)$ finishes the proof. ∎

There is one missing link which must be filled before we can characterize the compact subsets of Euclidean spaces. It has to do with our favorite space, namely, $[0, 1]$, and is the subject of the next theorem.

Theorem 2.7.4 $[0, 1]$ *is compact.*

PROOF. Let $\mathcal{U} = \{ U_\alpha : \alpha \in \mathcal{C} \}$ be an open cover of $[0, 1]$. Let $S = \{ x \in [0, 1] : [0, x]$ is covered by a finite subcollection of $\mathcal{U} \}$. Since $[0, \varepsilon]$ is contained in some U_α for some $\varepsilon > 0, \varepsilon/2$ is in S. Thus S is non-empty, so that the Completeness Axiom implies that S has a least upper bound t. Certainly $t \in [0, 1]$, so t is in some U_β, and for some positive δ, $(t - \delta, t] \subset U_\beta$. Since a finite subset of $\mathcal{U}$ must cover $[0, t - \delta]$, we can add U_β and conclude that some finite subset of $\mathcal{U}$ covers $[0, t]$, that is, $t \in S$.

If $t \neq 1$, then the δ above could have been chosen so that $(t - \delta, t + \delta) \subset U_\beta$, so that $t + \delta/2 \in S$. This contradicts the fact that t is an upper bound for S, so that $t = 1$ and we are done. ∎

Theorem 2.7.5 *A subset K of R^n is compact if and only if it is closed and bounded.*

PROOF. The *only if* part is Theorem 2.7.2. For the *if* part, let $K \subset N((x_1, x_2, \ldots, x_n), M)$. Then any coordinate of a point of K can differ from the corresponding coordinate of $(x_1, x_2, \ldots, x_n)$ by no more than M, so that $K \subset [x_1 - M, x_1 + M] \times [x_2 - M, x_2 + M] \times \cdots \times [x_n - M, x_n + M]$. Since compactness is topological, Theorem 2.7.3 implies that each $[x_i - M, x_i + M]$ is compact, and hence the product is also compact by Theorem 2.7.1. Thus K is a closed subset of a compact space and so is compact. ∎

EXAMPLES.

1. The spheres $S^n = \{ x \in R^{n+1} : |x| = 1 \}$ are compact, since they are closed bounded subsets of R^{n+1}.
2. $N(0, 1)$ is not a compact subset of R^n, for though it is bounded it is not closed.
3. R^n itself is not compact, for though it is closed it is not bounded.
4. If X is a discrete space, then $\{ \{x\} : x \in X \}$ is an open cover of X. Thus X is compact if and only if it is finite.
5. $S = \{ 1/n : n = 1, 2, \ldots \} \cup \{0\}$ is easily seen to be closed and bounded in R, and so is compact. A previous exercise showed that a convergent sequence together with its limit is a continuous image of S, and so is

compact, regardless of the space it is in. Theorem 2.7.2 then implies that a convergent sequence in a metric space is always bounded.

6. Consider the space $C([0,1])$. Define $\theta(x)=0$ for all x, and let $K = \{f \in C([0,1]) : \rho(\theta,f) \leq 1\}$. Then K is certainly a closed and bounded subset of $C([0,1])$. We will show that K is not compact, so that closed and bounded imply compact only for subsets of R^n. For $n \geq 2$ define f_n by

$$f_n\left(\frac{1}{n}\right) = 1, \quad f_n(0) = f_n\left(\frac{1}{n+1}\right) = f_n\left(\frac{1}{n-1}\right) = f_n(1) = 0$$

and extending f_n linearly to the rest of $[0,1]$. Then $f_n \in K$ for all n and $\rho(f_n,f_m)=1$ if $n \neq m$. Let $\mathfrak{U} = \{N(g,\frac{1}{2}) \cap K : g \in K\}$. $\mathfrak{U}$ is an open cover of K and if it has a finite subcover, then there is a g in K such that $N(g,\frac{1}{2})$ contains f_p and f_q for $p \neq q$. But then $\rho(f_p,f_q) \leq \rho(f_p,g)+\rho(g,f_q) < \frac{1}{2}+\frac{1}{2} = 1$. This contradiction shows that $\mathfrak{U}$ cannot have a finite subcover, so that K cannot be compact.

We now study another type of compactness called *sequential compactness*. It is not the same as compactness in the general case, but they do agree for metric spaces. Sequential compactness is often useful, since sequences arise frequently and are a nice way to tie together compactness, continuity, closure, etc. Section 3.6 will give the proper generalization to the topological case.

We have noted previously that sequences behave very nicely in metric spaces. In fact, any topological idea can be defined via sequences in the metric case. In particular, convergent sequences are crucial. It is far too much to ask that every sequence in a space be convergent, but it often happens that "part" of a sequence is convergent. For example, $[(-1)^n]$ does not converge, but $[(-1)^{2n}]$ does.

Definition Let $[n(j)]$ be any strictly increasing sequence of positive integers, i.e., $n(1)<n(2)<n(3)<\dots$. Let $[s(i)]$ be any sequence. Then $[s(n(i))]$ is a *subsequence* of $[s(i)]$.

Recall that $s(i)$ is usually denoted by s_i. Thus $n(i)$ would be n_i and $s(n(i))$ would be s_{n_i}. This is the usual notation for subsequences. Note also that since $[n(i)]$ is a strictly increasing sequence, $n(i) \geq i$. This fact is often useful in dealing with subsequences.

EXAMPLE.

7. Let $s_i = (-1)^i$, and $n(i)=2i$. Then $s_{n_i} = (-1)^{n_i} = (-1)^{2i} = 1$. Thus $1,1,1,\dots$ is a subsequence of $-1,1,-1,1,-1,\dots$.

We state and prove one easy fact about subsequences before delving into the compactness-related properties.

Theorem 2.7.6 *Let $[s_i]$ be a sequence in a space X which converges to q, and let $[s_{n_i}]$ be a subsequence of $[s_i]$. Then $[s_{n_i}]$ converges to q.*

PROOF. Let U be any neighborhood of q. There is an integer P such that $s_j \in U$ for $j \geqslant P$. Now if $i \geqslant P$, then $n_i \geqslant i \geqslant P$, so that $s_{n_i} \in U$ for $i \geqslant P$. ∎

Definition A space X is *sequentially compact* if every sequence in X has a subsequence which converges to a point of X.

Our first aim is to show that sequential compactness is equivalent to compactness for metric spaces. One might expect the proof to be somewhat involved, since the two concepts seem quite unrelated. In this case, expectations are fulfilled. The first step is Theorem 2.7.7, which relates sequential compactness to a covering property via Theorems 2.6.3 and 2.6.6.

Theorem 2.7.7 *A sequentially compact metric space is separable.*

PROOF. Let (X,d) be a sequentially compact metric space. We must construct a countable dense subset D of X. To do this we construct sets D_n such that every point of X is within $1/n$ of a point of D_n. Each D_n will be finite, so that $D = \cup \{D_n : n = 1, 2, \dots\}$ is countable. We leave as an exercise the proof that D is dense.

We now construct D_n. Let x_1 be any point of X. If $X \subset N(x_1, 1/n)$, then let $D_n = \{x_1\}$. Otherwise, let $x_2 \in X \setminus N(x_1, 1/n)$. If $X \subset N(x_1, 1/n) \cup N(x_2, 1/n)$, then let $D_n = \{x_1, x_2\}$. Otherwise, let $x_3 \in X \setminus (\cup \{N(x_i, 1/n) : i = 1, 2\})$. Suppose that for each j, X is not a subset of $\cup \{N(x_i, 1/n) : i = 1, 2, \dots, j\}$. Then we get a sequence $[x_i]$ which by construction satisfies $d(x_i, x_j) \geqslant 1/n$ for $i \neq j$. Since X is sequentially compact, $[x_i]$ has a subsequence $[x_{m_i}]$ which converges to the point q of X. Then there is an integer P such that $d(x_{m_i}, q) < 1/2n$ for $i \geqslant P$, so that

$$d(x_{m_p}, x_{m_{p+1}}) \leqslant d(x_{m_p}, q) + d(q, x_{m_{p+1}}) < \frac{1}{2n} + \frac{1}{2n} = \frac{1}{n}.$$

Thus for some $j, X \subset \cup \{N(x_i, 1/n) : i = 1, 2, \dots, j\}$, so that we may take D_n to be $\{x_1, x_2, \dots, x_j\}$. ∎

Theorem 2.7.8 *A metric space is compact if and only if it is sequentially compact.*

PROOF. We first build on Theorem 2.7.7 and prove that a sequentially compact metric space is compact. Let $\mathcal{U}$ be an open cover of such a space X. Theorem 2.7.7 implies that X is separable, and then Theorems 2.6.3 and 2.6.6 imply that $\mathcal{U}$ has a countable subcover $\mathcal{V} = \{ U_i : i = 1, 2, \ldots \}$.

Suppose that $\mathcal{V}$ has no finite subcover. Then for each positive integer i there is a point x_i in $X \setminus (U_1 \cup U_2 \cup \ldots \cup U_i)$. Then $[x_i]$ has a subsequence $[x_{n_i}]$ which converges to a point x of X. Since $\mathcal{V}$ is an open cover of X, there is a k such that $x \in U_k$. For some integer P, $x_{n_i} \in U_k$ for $i \geqslant P$. But then $x_{n_{P+k}}$ is both in U_k and in $X \setminus (U_1 \cup U_2 \cup \ldots \cup U_k \cup \ldots \cup U_{n_{P+k}})$, a contradiction. Hence $\mathcal{V}$ and therefore $\mathcal{U}$ have finite subcovers.

We must now show that a compact metric space Y is sequentially compact. Note that if q is a limit point of a subsequence of a sequence $[y_i]$ in Y, then each neighborhood of q must contain y_i for infinitely many i's. Note also that we can build an open cover from neighborhoods, and thus open the way to the use of compactness.

Suppose that each point y of Y is contained in an open set U_y containing y_i for only finitely many i's; that is, there is an integer N_y such that $y_i \in U_y$ only if $i < N_y$; then $\{ U_y : y \in Y \}$ is an open cover of Y, and so has a finite subcover $\{ U_{y_1}, U_{y_2}, \ldots, U_{y_n} \}$. Let $P = \max\{ N_{y_1}, N_{y_2}, \ldots, N_{y_n} \}$. Then y_P is not in U_{y_i} for $i = 1, 2, \ldots, n$, and so is not in $Y = U_{y_1} \cup U_{y_2} \cup \ldots \cup U_{y_n}$. This contradiction shows that some point y of Y has the property that every open set containing y also contains y_i for infinitely many i's.

Now we construct a subsequence of $[y_i]$ which converges to y. Choose n_1 such that $y_{n_1} \in N(y, 1)$. Since $N(y, \frac{1}{2})$ contains y_i for infinitely many i's, there is an n_2 such that $y_{n_2} \in N(y, \frac{1}{2})$ and $n_2 > n_1$. Similarly there is an n_3 such that $y_{n_3} \in N(y, \frac{1}{3})$ and $n_3 > n_2$. Continuing this procedure we obtain a strictly increasing sequence of integers $n_1, n_2, n_3, \ldots$ such that $y_{n_i} \in N(y, 1/i)$. Clearly $[y_{n_i}]$ is a subsequence of $[y_i]$ which converges to y. ∎

We illustrate the use of sequential compactness in the proof of the next theorem. This gives an important property of compact metric spaces which is used quite frequently in calculus and other parts of analysis. We first need a definition.

Definition Let (X, d) and (Y, ρ) be metric spaces, and f a function from X to Y. The function f is uniformly continuous if for each positive ε there is a positive α such that $\rho(f(x), f(y)) < \varepsilon$ whenever $d(x, y) < \alpha$.

The reader should carefully compare the definition of uniform continuity with the $\varepsilon - \alpha$ definition of continuity in Section 2.4. Note that uniform continuity requires that a single α work for each x, whereas for continuity the α may vary with x. "Uniform" concepts such as this do not generalize to the topological case. Instead, a new type of nearness structure called a *uniformity* has been invented, and "uniform" concepts then generalize to "uniform" spaces. The study of such spaces is beyond the scope of this book, and the interested reader is urged to consult more advanced texts for more information.

Theorem 2.7.9 *Let (X,d) be a compact metric space and f a continuous function from (X,d) to a metric space (Y,ρ). Then f is uniformly continuous.*

PROOF. We use the sequential compactness of X and argue by contradiction. Suppose ε is a positive number for which no positive α works. We need a sequence, so as usual we use the fact that $1/n$ does not work as α. This means that there are points a_n and b_n of X such that $d(a_n,b_n)<1/n$ but $\rho(f(a_n),f(b_n))\geqslant\varepsilon$. The sequence $[a_n]$ has a subsequence $[a_{n_i}]$ which converges to a point q of X. It is an easy exercise to show that $[b_{n_i}]$ also converges to q. Since f is continuous, both $[f(a_{n_i})]$ and $[f(b_{n_i})]$ converge to $f(q)$. But then for large enough i, $\rho(f(a_{n_i}),f(b_{n_i}))$ must be less than ε. This contradiction completes the proof. ∎

EXAMPLE.

8. Consider the function $f(x)=x^2$ from R to R. We show that f is not uniformly continuous by showing that no α works for $\varepsilon=1$. Suppose that x and α are positive. Then $(x+\alpha/2)^2-x^2=x\alpha+\alpha^2/4$. To make this larger than 1 we need only take $x=1/\alpha$. Note, however, that Theorem 2.7.9 says that f is uniformly continuous when restricted to any closed bounded subset of R.

Exercises

1. Fill in all the details of the proof of Theorem 2.7.7.

2. Fill in all the details of the proof of Theorem 2.7.9.

3. Tell which of the following spaces are compact and justify your answers.
   a. $[0,1)$.
   b. The subspace $P([0,1])$ of $C([0,1])$ consisting of all polynomials restricted to $[0,1]$.
   c. The subspace Z of R consisting of all the integers.
   d. The subspace of $P([0,1])$ consisting of all polynomials of degree less than 11 with coefficients lying in $[0,1]$.

4. Prove that I^n and R^n are not homeomorphic.

5. Prove that if $\{K_i:i=1,2,\ldots\}$ is a collection of non-empty compact subspaces of X such that $K_1\supset K_2\supset K_3\supset\ldots$, then $\cap\{K_i:i=1,2,\ldots\}\neq\varnothing$.

6. Suppose that X is a compact space, Y a metric space, and f a continuous map from X into Y. Prove that if C is a closed subset of X, then $f(C)$ is a closed subset of Y.

7. Suppose that X is a compact space, Y a metric space, and f a continuous one-to-one map from X onto Y. Prove that f is a homeomorphism.

8. The diameter of a subset A of a metric space (X,d) is defined by diam $A = \text{lub}\{d(x,y) : x,y \in A\}$. Let $\mathfrak{U}$ be an open cover of a compact metric space (X,d). Prove that there is a positive number S such that any set of diameter less than S lies in a single element of $\mathfrak{U}$. Hint: argue by contradiction and use sequences as in the proof of Theorem 2.7.9.

9. Prove that a continuous function f from R^n to a metric space (Y,ρ) is uniformly continuous on each bounded subset of R^n.

10. Prove that the union of two compact subsets of a space X is compact.

11. Prove that if $[s_i]$ is a convergent sequence in a metric space X and $[s_{n_i}]$ is a subsequence converging to p, then $[s_i]$ converges to p.

12. Fill in all details of the proof of Theorem 2.7.3.

Part B

In this section we investigate how the concepts from Part A behave in the general situation, and then localize the property of compactness. We first note that the definition of compact space and sequentially compact space given in Part A carry over without change to the topological case. So also do Theorems 2.7.1, 2.7.3, and their proofs. However, the remainder of the Theorems in Part A depend in one way or another on the fact that metric spaces are involved. A closer look shows that proofs of such theorems often use only part of the power of a metric, and so our first task is to discuss more precisely what properties are needed to obtain the same results.

Theorems 2.7.2, 2.7.4, 2.7.5, and 2.7.9 use metrics in a very essential way, so we concentrate on a more thorough study of Theorem 2.7.8. We first note that the proof of Theorem 2.7.8 conceals two properties of spaces which were not explicitly identified in Part A. They form the subject of the following definition.

Definition A space X is *countably compact* if every countable open cover of X has a finite subcover. A space Z has the *Bolzano—Weierstrass property* if every infinite subset of Z has a limit point.

The relationships between the four types of compactness thus far introduced (compact, sequentially compact, countably compact, and

Bolzano—Weierstrass property) are complicated. We only discuss some of them, leaving some proofs for exercises, and refer the reader to other texts for more details. In fact, we will not even formally state theorems.

The most important relationship is that all four properties are equivalent in metric spaces. In the general case, it is easy to see that compactness implies countable compactness, and that a countably compact Lindelöf space is compact. Further, the proof of Theorem 2.7.8 shows that a sequentially compact space is countably compact. It is also true that a countably compact space has the Bolzano—Weierstrass property. Finally, a countably compact first countable space is sequentially compact, and a space with the Bolzano—Weierstrass property and the property that finite sets are closed is countably compact. Again, for definitions of other closely related properties and proofs of these and even more facts, the reader is urged to consult other texts.

EXAMPLES.

1. Consider the set R with the cofinite topology $\mathcal{T}$. Let $K \subset R$, and let $\mathcal{U} = \{U_\alpha \cap K : \alpha \in \mathcal{C}\}$ be an open cover of K, where U_α is open in R. Now $R \setminus U_\alpha$ is finite for each α, so we can choose any $U_\alpha \cap K$ and then finitely many $U_\beta \cap K$'s which cover $K \setminus U_\alpha$, so that $\mathcal{U}$ has a finite subcover. Thus any subspace of $(R, \mathcal{T})$ is compact, so that compact subsets of $(R, \mathcal{T})$ need not be closed.

2. Consider the Sorgenfrey line $(R, \mathcal{S})$. Suppose that K is a compact subset of $(R, \mathcal{S})$ that contains $[x, x + \varepsilon)$ for some x and some positive ε. Since $[x, x + \varepsilon)$ is closed in $(R, \mathcal{S})$, it must also be compact. But

$$\left\{ \left[x + \frac{(n-1)}{n} \varepsilon, x + \frac{n}{n+1} \varepsilon \right) : n = 1, 2, \ldots \right\}$$

is an open cover of $[x, x + \varepsilon)$ with no finite subcover. Hence a compact subset of $(R, \mathcal{S})$ never contains a neighborhood of any of its points.

We now "localize" the property of compactness. The reader is again warned that there are several ways to do this, not all of which yield the same property. They are all equivalent in the important case of metric spaces, and our definition avoids some of the pathology which occurs in other formulations.

Definition A space S is *locally compact* if each neighborhood of any point x of X contains a compact set K which in turn contains a neighborhood of x.

EXAMPLES.

3. R^n is locally compact, since $\text{Cl}(N(x,r)) = \{y \in R^n : d(x,y) \leqslant r\}$ is always compact. Then any neighborhood U of x contains $N(x,s)$ for some s, and then $U \supset \text{Cl}(N(x,s/2)) \supset N(x,s/2)$. Thus locally compact spaces need not be compact.

4. Example 2 implies that the Sorgenfrey line is not locally compact.

5. Section 3.4 will deliver examples of compact spaces which are not locally compact.

We prove only one theorem dealing with local compactness and leave others for later sections.

Theorem 2.7.10 *Closed subsets of locally compact spaces are locally compact.*

PROOF.   Let K be a closed subset of a locally compact space X and let U be a neighborhood in K of a point x of K. There is a neighborhood V in X of x such that $U = V \cap K$, and then there is a compact set C which contains a neighborhood W of x in X and is contained in V. Since K is closed, $K \cap C$ is closed in C and so is compact. Further, $K \cap C$ contains $W \cap K$, which is a neighborhood of x in K, and certainly $K \cap C \subset K \cap V = U$. ■

We close this section with a theorem concerning the Hilbert cube I^∞, the definition of which was given in Part B of Section 2.2. Theorem 2.7.11 will have interesting consequences later, and its proof illustrates a diagonalizing process which is often useful in arguments involving sequences.

Theorem 2.7.11 *The Hilbert cube is compact.*

PROOF.   We use the fact that I^∞ is a metric space, and prove that it is sequentially compact. Recall that $I^\infty = [0,1] \times [0,\frac{1}{2}] \times [0,\frac{1}{3}] \times \dots$. To simplify notation, instead of using subscripts to denote coordinate position we employ the functions $\pi_i : I^\infty \to [0, 1/i]$ defined by $\pi_i((z_1, z_2, \dots)) = z_i$. Let $[x_i]$ be a sequence in I^∞. Since $[0,1]$ is compact and $[\pi_1(x_i)]$ is a sequence in $[0,1]$, $[x_i]$ has a subsequence which we will (somewhat unusually) denote by $[_1x_i]$, such that $[\pi_1(_1x_i)]$ converges to a point p_1 of $[0,1]$. A similar argument delivers a subsequence $[_2x_i]$ of $[_1x_i]$ such that $[\pi_2(_2x_i)]$ converges to a point p_2 of $[0,\frac{1}{2}]$. Continuing inductively we get sequences $[_1x_i],[_2x_i],[_3x_i],\dots$ such that $[_{n+1}x_i]$ is a subsequence of $[_nx_i]$ and $[\pi_n(_nx_i)]$ converges to a point p_n of $[0,1/n]$.

Consider the sequence $[_nx_n]$. It is clearly a subsequence of $[x_n]$, and we finish by showing that it converges to $(p_1,p_2,\ldots)$. Let ε be positive. There is an integer N such that $\sum_{i=N+1}^{\infty}(1/i)^2<\varepsilon^2/2$. Since $[\pi_j(_nx_n)]$ converges to p_j (an exercise), there is an integer M_j such that $|\pi_j(_nx_n)-p_j|<\varepsilon/\sqrt{2N}$ for $n\geqslant M_j$. Let $M=\max\{M_1,M_2,\ldots,M_j\}$. Then for $n\geqslant M$,

$$d(_nx_n,(p_1,p_2,\ldots))$$

$$=\sqrt{\sum_{i=1}^{\infty}|\pi_i(_nx_n)-p_i|^2}<\sqrt{\left(\sum_{i=1}^{N}\frac{\varepsilon^2}{2N}\right)+\frac{\varepsilon^2}{2}}$$

$$=\sqrt{\varepsilon^2}=\varepsilon. \qquad\blacksquare$$

Exercises

1. Fill in all details of the proof of Theorem 2.7.11.

2. Prove that open subsets of locally compact spaces are locally compact.

3. Prove that the subspace of R consisting of the rationals is not locally compact.

4. Prove that $B([0,1])$ is not locally compact. Hint: denote the zero function by θ. Define f_n by $f_n(1/n)=\varepsilon/2$, $f_n(x)=0$ otherwise. Then $[f_n]$ lies in $N(\theta,\varepsilon)$ but has no convergent subsequence.

5. Prove that X is compact if and only if it is countably compact and Lindelöf.

6. Prove that a second countable locally compact space is the union of an increasing sequence of compact sets (see Exercise 10 of Section 2.7, Part A).

7. Prove that a countably compact first countable space X is sequentially compact. Hint: let $[x_n]$ be a sequence in X, and suppose each point x of X has a neighborhood U_x containing x_n for only finitely many n. Let $V_n=\cup\{U_x:U_x\cap\{x_n:n=1,2,\ldots\}\subset\{x_1,x_2,\ldots,x_n\}\}$. $\{V_n:n=1,2,\ldots\}$ is an open cover of X. Proceed as in the proof of Theorem 2.7.8.

8. Prove that sequential compactness and countable compactness are preserved by continuous onto functions.

9. Show that the continuous image of a locally compact space need not be locally compact, but that local compactness is a topological property.

3

More concepts in topology

In this chapter we dig more deeply into some of the concepts already introduced, and develop some new ideas which are important for further study in topology. Section 3.1 deals with metric spaces exclusively and so can be read with only that knowledge, but the remaining sections deal with topological spaces, so that most of the Parts B are necessary for those. Many of the concepts here are not essential for the remainder of this book, but are for continued work and study in topology. We leave further introductory remarks for the individual sections.

3.1 Complete metric spaces

This section deals with a property of metric spaces, namely *completeness*, which is not topological but nevertheless has many applications in analysis, differential equations, and elsewhere. Much of its importance comes from the facts that Euclidean spaces are complete and many spaces of functions are complete. Section 4.4 exploits the latter fact. Also, completeness is a property which has many of the advantages of compactness but is not as restrictive.

The definition of completeness is motivated by the idea that a sequence that "clusters up" should converge. "Clustering up" here means that the farther out you go in the sequence, the closer together are all the remaining terms. This idea is made rigorous in the definition of Cauchy sequence, which is a necessary preliminary to the definition of completeness.

Definition A sequence $[x_n]$ in a metric space (X,d) is a *Cauchy sequence* if for each positive ε there is an integer P such that $d(x_m, x_n) < \varepsilon$ whenever $m \geqslant P$ and $n \geqslant P$. The space (X,d) is *complete* if every Cauchy sequence in (X,d) converges to a point of X.

EXAMPLES.

1. Consider the subspace Q of R consisting of all rationals. There is a sequence $[x_n]$ in Q which converges to $\sqrt{2}$. It is not hard to show that $[x_n]$ is a Cauchy sequence, but since it does not converge to a point of Q, the subspace Q is not complete.
2. Consider the subspace Z of R consisting of all integers. We show directly that Z is complete. Let $[x_n]$ be a Cauchy sequence in Z. Then there is a P such that $|x_n - x_m| < 1$ for $n, m \geqslant P$. But $|a - b| \geqslant 1$ for distinct elements a, b of Z, so that $x_n = x_m$ for $n, m \geqslant P$. Thus the sequence is eventually constant and so converges to x_P.

We now show that R with the usual metric is complete, which is the basic fact needed to show that many other spaces are also complete.

Theorem 3.1.1 *R is a complete metric space.*

PROOF. Let $[x_n]$ be a Cauchy sequence in R. We first show that $\{x_n : n = 1, 2, \ldots\}$ is bounded, so that we can use compactness to produce a limit point. There is a P such that $|x_n - x_m| < 1$ for $m, n \geqslant P$, so that in particular $|x_n - x_P| < 1$ for $n \geqslant P$. Letting

$$M = \max\{1, |x_1 - x_P|, |x_2 - x_P|, \ldots, |x_{P-1} - x_P|\}$$

we see that $\{x_n : n = 1, 2, \ldots\} \subset N(x_P, M + 1)$.

Since $[x_n]$ is a bounded sequence, it has a subsequence $[x_{n_i}]$ which converges to a point q of R. We finish by showing that $[x_n]$ converges to q.' Let ε be positive. There is an integer T such that $|x_{n_i} - q| < \varepsilon/2$ for $i \geqslant T$, and there is an integer S such that $|x_n - x_m| < \varepsilon/2$ for $n, m \geqslant S$. If $j \geqslant \max\{T, S\}$, then $|x_j - q| \leqslant |x_j - x_{n_j}| + |x_{n_j} - q| < \varepsilon/2 + \varepsilon/2 = \varepsilon$. ∎

Theorem 3.1.2

1. *Closed subspaces of complete metric spaces are complete.*
2. *Compact metric spaces are complete.*
3. *A finite product of complete metric spaces is complete.*

PROOF.
1. Let A be a closed subspace of the complete metric space (X,d). Let $[a_n]$ be a Cauchy sequence in A. Then $[a_n]$ is also a Cauchy sequence in X,

73

and so converges to a point x of X. But then $[a_n]$ is a convergent sequence in the closed set A, and so its limit belongs to A.

2. The essential part of this proof is in the proof of Theorem 3.1.1, and so we leave it as an exercise.

3. Let $(X_1, d_1), (X_2, d_2), \ldots, (X_n, d_n)$ be complete metric spaces, and let $X = X_1 \times X_2 \times \cdots \times X_n$. Recall that the product metric on X is

$$\rho((x_1, x_2, \ldots, x_n), (y_1, y_2, \ldots, y_n))$$
$$= \sqrt{(d_1(x_1, y_1))^2 + (d_2(x_2, y_2))^2 + \cdots + (d_n(x_n, y_n))^2}.$$

Let $[(_i x_1, _i x_2, \ldots, _i x_n)]$ be a Cauchy sequence in (X, ρ), where for notational purposes the "sequence index" is written on the left and the "coordinate index" on the right.

Now $d_i(_m x_i, _j x_i) \leqslant \rho((_m x_1, _m x_2, \ldots, _m x_n), (_j x_1, _j x_2, \ldots, _j x_n))$, so that $[_m x_i]$ is a Cauchy sequence in X_i for $i = 1, 2, \ldots, n$. It thus converges to a point p_i of X_i. Previous work then implies that $[(_i x_1, _i x_2, \ldots, _i x_n)]$ converges to $(p_1, p_2, \ldots, p_n)$. ∎

EXAMPLES.

3. Since R^n is a product of n copies of R, R^n is complete. Further, any closed subspace of R^n is complete, so all the spheres are complete.

4. We noted long ago that $(-1, 1)$ and R are homeomorphic. $[1 - 1/n]$ is a Cauchy sequence in $(-1, 1)$ which does not converge to a point of $(-1, 1)$, so that $(-1, 1)$ is not complete. Completeness is thus not a topological property. In particular, completeness often depends on the specific metric used, even when the metrics all yield the same topology.

We prove yet another theorem about construction of complete metric spaces. Theorems of this kind are extremely important in the study 'of power series and more general sequences of functions, as any advanced calculus or elementary analysis course will show. We first need some notation and terminology.

Definition Let X and Y be spaces. $C(X, Y)$ denotes the set of all continuous functions from X to Y. If Y has the metric d, then ρ is defined on $C(X, Y) \times C(X, Y)$ by

$$\rho(f, g) = \begin{cases} \text{lub}\{d(f(x), g(x)) : x \in X\} & \text{when this exists and is } < 1 \\ 1 & \text{otherwise.} \end{cases}$$

Theorem 3.1.3 $(C(X, Y), \rho)$ *is a metric space.*

PROOF. This is just a matter of checking the conditions that ρ be a metric and is left as an exercise. ∎

We note that the definition of $\rho(f,g)$ does not depend on the continuity of f and g, and we use this extended ρ in the proof of the next result.

Theorem 3.1.4 *If X is a space and (Y,d) a complete metric space, then $(C(X,Y),\rho)$ is a complete metric space.*

PROOF. Let $[f_n]$ be a Cauchy sequence in $C(X,Y)$. Since $d(f_n(x),f_m(x)) \leqslant \rho(f_n,f_m)$ for any x, then $[f_n(x)]$ is a Cauchy sequence in Y and so converges to a point $f(x)$ of Y. This defines a function f from X to Y.

We show that $[\rho(f_n,f)]$ converges to 0. Let ε be positive. There is an integer P such that $\rho(f_m,f_n) < \varepsilon/2$ for $m,n \geqslant P$. Fix m larger than P. Then $d(f_n(x),f_m(x)) < \varepsilon/2$ for $n \geqslant P$, and since $f_n(x) \to f(x)$, we must have $d(f(x), f_m(x)) \leqslant \varepsilon/2$. This is true for an arbitrary x, so that $\rho(f,f_m) \leqslant \varepsilon/2 < \varepsilon$ for $m > P$, which is the desired result.

We finish by showing that f is continuous. Let $x \in X$ and let ε be positive. We must find a neighborhood U of x such that $f(U) \subset N(f(x),\varepsilon)$. Since $[\rho(f_n,f)]$ converges to 0, there is an integer K such that $\rho(f_n,f) < \varepsilon/2$ for $n \geqslant K$. Then $f_K(x) \in N(f(x),\varepsilon/2)$, so there is a neighborhood U of x such that $f_K(U) \subset N(f(x),\varepsilon/2)$. If $y \in U$, then $d(f(x),f(y)) \leqslant d(f(x),f_K(y)) + d(f_K(y),f(y)) < \varepsilon/2 + \varepsilon/2 = \varepsilon$, so that $f(U) \subset N(f(x),\varepsilon)$. ∎

The fact that $[f_n]$ converges to f in $(C(X,Y),\rho)$ is often expressed by saying that $[f_n]$ converges uniformly to f or that f is the uniform limit of $[f_n]$. Note also that completeness of Y was used only to prove the existence of f, so that the proof shows that the uniform limit of continuous functions is continuous.

EXAMPLES.

5. Let X be a compact space and (Y,d) a metric space; the function $x \to d(f(x),g(x))$ can be written as the composition $x \to (f(x),g(x)) \to d(f(x),g(x))$ and so is easily shown to be continuous. Since X is compact, this function has a maximum value, so we can define $\hat{\rho}(f,g) = \max\{d(f(x),g(x)) : x \in X\}$. Now $\hat{\rho}(f,g) = \rho(f,g)$ when either is less than 1, so that $C(X,Y)$ has the same Cauchy sequences under either ρ or $\hat{\rho}$. Further, $N_\rho(f,\varepsilon) = N_{\hat{\rho}}(f,\varepsilon)$ when $\varepsilon < 1$, so that ρ and $\hat{\rho}$ have the same open sets in $C(X,Y)$ and thus sequences have the same convergence properties. As a result we can replace ρ by $\hat{\rho}$ in Theorem 3.1.4. In particular, $C([0,1])$ is a complete metric space since R is complete.
6. Let X be any space and let $C^*(X) = \{f : f$ is a bounded continuous real-valued function on $X\}$. It is easy to show that

$$\tilde{\rho}(f,g) = \text{lub}\{|f(x) - g(x)| : x \in X\}$$

is a metric on $C^*(X)$. Further, the proof of Theorem 3.1.4 shows that

$(C^*(X), \bar{\rho})$ is a complete metric space. We will make use of this example in Section 3.4.

The final result of this section is probably the most important single fact regarding complete metric spaces. It has innumerable uses in many phases of analysis, some of which are illustrated in Chapter 4.

Theorem 3.1.5 (Baire Category Theorem) *The intersection of any sequence of open dense subsets of a complete metric space is dense.*

PROOF. Let (X, d) be a complete metric space, and let $[O_i]$ be a sequence of open dense subsets of X. To show that $D = \cap \{ O_i : i = 1, 2, \ldots \}$ is dense, we choose any point x of X and any positive ε and show that D meets $N(x, \varepsilon)$. We use $B(z, r)$ to denote $\{ p \in X : d(z, p) \leqslant r \}$ as distinguished from $N(z, r) = \{ q \in X : d(z, q) < r \}$.

Since O_1 is dense, there is a point x_1 in $O_1 \cap N(x, \varepsilon)$. Since $O_1 \cap N(x, \varepsilon)$ is open, there is an $\varepsilon_1 < 1$ such that $B(x_1, \varepsilon_1) \subset O_1 \cap N(x, \varepsilon)$. Since O_2 is dense, there is a point x_2 in $O_2 \cap N(x_1, \varepsilon_1)$. Since $O_2 \cap N(x_1, \varepsilon_1)$ is open, there is an $\varepsilon_2 < \frac{1}{2}$ such that $B(x_2, \varepsilon_2) \subset O_2 \cap N(x_1, \varepsilon_1)$. Continuing inductively we obtain points $x_1, x_2, \ldots$ and positive numbers $\varepsilon_1, \varepsilon_2, \ldots$ such that $\varepsilon_i < 1/i$ and $B(x_{i+1}, \varepsilon_{i+1}) \subset O_{i+1} \cap N(x_i, \varepsilon_i)$. We thus have $N(x, \varepsilon) \supset B(x_1, \varepsilon_1) \supset N(x_1, \varepsilon_1) \supset B(x_2, \varepsilon_2) \supset N(x_2, \varepsilon_2) \supset B(x_3, \varepsilon_3) \supset \ldots$.

Since $x_n \in N(x_m, \varepsilon_m)$ for $n \geqslant m$ and $\varepsilon_m < 1/m$, $d(x_n, x_m) < 1/m$ when $n \geqslant m$. If ε is positive, then there is a positive integer P such that $1/P < \varepsilon$. Hence $d(x_n, x_m)$ will be less than ε whenever $m, n \geqslant P$, so that $[x_n]$ is a Cauchy sequence.

Since X is complete, $[x_n]$ converges to a point z of X. Eventually $[x_n]$ is in the closed set $B(x_i, \varepsilon_i)$, so that $z \in B(x_i, \varepsilon_i)$ for each i. Since $B(x_i, \varepsilon_i) \subset O_i$, $z \in O_i$ for each i, and since $N(x, \varepsilon) \supset B(x_1, \varepsilon_1)$, we have $z \in N(x, \varepsilon)$. Thus $z \in D \cap N(x, \varepsilon)$. ∎

The Baire Category Theorem is often phrased in other ways. A considerable amount of terminology has grown up around the theorem, which we will omit. However, one alternate statement is often useful, so we introduce the terminology necessary for it.

Definition A subset N of a space X is *nowhere dense* in X if $\mathrm{Cl}(N)$ contains no non-empty open set.

Theorem 3.1.6 *A complete metric space (X, d) is not the union of a sequence of nowhere-dense sets.*

PROOF. Let $N_1, N_2, \ldots$ be a sequence of nowhere-dense sets. Since $\mathrm{Cl}(N_i)$

contains no non-empty open set, $O_i = X \setminus \text{Cl}(N_i)$ meets every non-empty open set, and so O_i is open and dense in X. Hence $\cap \{O_i : i = 1, 2, \ldots\}$ is dense and in particular non-empty. Thus $\cap \{X \setminus \text{Cl}(N_i) : i = 1, 2, \ldots\} = X \setminus \cup \{\text{Cl}(N_i) : i = 1, 2, \ldots\}$ is not empty, so that X is not the union of the $\text{Cl}(N_i)$'s and certainly not of the N_i's. ∎

EXAMPLE.

7. Suppose we remove from the plane all circles that have rational radii and centers with rational coordinates. Then we have removed a sequence of nowhere-dense sets, namely the circles, so that the remainder is non-empty. In fact, Theorem 3.1.6 can be extended so as to imply that the remainder is still dense.

Exercises

1. Prove that a Cauchy sequence that has a convergent subsequence also converges to the same point.

2. Prove part 2 of Theorem 3.1.2.

3. Prove Theorem 3.1.3.

4. Prove in detail that the function $x \to d(f(x), g(x))$ in Example 5 is continuous.

5. Let A be a bounded subset of a metric space (X, d). The diameter of A is defined to be $\text{diam} A = \text{lub} \{d(x, y) : x, y \in A\}$. Prove that if $K_1, K_2, \ldots$ is a sequence of closed subsets of a complete metric space (X, d) such that $K_1 \supset K_2 \supset K_3 \supset \ldots$ and $\text{diam} K_i \to 0$, then $\cap \{K_i : i = 1, 2, \ldots\} \neq \varnothing$.

6. A metric space (X, d) is totally bounded if for each positive ε the set X is the union of finitely many sets of diameter less than ε.
   a. Prove that a bounded subset of R^n is totally bounded.
   b. Prove that total boundedness is not a topological property.
   c. Prove that a compact metric space is totally bounded.
   d. Prove that a totally bounded metric space is separable.
   e. Prove that a totally bounded complete metric space is compact. You may need to find a reference.

7. Prove that a uniformly continuous function takes Cauchy sequences to Cauchy sequences.

8. Verify all the details of Example 6.

9. Prove that if Y is a subspace of a metric space (X, d) and Y is complete, then Y is closed.

3.2 Separation properties

This section deals with various properties of topological spaces which describe how the points and/or closed sets of the space are separated. It has been a fruitful project in topology to study the influence of these properties and their combinations. There are a large number of different concepts of separation, but we restrict ourselves here to the four or five most important.

Most separation axioms are mutations of the statement: "disjoint things are contained in disjoint open sets," so our next definition includes terminology that facilitates discussion of such concepts. The first separation property is motivated by the idea that a finite set should have no limit points, though we do not state it that way in order to preserve the analogies between the different properties. A final remark is that the T-terminology derives from *Trennungsaxiom*, which is the German word for *separation axiom*.

Definition A *neighborhood* of a subset A of a space X is any open set containing A. A space X is T_1 if each of a pair of distinct points has a neighborhood not containing the other.

Our overall plan is to define separation properties in succession, and after each definition to state and prove the relevant subspace and product theorems, along with giving appropriate examples. We note that all of the separation axioms are topological properties, even though we may not explicitly say so. We leave the proofs as easy exercises. Keep in mind that metric spaces possess each of the properties discussed, though we leave the proof of this until later.

EXAMPLES.

1. An indiscrete space with two or more points is not T_1, since the only neighborhood of a point is the space itself.
2. R with the cofinite topology $\mathfrak{T}$ is T_1, since if x and y are distinct points, then $R \setminus \{y\}$ is a neighborhood of x not containing y, and similarly for the reverse. Note that the identity function is continuous from $(R, \mathfrak{T})$ to R with the indiscrete topology, so that continuous images of T_1 spaces need not be T_1.

Theorem 3.2.1 *A space X is T_1 if and only if each finite subset of X is closed.*

PROOF. Suppose that X is T_1, and let $x \in X$. We show that $\{x\}$ is closed, and our result follows since finite unions of closed sets are closed. If $y \neq x$, then y has a neighborhood U_y not containing x, so that $y \notin \text{Cl}(\{x\})$. Thus $\{x\} = \text{Cl}(\{x\})$ and $\{x\}$ is closed.

To show the converse, we let x and y be distinct points of X. Then $\{y\}$ is closed, so $X \setminus \{y\}$ is a neighborhood of x not containing y. Similarly, $X \setminus \{x\}$ is a neighborhood of y not containing x. ∎

Theorem 3.2.2

1. *A subspace of a T_1 space is T_1.*
2. *A finite product of T_1 spaces is T_1.*

PROOF.

1. Let A be a subspace of a T_1 space X. A finite subset of A is closed in X and hence closed in A, so that A is T_1 by Theorem 3.2.1.
2. Let $(x_1, x_2, \ldots, x_n)$ and $(y_1, y_2, \ldots, y_n)$ be two distinct points of the product $X_1 \times X_2 \times \cdots \times X_n$, where each X_i is T_1. For some j, $x_j \neq y_j$, so that x_j has a neighborhood U_j in X_j which does not contain y_j. Then $X_1 \times X_2 \times \cdots \times U_j \times \cdots \times X_n$ is a neighborhood of $(x_1, x_2, \ldots, x_n)$ in $X_1 \times X_2 \times \cdots \times X_n$ which does not contain $(y_1, y_2, \ldots, y_n)$. The reverse is similar. ∎

The next step up the ladder of separation axioms is probably the most important. In fact, some topologists refuse to deal with a space not possessing it. One reason for its importance is its extremely nice behavior in the presence of compactness, as evidenced by some of the theorems and exercises in this section.

Definition A space X is *Hausdorff* or T_2 if distinct points of X always have disjoint neighborhoods.

EXAMPLE.

3. R with the co-finite topology is not T_2, since the complement of any neighborhood of a point is finite and so cannot contain a neighborhood of another point. Thus T_1 spaces need not be T_2.

Theorem 3.2.3

1. *Subspaces of Hausdorff spaces are Hausdorff.*
2. *Finite products of Hausdorff spaces are Hausdorff.*

PROOF.

1. Let p and q be distinct points of the subset A of a Hausdorff space X. There are disjoint neighborhoods U_p, U_q of p, q respectively in X, and $U_p \cap A$, $U_q \cap A$ are disjoint neighborhoods of p, q in A.

2. This proof is very similar to that of part 2 of Theorem 3.2.2, so we leave it as an exercise. ∎

Some confusion in terminology sets in with our next definition. For some authors our T_3 and regular are synonymous, and others reverse the two. Naturally, we prefer our terminology, but the reader is warned to take care when reading other texts.

Definition A space X is *regular* if x and C have disjoint neighborhoods whenever C is a closed subset of X not containing the point x of X. A space is T_3 if it is regular and T_1.

EXAMPLES.

4. We first note that any indiscrete space X is regular, since the only closed sets are $\varnothing$ and X. A somewhat more interesting example is given by $X = \{a,b,c\}$ with the topology $\mathfrak{T} = \{\varnothing, X, \{a\}, \{b,c\}\}$. The point a and the closed set $\{b,c\}$ have the disjoint neighborhoods $\{a\}$ and $\{b,c\}$. This is the only nontrivial case to check so that X is regular. The points b and c do not have disjoint neighborhoods, so that X is not T_2. We note that X is not T_1 either, which fact is related to Theorem 3.2.8.
5. We give an example of a T_2 space which is not T_3. Consider the set R, and let $A = \{1/n : n = 1, 2, \ldots\}$. It is not hard to verify that $\mathcal{V} = \{U \cup (V \setminus A) : U$ and V are open in the Euclidean topology on $R\}$ is a topology on R. Since each Euclidean-open set is $\mathcal{V}$-open, $(R, \mathcal{V})$ is a Hausdorff space. To show that $(R, \mathcal{V})$ is not T_3, we show that the point 0 and the closed set A (verification: an exercise) do not have disjoint neighborhoods. A neighborhood of 0 missing A must be of the form $V \setminus A$, where V is Euclidean-open. Thus there is a positive integer P such that $1/P \in V$, and any neighborhood of A must contain a neighborhood of $1/P$, which must meet $V \setminus A$.

Theorem 3.2.4

1. *Subspaces of regular or T_3 spaces are regular or T_3.*
2. *Finite products of regular or T_3 spaces are regular or T_3.*

PROOF. We need worry only about regularity, since Theorem 3.2.2 will then yield the T_3 part of this theorem. Further, the proof of (1) is similar to preceding subspace proofs, and is left as an exercise.

Let $x = (x_1, x_2, \ldots, x_n)$ be a point of the product $X = X_1 \times X_2 \times \cdots \times X_n$ of regular spaces which does not lie in the closed subset C of X. The definition of the product topology delivers open subsets U_i of each X_i such that $x_i \in U_i$ and $(U_1 \times U_2 \times \cdots \times U_n) \cap C = \varnothing$. Since each X_i is regular, there are disjoint neighborhoods V_i, W_i of $x_i, X_i \setminus U_i$, respectively, in X_i. Then $V = V_1 \times V_2 \times \cdots \times V_n$ is a neighborhood of x in X, and we let $W = \cup \{X_1 \times X_2 \times \cdots \times W_j \times \cdots \times X_n : j = 1, 2, \ldots, n\}$. W is open in X, and a point $(y_1, y_2, \ldots, y_n)$ of C must have $y_j \notin U_j$ for some j since C and $U_1 \times U_2 \times \cdots \times U_n$ are disjoint, so that $(y_1, y_2, \ldots, y_n) \in X_1 \times X_2 \times \cdots \times W_j \times \cdots \times X_n$. Thus W is a neighborhood of C. Finally, a point lying in $V \cap W$ must have its jth coordinate in both of the disjoint sets V_j, W_j for some j. This contradiction shows that V and W are disjoint. ∎

We now introduce a separation property whose definition departs from the pattern thus far established. Spaces with this property have become very important in topology, mostly because their topologies are intimately tied to their continuous real-valued functions. The definition fuzzily implies this, but we leave further details for other texts.

Definition A space X is *completely regular* if whenever C is a closed set in X and x a point not in C, there is a continuous function $f : X \to [0, 1]$ such that $f(x) = 1$ and $f(C) = 0$. A completely regular T_1 space is a *Tychonoff space*.

EXAMPLE.

6. A completely regular space need not be T_2, as any space of more than one point with the indiscrete topology shows. Also, a regular space need not be completely regular, but the example is formidable and we omit it.

Theorem 3.2.5

1. *Subspaces of completely regular or Tychonoff spaces are completely regular or Tychonoff.*
2. *Finite products of completely regular or Tychonoff spaces are completely regular or Tychonoff.*

PROOF. Again we deal only with complete regularity, and again leave (1) as an exercise. Let $x = (x_1, x_2, \ldots, x_n)$ be a point of the product $X = X_1 \times X_2 \times \cdots \times X_n$ of completely regular spaces which does not lie in the closed subset C of X. There are open sets U_i in X_i such that $x \in U_1 \times U_2 \times \cdots \times U_n = U$ and $U \cap C = \emptyset$. Since each X_i is completely regular there are continuous functions $f_i : X_i \to [0, 1]$ such that $f_i(x_i) = 1$ and $f_i(X_i \setminus U_i) = 0$. Define $g : X \to [0, 1]$ by $g((y_1, y_2, \ldots, y_n)) = \min\{f_1(y_1), f_2(y_2), \ldots, f_n(y_n)\}$. It is not hard to verify that g is a continuous function such that $g(x) = 1$ and $g(C) = 0$. ∎

81

We now come to the last and most troublesome of our separation axioms. It is troublesome in that it does not behave as nicely as the others, as some examples will show. However, as later theorems will show, this property is precisely what is needed in many situations.

Definition A space X is *normal* if disjoint closed subsets of X have disjoint neighborhoods. X is T_4 if it is normal and T_1.

EXAMPLE.

7. A normal space need not be regular. Consider R with the topology $\mathcal{U} = \{\varnothing, R\} \cup \{(a, +\infty) : a \in R\}$. There are no nontrivial disjoint closed sets in $(R, \mathcal{U})$, so that the space is normal. However, any neighborhood of the closed set $(-\infty, 0]$ must contain $(a, +\infty)$ for each $a < 0$ and so the only neighborhood of $(-\infty, 0]$ is R itself. Hence $(-\infty, 0]$ and 1 do not have disjoint neighborhoods.

Our first theorem gives an alternative characterization of normality which is often useful. Regularity also has such a characterization, which we leave as an exercise.

Theorem 3.2.6 *A space X is normal if and only if whenever U is a neighborhood of a closed set C, then there is a neighborhood V of C such that $\mathrm{Cl}(V) \subset U$.*

PROOF. Suppose X is normal and U is a neighborhood of a closed set C. Then C and $X \setminus U$ are disjoint closed sets and so have disjoint neighborhoods V and W. Then $\mathrm{Cl}(V) \subset X \setminus W \subset X \setminus (X \setminus U) = U$. The converse is left as an exercise. ∎

The next theorem turns out to be about all that can be said about subspaces and products of normal spaces. However, we postpone more examples until after some machinery has been built.

Theorem 3.2.7 *Closed subspaces of normal or T_4 spaces are normal or T_4.*

PROOF. An exercise. ∎

The notation T_1, T_2, T_3, T_4 suggests that these properties are successively stronger. This is precisely the next theorem. It is also true that T_4 spaces are Tychonoff, but the proof of this fact must wait until the next section.

Theorem 3.2.8

1. T_4 *implies* T_3 *implies* T_2 *implies* T_1.
2. *Completely regular spaces are regular, so that Tychonoff implies* T_3.

PROOF.

1. Let x be a point of the T_4 space X which is not in the closed set C. Since X is T_1, $\{x\}$ is a closed set disjoint from C. Normality then says that x and C have disjoint neighborhoods, so that X is T_3. The other proofs are similar and are left for the ambitious reader.

2. Let x be a point of the completely regular space X which is not in the closed set C. There is a continuous function $f: X \to [0, 1]$ such that $f(x) = 1$ and $f(C) = 0$. Then $f^{-1}((\frac{1}{2}, 1])$ and $f^{-1}([0, \frac{1}{2}))$ are disjoint neighborhoods of x and C, respectively. ∎

Our next result is that metric spaces satisfy the most powerful of our separation axioms. In particular, then, all subspaces of Euclidean spaces are T_4. In fact, metric spaces have separation properties even stronger than T_4, but we have no need for these properties and leave them for the hungry reader to pursue.

Theorem 3.2.9 *A metric space is T_4.*

PROOF. Let A and B be disjoint closed subsets of the metric space (X, d). Each point x of A has a neighborhood $N(x, \varepsilon_x)$ not meeting B, and each point y of B has a neighborhood $N(y, \delta_y)$ not meeting A. Let $U = \cup \{N(x, \frac{1}{3}\varepsilon_x) : x \in A\}$ and $V = \cup \{N(y, \frac{1}{3}\delta_y) : y \in B\}$. Suppose $U \cap V \neq \varnothing$, and let x, y be points of A, B respectively such that $N(x, \frac{1}{3}\varepsilon_x) \cap N(y, \frac{1}{3}\delta_y)$ contains a point z. Suppose also that $\varepsilon_x \geq \delta_y$, since the reverse inequality leads to a similar proof. Then $d(x, y) \leq d(x, z) + d(z, y) < \frac{1}{3}\varepsilon_x + \frac{1}{3}\delta_y \leq \frac{2}{3}\varepsilon_x < \varepsilon_x$, so that $N(x, \varepsilon_x)$ meets B. This contradiction shows that U and V are disjoint neighborhoods of A and B, respectively. Since $N(x, \frac{1}{2}d(x, y)) \cap N(y, \frac{1}{2}d(x, y)) = \varnothing$ when $x \neq y$, (X, d) is T_2 and hence T_4. ∎

We next investigate conditions under which a T_i space is T_{i+1}. We concentrate on only two theorems, the first of which will be useful in the next section. The second theorem is one reason for the importance of compactness, and its essence is that in a compact space closed sets behave like points.

Theorem 3.2.10 *A regular Lindelöf space is normal.*

PROOF. Let A and B be disjoint closed sets in the regular Lindelöf space X. For each point a of A there are disjoint open neighborhoods U_a, V_a of a and B, respectively. $\{X \setminus A\} \cup \{U_a : a \in A\}$ is an open cover of X, so we may choose countably many U_a's, which we denote by $U_1, U_2, \ldots$, whose union contains A. Further, since $U_a \cap V_a = \varnothing$, $\mathrm{Cl}(U_i) \cap B = \varnothing$ for each i. Similarly, there are open sets $O_1, O_2, \ldots$ whose union contains B and such that $\mathrm{Cl}(O_i) \cap A = \varnothing$ for each i.

Now construct open sets S_i, T_i inductively as follows. Let $S_1 = U_1$, $T_1 = O_1 \backslash \text{Cl}(U_1), S_2 = U_2 \backslash \text{Cl}(T_1), T_2 = O_2 \backslash \text{Cl}(S_1 \cup S_2), S_3 = U_3 \backslash \text{Cl}(T_1 \cup T_2), T_3 = O_3 \backslash \text{Cl}(S_1 \cup S_2 \cup S_3), \dots$. Let $S = \cup \{S_i : i = 1, 2, \dots\}$ and $T = \cup \{T_i : i = 1, 2, \dots\}$. By construction S_i misses $T_1 \cup T_2 \cup \cdots \cup T_{i-1}$ and T_j misses $S_1 \cup S_2 \cup \cdots \cup S_j \supset S_i$ when $j \geqslant i$. Thus $S_i \cap T_j = \varnothing$ for all i and j, so that S and T are disjoint open sets. If $a \in A$, then $a \in U_j$ for some j. Since $\text{Cl}(T_1 \cup T_2 \cup \cdots \cup T_{j-1}) \subset \text{Cl}(O_1 \cup O_2 \cup \cdots \cup O_{j-1}) = \text{Cl}(O_1) \cup \text{Cl}(O_2) \cup \cdots \cup \text{Cl}(O_{j-1})$ and each $\text{Cl}(O_k)$ misses A, the point a is in S_j. Thus S is a neighborhood of A, and similarly T is a neighborhood of B. ∎

Theorem 3.2.11 *A compact Hausdorff space is* T_4.

PROOF. By Theorem 3.2.10 we need only show that a compact T_2 space X is regular. Thus let x be a point not in the closed set C. Since X is T_2, for each point y of C there are disjoint neighborhoods U_y, V_y of x, y respectively. Compactness implies that C lies in the union of a finite collection $V_{y_1}, V_{y_2}, \dots, V_{y_n}$. Let $U = U_{y_1} \cap U_{y_2} \cap \cdots \cap U_{y_n}$ and $V = V_{y_1} \cup V_{y_2} \cup \cdots \cup V_{y_n}$. It is easy to see that U, V are disjoint neighborhoods of x and C, respectively. ∎

EXAMPLE.

8. We first show that the Sorgenfrey line $(R, \mathcal{S})$ is T_4. It is clearly T_1 and we have previously seen that it is Lindelöf. Thus we need only show that it is regular. If x is a point not in the closed set C, then for some positive ε, the set $[x, x + \varepsilon)$ misses C. But $R \backslash [x, x + \varepsilon)$ is also open, so that x and C have disjoint neighborhoods.

Now consider the Sorgenfrey plane $(R^2, \mathcal{S}')$. We show by contradiction that $(R^2, \mathcal{S}')$ is not normal. Let D be the dense subset of $(R^2, \mathcal{S}')$ consisting of the points with rational coordinates. Recall that every subset of $L = \{(x, y) \in R^2 : y = -x\}$ is closed in $(R^2, \mathcal{S}')$. If $(R^2, \mathcal{S}')$ were normal, then for every subset A of L there would be disjoint open sets S_A, T_A such that $A \subset S_A$ and $L \backslash A \subset T_A$. If $A_1 \backslash A_2 \neq \varnothing$, then certainly $S_{A_1} \cap T_{A_2}$ is not empty, so that $S_{A_1} \cap T_{A_2} \cap D$ is not empty. But then $S_{A_1} \cap T_{A_2} \cap D$ is a subset of $S_{A_1} \cap D$ but not of $S_{A_2} \cap D$, since $S_{A_2} \cap T_{A_2} = \varnothing$. Thus if A_1 and A_2 are different subsets of L, then $S_{A_1} \cap D$ and $S_{A_2} \cap D$ are different subsets of D. But L is uncountable and so has more subsets (see the Appendix for more rigor) than the countable set D. Thus $(R^2, \mathcal{S}')$ is not normal.

This example shows that the product of normal spaces need not be normal. Further, Theorem 3.2.5 implies that $(R^2, \mathcal{S}')$ is Tychonoff, so that Tychonoff spaces need not be normal. A consequence of techniques of

Sections 3.3 and 3.5 is that every Tychonoff space is a subspace of a T_4 space. Hence the nonnormal Sorgenfrey plane is a subspace of some T_4 space, so that subspaces of normal spaces need not be normal.

Exercises

1. Complete the proof of Theorem 3.2.3.

2. Verify all details in Example 5.

3. Complete the proof of Theorem 3.2.4.

4. Complete the proof of Theorem 3.2.5.

5. Prove Theorem 3.2.7.

6. Prove that any space with more than three points has a nonindiscrete topology which is regular and normal but not Hausdorff.

7. Prove that a space X is completely regular if and only if whenever x is a point not in the closed set C and a, b are real numbers with $a < b$, then there is a continuous function f from X to $[a, b]$ such that $f(x) = a$ and $f(C) = b$.

8. Prove that the continuous image of a Hausdorff space need not be Hausdorff.

9. Prove that a finite T_1 space is discrete.

10. Prove that a convergent sequence in a Hausdorff space has a unique limit point.

11. **a.** Prove that a compact subset of a Hausdorff space is closed.
    b. Prove that a one-to-one continuous function from a compact space X onto a Hausdorff space Y is a homeomorphism.

12. **a.** Complete the proof of Theorem 3.2.6.
    b. State and prove a theorem similar to Theorem 3.2.6 for regularity.

3.3 Construction of continuous functions and metrics

Questions concerning the existence of various kinds of functions permeate not only topology but analysis and other areas of mathematics. Is there a continuous real-valued function which takes specified values on a closed subset A of a space X? When can a function defined on a dense subset of a space be extended to a continuous function on the entire space? When can a metric on a closed subset be extended to a compatible metric on the entire space? When can a homeomorphism from subspace A to subspace B be extended to a homeomorphism between the containing spaces? When can one construct a homeomorphism from a space X to a space Y? This section exposes just the tip of the iceberg of results and questions in this area.

Our first result is perhaps the most basic, since it bare-handedly constructs a continuous function using only topological properties of a space. Its converse is also true (an exercise) and so we get another characterization of normality, as well as an indication of why normality is so important.

Theorem 3.3.1 (Urysohn's Lemma) *Let A and B be disjoint non-empty closed subsets of a normal space X. Then there is a continuous function $f: X \to [0, 1]$ such that $f(A) = 0$ and $f(B) = 1$.*

PROOF. The idea of the proof lies in the fact that such a function f is essentially determined by the sets $f^{-1}([0, r))$ for $0 \leqslant r \leqslant 1$. We turn this around, and first construct the sets which will almost be the $f^{-1}([0, r))$'s, and then use them to define the function.

We use induction on n to define open sets $U_{k/2^n}$ for $k = 0, 1, \ldots, 2^n$ and $n = 0, 1, 2, \ldots$ which satisfy $\text{Cl}(U_{j/2^n}) \subset U_{i/2^n}$ for $j < i$. First, define U_1 to be $X \setminus B$. Then Theorem 3.2.6 implies that there is an open set U_0 such that $A \subset U_0$ and $\text{Cl}(U_0) \subset U_1$. Now suppose that such sets have been defined for $k = 0, 1, \ldots, 2^n$ and $n = 0, 1, \ldots, i$. We must define $U_{(2j+1)/2^{i+1}}$ for $j = 0, 1, \ldots, 2^i - 1$. The sets already constructed satisfy $\text{Cl}(U_{j/2^i}) \subset U_{(j+1)/2^i}$, so Theorem 3.2.6 implies that there is an open set $U_{(2j+1)/2^{i+1}}$ such that $\text{Cl}(U_{j/2^i}) \subset U_{(2j+1)/2^{i+1}}$ and $\text{Cl}(U_{(2j+1)/2^{i+1}}) \subset U_{(j+1)/2^i}$. The induction is thus complete.

We can now define the function f by

$$f(x) = \begin{cases} 1 & \text{if } x \text{ belongs to no } U_{k/2^n} \\ \text{glb}\left\{ \dfrac{k}{2^n} : x \in U_{k/2^n} \right\} & \text{otherwise.} \end{cases}$$

Note that 1) $f(x) \geqslant k/2^n$ if $x \notin \text{Cl}(U_{k/2^n})$ and that 2) $f(x) \leqslant j/2^n$ if $x \in U_{j/2^n}$. Further, $U_1 = X \setminus B$, so that $f(B) = 1$, and $A \subset U_0$, so that $f(A) = 0$.

We now show that f is continuous. Let ε be positive and let x be an arbitrary point of X. We find a neighborhood of x that f takes into $N(f(x), \varepsilon)$. If $f(x) = 1$, then choose $k/2^n$ such that $1 - \varepsilon < k/2^n < 1$, so that $X - \text{Cl}(U_{k/2^n})$ is a neighborhood of x with $f(X - \text{Cl}(U_{k/2^n})) \subset [k/2^n, 1] \subset N(f(x), \varepsilon)$. If $0 < f(x) < 1$, then choose $k/2^n$ and $j/2^n$ in $(0, 1)$ such that $f(x) - \varepsilon < k/2^n < f(x) < j/2^n < f(x) + \varepsilon$. Then $U_{j/2^n} \setminus \text{Cl}(U_{k/2^n})$ is a neighborhood of x which f takes into $[k/2^n, j/2^n] \subset N(f(x), \varepsilon)$. If $f(x) = 0$, then choose $k/2^n$ such that $0 < k/2^n < \varepsilon$, so that $U_{k/2^n}$ is a neighborhood of x with $f(U_{k/2^n}) \subset [0, k/2^n] \subset N(f(x), \varepsilon)$. ∎

Corollary 3.3.2 *A T_4 space is Tychonoff.*

We now use Urysohn's Lemma to construct a metric on a suitable space. It should be clear by now that a metric space has much nicer properties than a general topological space, so it is of great interest to find topological properties which will imply that a space is metric. It is clear that the topology of a space does not determine a unique metric, so we have the following definition.

Definition A topological space $(X, \mathfrak{T})$ is *metrizable* if there is a metric d on X whose collection of open sets is precisely $\mathfrak{T}$.

It is easy to see that metrizability is a topological property. Further, subspaces and finite products of metrizable spaces are metrizable since the topologies of subspaces and products of metric spaces are the subspace and product topologies, respectively.

The question of which spaces are metrizable was not satisfactorily settled until the 1950's. We will not state or prove a general metrization theorem, but will be content with the following classical theorem proved in 1925.

Theorem 3.3.3 **(Urysohn's Metrization Theorem)** *A space is separable and metrizable if and only if it is T_3 and second countable.*

PROOF. We have shown earlier that a metric space is T_4 and hence T_3, and that a separable metric space is second countable. Hence our hard work involves the converse.

We first note that a second countable space is Lindelöf, and hence a second countable T_3 space is T_4 by Theorem 3.2.10. We can thus apply Urysohn's Lemma to produce continuous real-valued functions. Note further that any closed bounded interval would serve as well as $[0,1]$ for the range space of the functions delivered by Urysohn's Lemma.

The plan is to produce a homeomorphism ϕ from the second countable T_3 space X onto a subspace of the Hilbert cube I^∞. Recall that $I^\infty = [0,1] \times [0, \frac{1}{2}] \times [0, \frac{1}{3}] \times \ldots$, so we can construct such a homeomorphism ϕ by specifying the n-th coordinate of $\phi(x)$ for each n. This is done by constructing a suitable sequence $[f_n]$ of functions, where f_n goes from X to $[0, 1/n]$.

Let $\{ U_i : i = 1, 2, \ldots \}$ be a countable base for X. Let $[(i_n, j_n)]$ be the sequence of ordered pairs of integers for which $\mathrm{Cl}(U_{i_n}) \subset U_{j_n}$. For each n Urysohn's Lemma then produces a continuous function $f_n : X \to [0, 1/n]$ such that $f_n(\mathrm{Cl}(U_{i_n})) = 0$ and $f_n(X \setminus U_{j_n}) = 1/n$. Define $\phi : X \to I^\infty$ by $\phi(x) = (f_1(x), f_2(x), \ldots)$. It is not hard to show that ϕ is continuous, and we leave this as an exercise.

We next show that ϕ is one-to-one. Let x and y be distinct points of X. Since X is T_3, there is a j such that $x \in U_j$ but $y \notin U_j$, and then there is an i such that $x \in U_i$ and $\mathrm{Cl}(U_i) \subset U_j$. For some n, (i,j) is (i_n, j_n), and then $f_n(x) = 0$ whereas $f_n(y) = 1/n$. Thus $\phi(x)$ and $\phi(y)$ differ in the n-th coordinate, so that ϕ is one-to-one.

We are done when we show that $\phi^{-1}:\phi(X)\to X$ is continuous. This is the same as showing that $\phi(V)$ is open in $\phi(X)$ whenever V is open in X. In turn, this can be done by showing that for each point x of the open set V of X there is a neighborhood W of $\phi(x)$ in I^∞ such that $\phi(V)\supset W\cap \phi(X)$. Using the regularity of X we can find an n such that $x\in U_{i_n}$ and $\mathrm{Cl}(U_{i_n})\subset U_{j_n}\subset V$. The set $W=[0,1]\times[0,1/2]\times\cdots\times[0,1/2n)\times\ldots$ is then a neighborhood of $\phi(x)$ in I^∞. If $\phi(y)\in W$, then $f_n(y)\in[0,1/2n)$, whereas $f_n(X-V)\subset f_n(X-U_{j_n})=1/n$. Hence $y\in V$, so that $W\cap\phi(X)\subset\phi(V)$. ∎

This theorem has several interesting corollaries, two of which we state now but develop further in later sections. The second corollary follows when we recall that I^∞ is compact.

Corollary 3.3.4 *Every second countable T_3 space is homeomorphic to a subspace of the Hilbert cube.*

Corollary 3.3.5 *Every separable metric space is homeomorphic to a subspace of a compact metric space.*

We turn now to our first theorem dealing with the extension of a continuous function. This is a highly important and interesting area which has spawned some of the nicest results in all of topology. Again, we must content ourselves with one basic and very useful theorem plus a very few remarks and elementary results.

Theorem 3.3.6 (**Tietze's Extension Theorem**) *Let A be a closed subset of a normal space X and f a continuous function from A to $[-1,1]$. Then there is a continuous function F from X to $[-1,1]$ such that $F|A=f$.*

PROOF. The idea is to construct a sequence $f_1,f_2,\ldots$ of functions on X such that $|f(x)-\sum_{i=1}^n f_i(x)|\leqslant(\frac{2}{3})^n$ for $x\in A$. If we do this in such a way that $\sum_{i=1}^\infty f_i(x)$ always exists, then this will be a good candidate for the function F.

To define f_1 we use the sets $A_1=\{x\in A:f(x)\geqslant\frac{1}{3}\}$ and $B_1=\{x\in A:f(x)\leqslant-\frac{1}{3}\}$. These are disjoint closed sets in X, so Urysohn's Lemma produces a continuous $f_1:X\to[-\frac{1}{3},\frac{1}{3}]$ such that $f_1(A_1)=\frac{1}{3}$ and $f_1(B_1)=-\frac{1}{3}$. Hence $|f(x)-f_1(x)|\leqslant\frac{2}{3}$ for $x\in A$.

Now repeat this process with f replaced by $f-f_1$ and $[-1,1]$ replaced by $[-\frac{2}{3},\frac{2}{3}]$. That is, let $A_2=\{x\in A:(f-f_1)(x)\geqslant\frac{2}{9}\}$ and $B_2=\{x\in A:(f-f_1)(x)\leqslant-\frac{2}{9}\}$. These are disjoint closed sets in X, so Urysohn's Lemma produces a continuous $f_2:X\to[-\frac{2}{9},\frac{2}{9}]$ such that $f_2(A_2)=\frac{2}{9}$ and $f_2(B_2)=-\frac{2}{9}$. Then $|f(x)-(f_1+f_2)(x)|=|(f-f_1)(x)-f_2(x)|\leqslant\frac{4}{9}=(\frac{2}{3})^2$.

We can continue this process inductively to produce a sequence $[f_n]$ of continuous real-valued functions on X such that the range of f_n is contained in $[-2/3^n, 2/3^n]$ for $n \geq 2$ and $|f(x) - (f_1 + f_2 + \cdots + f_n)(x)| \leq (\frac{2}{3})^n$ for $n \geq 1$. Now for each x in X,

$$\left| \sum_{i=1}^{n+r} f_i(x) - \sum_{i=1}^{n} f_i(x) \right| = |f_{n+1}(x) + f_{n+2}(x) + \cdots + f_{n+r}(x)|$$

$$\leq \frac{2}{3^{n+1}} + \frac{2}{3^{n+2}} + \cdots + \frac{2}{3^{n+r}} < \frac{1}{3^n}.$$

(Here we have used the fact that $1 + a + a^2 + \cdots + a^s = (1 - a^{s+1})/(1 - a)$ for $a \neq 1$.) Since R is complete, Theorem 3.1.4 implies that $[\sum_{i=1}^{n} f_i]$ converges to a continuous function F on X. Now

$$|f_1(x) + f_2(x) + \cdots + f_n(x)| \leq \frac{1}{3} + \frac{2}{3^2} + \frac{2}{3^3} + \cdots + \frac{2}{3^n}$$

$$< \frac{2}{3}\left(1 + \frac{1}{3} + \frac{1}{3^2} + \cdots + \frac{1}{3^{n-1}}\right)$$

$$= \frac{2}{3}\left[1 - \left(\frac{1}{3}\right)^n \Big/ 1 - \frac{1}{3}\right] < \frac{2}{3} \cdot \frac{3}{2} = 1.$$

Hence $|F(x)| \leq 1$ for each $x \in X$. Finally, for $x \in A$ we have

$$|f(x) - F(x)| \leq \left| f(x) - \left(\sum_{i=1}^{n} f_i(x) \right) \right| + \left| \sum_{i=1}^{n} f_i(x) - F(x) \right|$$

$$\leq \left(\frac{2}{3} \right)^n + \left| \sum_{i=1}^{n} f_i(x) - F(x) \right|.$$

Since

$$F(x) = \lim_{n \to \infty} \sum_{i=1}^{n} f_i(x), \qquad \left| \sum_{i=1}^{n} f_i(x) - F(x) \right| \to 0$$

as $n \to \infty$. Thus $|f(x) - F(x)|$ is arbitrarily small and so must be 0, and F is the desired function. ∎

There are two points of view that can be taken regarding Tietze's Extension Theorem. The first is that it expresses a property of normal spaces, and in this case we leave it as an exercise to show that the property is actually equivalent to normality. The second point of view is that it expresses a property of the space $[-1, 1]$. We now introduce some terminology and discuss the latter idea.

Definition If $A \subset X$ and $f : A \to Y$, $F : X \to Y$ are functions such that $F|A = f$, then F is called an *extension* of f to X and we also say that f *extends to* F.

Definition A space Y is called an *absolute extensor for normal spaces* if whenever f is a continuous function from a closed subset A of a normal space X into Y then f extends to a continuous function from X into Y.

Tietze's Extension Theorem says precisely that $[-1,1]$ is an absolute extensor for normal spaces. It is easy to show that this is a topological property, so that we conclude that any closed bounded interval is an absolute extensor for normal spaces. Our next theorem shows that R is also.

Theorem 3.3.7 *R is an absolute extensor for normal spaces.*

PROOF. Since R is homeomorphic to $(-1,1)$, we prove the theorem for $(-1,1)$ instead. Let f be a continuous function from a closed subset A of a normal space X into $(-1,1)$. The function f can be regarded as a function into $[-1,1]$, and so has a continuous extension $F':X\to[-1,1]$. Let $B=\{x \in X:F'(x)=-1$ or $F'(x)=1\}$. Then A and B are disjoint closed sets in X, so Urysohn's Lemma delivers a continuous function $g:X\to[0,1]$ such that $g(B)=0$ and $g(A)=1$. Let $F=g\cdot F'$. Then F is a continuous function from X into $(-1,1)$, and if $x\in A$, then $F(x)=g(x)\cdot F'(x)=1\cdot f(x)=f(x)$. ∎

Absolute extensors for normal spaces have a very nice property expressed in the following theorem. It has a converse which is also true and which opens the door to the *theory of retracts*, of which every young topologist should know something. Unfortunately, he/she will have to find the knowledge elsewhere.

Theorem 3.3.8 *Let A be a closed subspace of a normal space X, and let A be an absolute extensor for normal spaces. Then there is a continuous function r from X to A such that $r(a)=a$ for each $a\in A$.*

PROOF. Define $f:A\to A$ by $f(a)=a$. Since A is an absolute extensor for normal spaces, f extends to the desired continuous function r from X to A. ∎

Definition A subspace A of a space X is a *retract* of X if there is a continuous function $r:X\to A$ such that $r(a)=a$ for each $a\in A$. The function r is called a *retraction*. A normal space Y is an *absolute retract* if Y is a retract of X whenever Y is embedded as a closed subspace of the normal space X.

Theorem 3.3.8 shows that there is an intimate connection between absolute extensors and absolute retracts. As mentioned earlier we must leave further study of these spaces for other books, and reluctantly content ourselves with the above theorems and some exercises.

Exercises

1. Prove that metrizability is a topological property.

2. Prove that the function ϕ in the proof of Urysohn's Metrization Theorem is continuous.

3. Supply all details in the construction of the sequence $[f_n]$ in the proof of Tietze's Extension Theorem.

4. Prove that $[0, 1)$ is an absolute extensor for normal spaces.

5. Prove that a product of absolute extensors for normal spaces is an absolute extensor for normal spaces. Conclude that R^n is such a space.

6. Prove that a retract of a Hausdorff space is closed.

7. Prove that if A is a retract of X, then every continuous function $f: A \to Z$ extends to a continuous function from X to Z. Hint: $f \circ$ retraction.

8. Construct a retraction from R to $[-1, 1]$.

9. Prove that a retract of a connected space is connected, and that a retract of a compact space is compact.

10. Prove that the Sorgenfrey line is not metrizable. Thus a regular Lindelöf space need not be metrizable.

11. Give an example of a second countable Hausdorff space which is not regular and hence not metrizable.

3.4 New spaces from old, II: compactification and completion

It should by now be clear that compact spaces and complete metric spaces have very nice properties. It is thus of interest and often useful to construct a compact or complete space which is in some sense very close to a given noncompact or noncomplete space X. It is the purpose of this section to give two methods for doing so and to investigate some of the properties of the resulting spaces.

We look first at the metric case. The idea is to construct a complete metric space which contains a dense exact copy of a given metric space. If we identify the copy with the original, then we can also view the procedure as one of adding enough points to a metric space so that the result is complete. This point of view is intuitively satisfying, since it corresponds to adding new points which will be the limit points of the nonconvergent Cauchy sequences.

As usual, we need some terminology. We leave proofs of many of the elementary results as exercises.

Definition A function f from a metric space (X, d) to a metric space (Y, ρ) is an *isometry* if $\rho(f(x), f(y)) = d(x, y)$ for all $x, y \in X$.

Definition   A *completion* of a metric space (X,d) is a complete metric space $(\hat{X},\hat{d})$ and an isometry e from (X,d) into $(\hat{X},\hat{d})$ such that $e(X)$ is dense in $\hat{X}$.

Intuitively, we identify X and $e(X)$, so that $\hat{X}\setminus e(X)$ is the set of points we have added. It is easy to show that an isometry is a homeomorphism, so that X and $e(X)$ have the same topological properties. It is also true that X and $e(X)$ have the same metric properties, since e preserves distances.

Our next theorem says that every metric space has a completion, and the following result is that the completion is essentially unique. These results are often applied in analysis, and perhaps their most important application is in the construction of the real numbers from the rationals. There are two popular ways to prove the existence of completions, the first of which makes the construction more or less from scratch. In this case the main idea is fairly simple, but the details are excruciating.

Our proof avoids some of the mess and uses instead some previous results plus a trick or two. It is also capable of being used to prove other results in the theory of metrics and in the theory of absolute extensors. The reader is urged to consult other texts.

Theorem 3.4.1   *Every metric space has a completion.*

PROOF.   Let (X,d) be a metric space. The idea is to embed (X,d) in a complete metric space, and then the closure of the copy of X will be the desired completion. Recall from Section 3.1 that the set $C^*(X)$ of bounded continuous real-valued functions on X with the metric $\tilde{\rho}(f,g)=\mathrm{lub}\{|f(x)-g(x)|:x\in X\}$ is a complete metric space.

We now construct an isometry e from X into $C^*(X)$. For any point x of X let r_x be the function $r_x(y)=d(x,y)$. Fix a point a in X, and let $e(z)=r_z-r_a$. Now for any y in X we have $r_z(y)-r_a(y)=d(z,y)-d(a,y)\leqslant d(z,a)$, since $d(z,y)\leqslant d(z,a)+d(a,y)$. Similarly, $r_a(y)-r_z(y)\leqslant d(a,z)$, so that $|r_z(y)-r_a(y)|\leqslant d(a,z)$. Thus $e(z)$ is a continuous bounded real-valued function and so is in $C^*(X)$. Also,

$$\tilde{\rho}(e(p),e(q)) = \mathrm{lub}\{|e(p)(y)-e(q)(y)|:y\in X\}$$
$$= \mathrm{lub}\{|r_p(y)-r_a(y)-r_q(y)+r_a(y)|:y\in X\}$$
$$= \mathrm{lub}\{|r_p(y)-r_q(y)|:y\in X\},$$

and the above results show that this is no larger than $d(p,q)$. Finally, $|r_p(q)-r_q(q)|=|d(p,q)-d(q,q)|=d(p,q)$, so that $\tilde{\rho}(e(p),e(q))=d(p,q)$.

Let $\hat{X}=\mathrm{Cl}(e(X))$ and let $\hat{d}$ be $\tilde{\rho}|\hat{X}$. As a closed subset of the complete space $C^*(X)$, $\hat{X}$ is complete, and $e(X)$ is clearly dense in $\hat{X}$. The desired completion of (X,d) is thus $(\hat{X},\hat{d})$. ∎

Before we prove that completions are essentially unique, we need a result that is of independent interest. It is another in our collection of *function-extension* facts.

Theorem 3.4.2 *Let D be a dense subset of a metric space (X,d) and f a uniformly continuous function from D to a complete metric space (Y,ρ). Then there is a uniformly continuous function $F : X \to Y$ such that $F|D = f$.*

PROOF. Let $x \in X$. Since D is dense in X, there is a sequence $[d_n]$ in D converging to x. Then $[d_n]$ is a Cauchy sequence, and Exercise 7 of Section 3.1 implies that $[f(d_n)]$ is a Cauchy sequence in Y. Since Y is complete, $[f(d_n)]$ converges to a point q of Y. If $[d_n']$ is another sequence in D converging to x, then $d_1, d_1', d_2, d_2', \dots$ is a sequence converging to x. Its image under f is a Cauchy sequence in Y of which $[f(d_n)]$ and $[f(d_n')]$ are both subsequences. Hence $[f(d_n')]$ also converges to q, so we may without ambiguity define $F(x) = q$.

Since $d, d, d, \dots$ is a sequence converging to the point d of D, it is clear that $F|D = f$. It remains only to show that F is uniformly continuous. Let ε be positive, and choose a positive δ such that $\rho(f(p), f(q)) < \varepsilon/2$ whenever $d(p,q) < \delta$ and p, q are in D. Let $d(x,z)$ be less than $\delta/2$, and let $[p_n], [q_n]$ be sequences in D converging to x, z, respectively. There is an integer N such that $d(p_n, q_m) < \delta$ for $n, m \geqslant N$, so that $\rho(f(p_n), f(q_m)) < \varepsilon/2$ for $n, m \geqslant N$. Since $F(x) = \lim_{n \to \infty} f(p_n)$, $\rho(F(x), f(q_m)) \leqslant \varepsilon/2$, and then $\rho(F(x), F(z)) \leqslant \varepsilon/2 < \varepsilon$ since $F(z) = \lim_{m \to \infty} f(q_m)$. ∎

Theorem 3.4.3 *Let $(\hat{X}, \hat{d})$ and (X', d') be complete spaces with isometries $\hat{e}, e'$ from (X,d) onto dense subsets of $\hat{X}, X'$, respectively. Then there is an isometry ϕ from $(\hat{X}, \hat{d})$ onto (X', d') such that $\phi \circ \hat{e} = e'$.*

PROOF. Define $f : \hat{e}(X) \to e'(X)$ by $f(\hat{e}(x)) = e'(x)$. Since $\hat{e}, e'$ are isometries it is clear that f is an isometry and hence f is uniformly continuous. Theorem 3.4.2 implies that there is a function $\phi : \hat{X} \to X'$ such that $\phi|\hat{e}(X) = f$, that is, $\phi \circ \hat{e} = e'$. Let x and z be points of $\hat{X}$, and let $[p_n], [q_n]$ be sequences in $\hat{e}(X)$ converging to x, z, respectively. It is not hard to check (an exercise) that $\hat{d}(x, z) = \lim_{n \to \infty} \hat{d}(p_n, q_n) = \lim_{n \to \infty} d'(f(p_n), f(q_n)) = d'(\phi(x), \phi(z))$. Thus ϕ is an isometry from $\hat{X}$ into X'. Since $\phi(\hat{X})$ is complete, it is closed in X', and since it also contains the dense subset $e'(X)$ of X', $\phi(\hat{X}) = X'$ and ϕ is onto. ∎

The preceding theorem says that there is an essentially unique complete metric space which contains a dense isometric copy of a given metric space. One can conclude that a complete metric space is its own completion, and that the real numbers form the completion of the rationals.

Note should be taken here that we have assumed completeness of the real numbers. The other approach to the proof of Theorem 3.4.1 does not use this fact, and so must be the approach taken when the real numbers are constructed. This is the price we pay for the simplicity of our proof of the existence of completions.

We now turn to the topological case and investigate compactifications of spaces. The basic definition is quite similar to that for completions, but there the similarity ends. There are many compactifications of a given space, rather than a unique one, and in fact work is still being done on various questions concerning this idea. We content ourselves with just one kind of compactification, leaving another for Section 3.6.

Definition A *compactification* of a space X is a compact space $\hat{X}$ and a homeomorphism e from X onto the subset $e(X)$ of $\hat{X}$ such that $e(X)$ is dense in $\hat{X}$.

We note that Corollary 3.3.5 says that every separable metric space has a metrizable compactification. We leave it as an exercise to show that a nonseparable metric space cannot have a metrizable compactification. In fact, right now we do not know if it has a compactification of any kind. We now remedy this defect.

Definition Let $(X, \mathcal{T})$ be a topological space and ∞ a point not in X. Then we set $\tilde{X} = X \cup \{\infty\}$ and $\tilde{\mathcal{T}} = \{U \subset \tilde{X} : \tilde{X} \setminus U$ is a closed compact subset of X or U is open in $X\}$.

Theorem 3.4.4 $(\tilde{X}, \tilde{\mathcal{T}})$ *is a compact topological space containing X as a subspace.*

PROOF. Since $\tilde{X} \setminus \tilde{X}$ is a closed compact subset of X, $\tilde{X} \in \tilde{\mathcal{T}}$, and $\varnothing \in \tilde{\mathcal{T}}$ since $\varnothing$ is open in X. Suppose U_1 and U_2 are in $\tilde{\mathcal{T}}$. If U_1 and U_2 are both open in X, then so is $U_1 \cap U_2$. If $\tilde{X} \setminus U_1$ and $\tilde{X} \setminus U_2$ are both closed compact subsets of X, then so is $(\tilde{X} \setminus U_1) \cup (\tilde{X} \setminus U_2) = \tilde{X} \setminus (U_1 \cap U_2)$. If $\tilde{X} \setminus U_1$ is a closed compact subset of X and U_2 is open in X, then $U_1 \cap U_2 = U_2 \cap (X \cap U_1) = U_2 \cap (X \setminus (X \setminus U_1)) = U_2 \cap (X \setminus (\tilde{X} \setminus U_1))$ is the intersection of two open subsets of X and so is open in X. Hence in any case $U_1 \cap U_2$ is in $\tilde{\mathcal{T}}$. Finally, if U_α is open in X for each $\alpha \in \mathcal{C}$, then so is $\cup \{U_\alpha : \alpha \in \mathcal{C}\}$. If $\tilde{X} \setminus U_\beta$ is closed and compact in X for each $\beta \in \mathcal{B}$, then $\tilde{X} \setminus (\cup \{U_\beta : \beta \in \mathcal{B}\}) = \cap \{\tilde{X} \setminus U_\beta : \beta \in \mathcal{B}\}$ is also. Further, $\tilde{X} \setminus [(\cup \{U_\alpha : \alpha \in \mathcal{C}\}) \cup (\cup \{U_\beta : \beta \in \mathcal{B}\})] = (X \setminus \cup \{U_\alpha : \alpha \in \mathcal{C}\}) \cap (\cap \{\tilde{X} \setminus U_\beta : \beta \in \mathcal{B}\})$ is a closed compact subset of X. Hence unions of sets in $\tilde{\mathcal{T}}$ are in $\tilde{\mathcal{T}}$. Thus $\tilde{\mathcal{T}}$ is a topology.

To show that $(\tilde{X}, \tilde{\mathcal{T}})$ is compact, let $\mathcal{U} = \{U_\alpha : \alpha \in \mathcal{C}\}$ be an open cover of $\tilde{X}$. Then for some $\beta \in \mathcal{C}$, $\infty \in U_\beta$, so that $\tilde{X} \setminus U_\beta$ is a compact subset of

X. Noting that $U_\alpha \cap X$ is always open in X, we see that $\{U_\alpha \cap X : \alpha \in \mathcal{C}\}$ is an open cover of $\tilde{X} \setminus U_\beta$ and so has a finite subcover $\{U_{\alpha_1} \cap X, U_{\alpha_2} \cap X, \ldots, U_{\alpha_n} \cap X\}$. Then $\{U_\beta, U_{\alpha_1}, \ldots, U_{\alpha_n}\}$ is a finite subcover of $\tilde{\mathcal{U}}$.

Finally, note that $U \cap X$ is always open in X when U is in $\tilde{\mathcal{I}}$, and every open subset of X lies in $\tilde{\mathcal{I}}$. Thus $\tilde{\mathcal{I}}$ coincides with the subspace topology on X. ∎

Note that if X is compact, then $\tilde{X} \setminus \{\infty\} = X$ is a closed compact subset of X and so $\{\infty\}$ is an open subset of $\tilde{X}$. On the other hand, if X is not compact and U is an open set containing ∞, then $\tilde{X} \setminus U$ is a compact subset of X and so cannot be all of X. Thus $U \cap X \neq \varnothing$, so that X is dense in $\tilde{X}$. We thus have the following theorem.

Theorem 3.4.5 *X is dense in $\tilde{X}$ if and only if X is not compact.*

If we let $e(x) = x$ for each $x \in X$, then $\tilde{X}$ is a compactification of X precisely in the interesting case, namely, when X is not compact. Thus every space has at least one compactification. The next theorem lists some properties of this space, but first we give it a name.

Definition If X is not compact, then the space $(\tilde{X}, \tilde{\mathcal{I}})$ defined above is called the *Alexandroff* or *one-point compactification* of X.

Theorem 3.4.6 *Let X be a noncompact space and $\tilde{X}$ its one-point compactification.*

1. *$\tilde{X}$ is Hausdorff if and only if X is Hausdorff and locally compact.*
2. *If X is locally compact Hausdorff and second countable, then $\tilde{X}$ is second countable.*
3. *$\tilde{X}$ is metrizable if and only if X is separable metrizable and locally compact.*

PROOF.
1. If $\tilde{X}$ is Hausdorff, then so is X as a subspace of $\tilde{X}$. Further, $\{\infty\}$ is then a closed subset of $\tilde{X}$, so that $X = \tilde{X} \setminus \{\infty\}$ is open, and open subsets of compact Hausdorff spaces are easily shown to be locally compact.

   Now suppose that X is Hausdorff and locally compact. Clearly any two points of X have disjoint neighborhoods in $\tilde{X}$, since open sets in X are also open in $\tilde{X}$. Thus we must find disjoint neighborhoods of ∞ and a point x of X. Since X is locally compact, there is a compact set K in X containing a neighborhood U of x. Since X is T_2, K is closed, so that $\tilde{X} \setminus K$ is a neighborhood of ∞. Thus $\tilde{X} \setminus K$ and U are the desired neighborhoods of ∞ and x respectively.

2. Let X be locally compact Hausdorff with countable base $\mathcal{U} = \{ U_n : n = 1, 2, \ldots \}$. Let $\{ V_n : n = 1, 2, \ldots \}$ be the subcollection of $\mathcal{U}$ consisting of all those U_j's which have compact closure. Since any neighborhood of a point in X contains a neighborhood whose closure is compact, and this neighborhood in turn contains some U_r, $\{ V_n : n = 1, 2, \ldots \}$ is also a countable base for X. Let $W_n = \tilde{X} \backslash \mathrm{Cl}(V_1 \cup V_2 \cup \cdots \cup V_n)$ for $n = 1, 2, \ldots$. The W_n's are by definition open in $\tilde{X}$.

   Let O be open in $\tilde{X}$. Then $O \cap X$ is open in X and so is a union of V_n's. We will be done when we show that if $\infty \in O$, then there is a W_n with $W_n \subset O$. But if $\infty \in O$, then $\tilde{X} \backslash O$ is a compact subset of X and so is covered by finitely many V_j's, say $V_1, V_2, \ldots, V_N$. Then clearly $W_N \subset O$.

3. If $\tilde{X}$ is metrizable, then it is T_2, so that X is locally compact. Further, X is then a subspace of a compact metric space and so is separable and metrizable.

   Conversely, if X is separable metrizable and locally compact, then the above results imply that $\tilde{X}$ is compact Hausdorff and second countable. Hence $\tilde{X}$ is T_3 and second countable, and so is metrizable by Urysohn's Metrization Theorem. ∎

EXAMPLES.

1. The following picture indicates a function from R to the circle S^1.

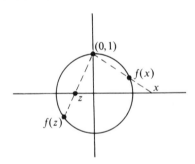

   We can extend f to $\tilde{R}$ by setting $f(\infty) = (0, 1)$. It is not hard to check that f is then a continuous one-to-one function from $\tilde{R}$ onto S^1, so that these spaces are homeomorphic. An analogous procedure shows that S^n is the one-point compactification of R^n for $n = 1, 2, \ldots$.

2. Consider the space $(0, 1)$. Its one-point compactification is S^1 as shown above. It also has a two-point compactification, namely $[0, 1]$. The subset $(0, 1) \cup (1, 2)$ of R has one-point, two-point, and three-point compactifications.

   We conclude this section with a nice application of the one-point compactification.

Theorem 3.4.7 *A locally compact Hausdorff space X is Tychonoff.*

PROOF. If X is compact, we are done by Theorem 3.2.11 and Corollary 3.3.2. Otherwise, $\tilde{X}$ is a compact Hausdorff space and hence is Tychonoff. X is then a subspace of a Tychonoff space and so is Tychonoff. ∎

Exercises

1. Prove that an isometry from (X,d) onto (Y,ρ) is a homeomorphism.

2. Supply all the details of the proof of Theorem 3.4.3.

3. Prove that a nonseparable metric space cannot have a metrizable compactification.

4. Prove that a compact Hausdorff space is locally compact and hence that open subspaces of compact Hausdorff spaces are locally compact.

5. Furnish all the details of Example 1 for R and S^1.

6. For each positive integer n, find a subspace of R which has $1, 2, \ldots, n$-point compactifications.

7. Prove that the one-point compactification of R^n is S^n for each n.

8. Prove that the one-point compactification of X is T_1 if and only if X is T_1.

9. Give an example to show that an open subset of a compact T_1 space need not be locally compact. Hint: use Exercise 8.

3.5 New spaces from old, III: quotients and arbitrary products

In this section we expand our treatment of some topics which we have touched in one way or another in earlier sections. We introduce in full generality two of the three fundamental methods for creating new spaces, namely, quotient spaces and product spaces. (The third is the taking of subspaces.)

We concentrate first on product spaces. We have had product spaces with us ever since Section 2.2, but only in the finite case. We now treat the general case, but often leave proofs as exercises, since many are very similar to the proofs of the analogous results for finite products.

Suppose we are given a collection of spaces $\{X_i : i \in J\}$. We must first define the Cartesian product $\times \{X_i : i \in J\}$, and the motivation for this lies in a closer examination of the finite case. Note that $X_1 \times X_2 \times \cdots \times X_n$ consists of ordered n-tuples $(x_1, x_2, \ldots, x_n)$, where $x_i \in X_i$ for each i. Such an ordered n-tuple is really an assignment of a point x_i in X_i to the index i, that is, $(x_1, x_2, \ldots, x_n)$ can be regarded as a function on $\{1, 2, \ldots, n\}$ whose value at i lies in X_i. We are thus led to the following.

Definition   Let $\{X_i : i \in J\}$ be a collection of sets. The *Cartesian product* of this collection is denoted by $\times \{X_i : i \in J\}$ and is defined to be $\{f : f$ is a function on J with $f(i) \in X_i$ for each i in $J\}$. X_i is the *i-th coordinate set*, and $f(i)$ is the *i-th coordinate* of the point f of the product. The function $\pi_i : \times \{X_i : i \in J\} \to X_i$ defined by $\pi_i(f) = f(i)$ is called the *projection* into the *i*-th coordinate set. Finally, we often write f_i for $f(i)$ and even worse, we write x for a point of the product and x_i for its *i*-th coordinate.

A rather subtle but important set theory question now arises. Namely, if each X_j is non-empty, then is it true that $\times \{X_j : j \in J\}$ is non-empty? This query has no easy answer, contrary to intuition, and a rigorous treatment requires a thorough discussion of the Axiom of Choice (see the Appendix). We proceed naively and assume the answer is yes. For more details, see other texts.

Our previous discussion shows that we actually have a generalization of finite products. The question now remains as to how to put a topology on a Cartesian product of topological spaces. Analogy with the finite case would suggest that $\times \{U_i : i \in J\}$ should be an open set in the product if each U_i is open in X_i. This construction does yield an interesting topology, but it turns out to be the wrong one for most purposes. Experience has shown that the following definition is the correct one.

Definition   Let $(X_i, \mathcal{T}_i)$ be a topological space for each $i \in J$, and let $X = \times \{X_i : j \in J\}$. Define $\mathcal{T}$ to be the collection of all unions of sets of the form $W = \times \{W_j : j \in J, W_j$ is open in X_j, $W_j = X_j$ except for finitely many j's$\}$.

Theorem 3.5.1 $\mathcal{T}$ *is a topology on* X.

PROOF. X is clearly of the form of W in the definition, and $\varnothing = W$ if some $W_j = \varnothing$, so X and $\varnothing$ are both in $\mathcal{T}$. Since unions of unions are unions, unions of sets in $\mathcal{T}$ lie in $\mathcal{T}$. Finally, suppose that O_1 and O_2 are in $\mathcal{T}$ and that $x \in O_1 \cap O_2$. There are sets $W = \times \{W_j : j \in J, W_j$ is open in X_j, $W_j = X_j$ except for finitely many j's$\}$ and $V = \times \{V_j : j \in J, V_j$ is open in $X_j, V_j = X_j$ except for finitely many j's$\}$ such that $x \in W \subset O_1$ and $x \in V \subset O_2$. If $U_j = W_j \cap V_j$ and $U = \times \{U_j : j \in J\}$, then U has the proper form and $x \in U \subset O_1 \cap O_2$. Thus $O_1 \cap O_2$ is a union of sets of the correct form and so lies in $\mathcal{T}$.   ∎

Definition $\mathcal{T}$ is called the *product topology* on X, and $(X, \mathcal{T})$ is a *product space*, or *the product of the spaces* X_j. The spaces X_j are called *factors* of X.

We now look at the properties of the projection functions π_i. It is their nice behavior under the product topology which is one of the justifications for its use.

Theorem 3.5.2 *Let* $(X, \mathfrak{I})$ *be the product of the collection of spaces* $\{(X_i, \mathfrak{I}_i) : i \in J\}$, *and let* $\pi_i : X \to X_i$ *be the projection function.*

1. π_i *is continuous and takes open sets to open sets.*
2. *If* $(Y, \mathfrak{U})$ *is a space and* f *a function from* Y *to* X, *then* f *is continuous if and only if* $\pi_i \circ f$ *is continuous for each* $i \in J$.

PROOF.
1. If U_i is open in X_i, then $\pi_i^{-1}(U_i) = \times \{W_j : j \in J\}$, where $W_i = U_i$ and $W_j = X_j$ for $j \neq i$. Thus $\pi_i^{-1}(U_i)$ lies in $\mathfrak{I}$, so that π_i is continuous. Since π_i preserves unions, to show that π_i takes open sets to open sets we need only show that $\pi_i(W)$ is open, where $W = \times \{W_j : j \in J, W_j$ is open in $X_j, W_j = X_j$ except for finitely many j's$\}$. But clearly $\pi_i(W) = W_i$ which is open in X_i.

2. If f is continuous, then part 1 implies that $\pi_i \circ f$ is continuous for each i. Conversely, suppose that each $\pi_i \circ f$ is continuous. Since f^{-1} preserves unions, we need only show that $f^{-1}(W)$ is open when W has the usual form. If $j_1, j_2, \ldots, j_n$ are the only j's for which $W_j \neq X_j$, then

$$W = \pi_{j_1}^{-1}(W_{j_1}) \cap \pi_{j_2}^{-1}(W_{j_2}) \cap \cdots \cap \pi_{j_n}^{-1}(W_{j_n}),$$

and

$$f^{-1}(W) = f^{-1}\left[\pi_{j_1}^{-1}(W_{j_1}) \cap \pi_{j_2}^{-1}(W_{j_2}) \cap \cdots \cap \pi_{j_n}^{-1}(W_{j_n}) \right]$$
$$= f^{-1}\pi_{j_1}^{-1}(W_{j_1}) \cap f^{-1}\pi_{j_2}^{-1}(W_{j_2}) \cap \cdots \cap f^{-1}\pi_{j_n}^{-1}(W_{j_n}).$$

This is a finite intersection of open sets, since each $\pi_{j_r} \circ f$ is continuous and W_{j_r} is open. Thus $f^{-1}(W)$ is open and f is continuous. ∎

A consideration of elementary examples suggests that a product space always contains a copy of each of its factors. For instance, the plane contains many copies of the real line. That this is true in general is our next result.

Theorem 3.5.3 *Let* $(X_j, \mathfrak{I}_j)$ *be a non-empty topological space for each* j *in* J, *and let* $(X, \mathfrak{I})$ *be the product of the spaces* $(X_j, \mathfrak{I}_j)$. *The space* $(X, \mathfrak{I})$ *contains a subspace homeomorphic to* $(X_j, \mathfrak{I}_j)$ *for each* $j \in J$.

PROOF. Fix $j \in J$, and for each i in J choose $x_i \in X_i$. Let $X_j' = X_j \times \times \{\{x_i\} : i \in J, i \neq j\}$. Define $e : X_j \to X$ by $e(z) = \{z\} \times \times \{\{x_i\} : i \in J, i \neq j\}$, that is,

$$(e(z))_k = \begin{cases} z & k = i \\ x_k & k \neq i \end{cases}.$$

The function e is clearly one-to-one and onto from X_j to X_j'. Further, $\pi_k \circ e$ is clearly continuous for each k, so Theorem 3.5.2 implies that e is continuous. Finally, $e^{-1} = \pi_j | X_j'$, so that e^{-1} is continuous. Hence e is a homeomorphism and X_j' is a subspace of X homeomorphic to X_j. ■

We now turn to an investigation of some topological properties which are preserved by products. Not all properties are, and in particular countability properties are often not preserved when a product has too many factors. We leave a more detailed discussion for more advanced texts and prove just two of the more important theorems. Note that we do not deal with compactness, the reason being that the necessary tools will not be developed until Section 3.6.

Theorem 3.5.4 *Let* $(X, \mathcal{T})$ *be the product of the collection of non-empty spaces* $\{(X_j, \mathcal{T}_j) : j \in J\}$.

1. $(X, \mathcal{T})$ *is* T_1 *if and only if each* $(X_j, \mathcal{T}_j)$ *is* T_1.
2. $(X, \mathcal{T})$ *is* T_2 *if and only if each* $(X_j, \mathcal{T}_j)$ *is* T_2.
3. $(X, \mathcal{T})$ *is regular if and only if each* $(X_j, \mathcal{T}_j)$ *is regular.*
4. $(X, \mathcal{T})$ *is completely regular if and only if each* $(X_j, \mathcal{T}_j)$ *is completely regular.*
5. $(X, \mathcal{T})$ *is connected if and only if each* $(X_j, \mathcal{T}_j)$ *is connected.*

PROOF. Since open sets in a product space can almost be thought of as unions of finite products of open sets in the factors, the proofs of these results are almost identical with their proofs in the case of finite products. Also, Theorem 3.5.3 says that the factors inherit from the product space all those properties which are inherited by subspaces. With these remarks we leave the proofs of $(1-4)$ as exercises.

To prove (5), we fix a point x in X and note that if y is a point in X which differs from x only in the j-th coordinate, then x and y both lie in $X_j' = X_j \times \times \{\{x_i\} : i \in J, i \neq j\}$. The proof of Theorem 3.5.3 shows that X_j' is homeomorphic to X_j, so we conclude that x and y lie together in a connected subset C_1 of X. If z differs from y only in the k-th coordinate, then similarly z and y lie together in a connected subset C_2 of X, so that x and z lie in the connected subset $C_1 \cup C_2$. Induction then shows that any point of X which differs from x in at most finitely many coordinates lies in $C = \cup \{K : K \text{ connected}, x \in K \subset X\}$.

Let p be any point of X, and let O be any neighborhood of p. There are open sets W_j in X_j such that $p_j \in W_j$, $W_j = X_j$ except for $j = i_1, i_2, \ldots, i_n$, and

$p \in \times \{ W_j : j \in J \} \subset O$. Then the point q defined by

$$q_j = \begin{cases} x_j & j \neq i_1, i_2, \ldots, i_n \\ p_j & j = i_1, i_2, \ldots, i_n \end{cases}$$

lies in $O \cap C$. Thus X is the closure of the connected set C and so is connected.

Conversely, if X is connected, then X_j is the continuous image of X under π_j and so each factor is connected. ∎

The next theorem collects some results concerning product spaces and countability properties. There are more results along these lines, including necessary and sufficient conditions for a product to enjoy certain countability properties, but we will not pursue them.

Theorem 3.5.5 *Let* $(X, \mathfrak{T})$ *be the product of the countable collection of non-empty spaces* $\{(X_i, \mathfrak{T}_i) : i = 1, 2, \ldots \}$.

1. $(X, \mathfrak{T})$ *is first countable if each* $(X_i, \mathfrak{T}_i)$ *is first countable.*
2. $(X, \mathfrak{T})$ *is second countable if each* $(X_i, \mathfrak{T}_i)$ *is second countable.*
3. $(X, \mathfrak{T})$ *is metrizable if each* $(X_i, \mathfrak{T}_i)$ *is metrizable.*

PROOF.
1. In the case of countable products we allow ourselves the liberty of writing $X_1 \times X_2 \times \cdots$ for $\times \{ X_i : i = 1, 2, \ldots \}$ and $(p_1, p_2, \ldots)$ for the point whose i-th coordinate is p_i. Let $p = (p_1, p_2, \ldots)$ be any point of X, and for each i let $\mathfrak{U}_i = \{ U_{i,n} : n = 1, 2, \ldots \}$ be a countable collection of neighborhoods of p_i such that each neighborhood of p_i contains some $U_{i,n}$.
   Consider the collection $\{ U_{1,n_1} \times U_{2,n_2} \times \cdots \times U_{r,n_r} \times X_{r+1} \times X_{r+2} \cdots : r = 1, 2, \ldots$ and $n_i = 1, 2, \ldots$ for each $i = 1, 2, \ldots, r \}$. This is a countable collection of neighborhoods of p. If O is any neighborhood of p, then there are open sets $W_1, W_2, \ldots, W_s$ in $X_1, X_2, \ldots, X_s$, respectively, such that $p \in W_1 \times W_2 \times \cdots \times W_s \times X_{s+1} \times X_{s+2} \times \cdots \subset O$. There are then neighborhoods U_{i,n_i} of p_i such that $U_{i,n_i} \subset W_i$ for $i = 1, 2, \ldots, s$. Clearly, $p \in U_{1,n_1} \times U_{2,n_2} \times \cdots \times U_{s,n_s} \times X_{s+1} \times X_{s+2} \times \cdots \subset O$.
2. This proof is similar to and easier than the proof of 1, so we leave it as an exercise.
3. Let p_i be a metric for X_i whose topology is $\mathfrak{T}_i$ for $i = 1, 2, \ldots$. It is easy to check that $d_i(x,y) = \min \{ p_i(x,y), 1/i \}$ is also a metric for X_i whose topology is $\mathfrak{T}_i$, so we use the d_i's instead. We then define a function d on $X \times X$ by

$$d((x_1, x_2, \ldots), (y_1, y_2, \ldots)) = \sqrt{\sum_{i=1}^{\infty} (d_i(x_i, y_i))^2}.$$

101

Results from the Appendix and our previous work on the Hilbert cube (p. 24) imply that d is a metric on X.

We show that d generates the product topology on X. First note that $d((x_1, x_2, \ldots), (y_1, y_2, \ldots)) \geqslant d_i(x_i, y_i)$, so that $\pi_i : (X, d) \to (X_i, d_i)$ is continuous for each i. Since

$$U_1 \times U_2 \times \cdots \times U_n \times X_{n+1} \times X_{n+2} \times \cdots$$
$$= \pi_1^{-1}(U_1) \cap \pi_2^{-1}(U_2) \cap \cdots \cap \pi_n^{-1}(U_n),$$

each set of this form is open in (X, d) when $U_1, U_2, \ldots, U_n$ are open sets in $X_1, X_2, \ldots, X_n$. Hence the topology generated by d contains the product topology.

Suppose that $p = (p_1, p_2, \ldots)$ is a point of the d-open set O in X. There is a positive ε such that $N(p, \varepsilon) \subset O$. Then there is an integer n such that $\sum_{i=n+1}^{\infty} 1/i^2 < \varepsilon^2/2$. If $y = (y_1, y_2, \ldots)$ is a point of

$$N\left(p_1, \frac{\varepsilon}{\sqrt{2n}}\right) \times N\left(p_2, \frac{\varepsilon}{\sqrt{2n}}\right) \times \cdots \times N\left(p_n, \frac{\varepsilon}{\sqrt{2n}}\right)$$
$$\times X_{n+1} \times X_{n+2} \times \cdots,$$

then

$$d(p, y) = \sqrt{\sum_{i=1}^{\infty} \left(d_i(p_i, y_i)\right)^2} < \sqrt{\frac{\varepsilon^2}{2n} + \frac{\varepsilon^2}{2n} + \cdots + \frac{\varepsilon^2}{2n} + \sum_{i=n+1}^{\infty} \frac{1}{i^2}}$$
$$< \sqrt{\frac{\varepsilon^2}{2} + \frac{\varepsilon^2}{2}} = \varepsilon,$$

so that $y \in N(p, \varepsilon) \subset O$. Thus O is a union of $\mathfrak{T}$-open sets and so is $\mathfrak{T}$-open, and the topology generated by d coincides with the product topology. ∎

EXAMPLES.

1. Our previous work on the Hilbert cube I^{∞} can now be summed up by saying that I^{∞} is the product of the spaces $[0, 1/i]$ for $i = 1, 2, \ldots$. Since $[0, 1/i]$ and $[0, 1]$ are homeomorphic, we can also say that I^{∞} is $[0, 1] \times [0, 1] \times \cdots$ (see Exercise 7).

2. For each positive integer i let X_i be the discrete space $\{0, 1\}$, and let X be the product of the X_i's. Then X is a metric space by Theorem 3.5.5, but it is no longer discrete because any neighborhood of $(0, 0, \ldots)$ must contain a set of the form $\{0\} \times \{0\} \times \cdots \times \{0\} \times X_{n+1} \times X_{n+2} \times \cdots$ for some n and so must contain points other than $(0, 0, \ldots)$. This space in another disguise turns out to be quite important, and we will return to it in Chapter 4.

We now turn to a second important method for constructing new spaces from old. The study of this procedure has led to many important results in recent years, and the procedure itself is a basic tool used in constructing the important spaces of algebraic topology. Our motivation comes from the following example.

EXAMPLE.

3. Consider the unit segment [0, 1]. The following pictures show what happens when we identify the points 0 and 1 with a single point in a new space.

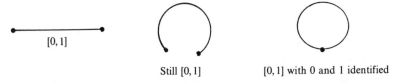

[0, 1]

Still [0, 1]   [0, 1] with 0 and 1 identified

Thus this identification procedure can be used to construct S^1 from [0, 1].

This idea of taking subsets of a space and regarding them as points of a new space is made rigorous by the following definition. Our terminology does not coincide precisely with some other texts, in that others sometimes make synonyms out of what to us are distinct terms, in particular, *decomposition space* and *quotient space*. Hopefully our approach will lend clarity to a slightly confusing situation, and all will be cleared up after a theorem or two.

Definition   Let $(X, \mathcal{T})$ be a topological space. Let $\mathcal{D}$ be a collection of pairwise disjoint non-empty subsets of X whose union is X. $\mathcal{D}$ is said to be a *decomposition* of X. Define the *projection map* P from X onto $\mathcal{D}$ by letting $P(x)$ be the unique set in $\mathcal{D}$ which contains x. Finally, let $\mathcal{T}' = \{\sigma \subset \mathcal{D} : P^{-1}(\sigma)$ is open in $X\}$. The topological space $(\mathcal{D}, \mathcal{T}')$ (verification: an exercise) is called a *decomposition space* of X.

We need to construct some more machinery and introduce some other ideas before we can turn to examples. The next theorem is a very useful tool for dealing with decomposition spaces and sort of corresponds dually with Theorem 3.5.2, part 2.

Theorem 3.5.6   *Let $(\mathcal{D}, \mathcal{T}')$ be a decomposition space of $(X, \mathcal{T})$ with projection map P.*

1. *P is continuous.*

2. *If* $(Y, \mathfrak{U})$ *is a space and* $f: \mathfrak{D} \to Y$ *a function, then* f *is continuous if and only if* $f \circ P$ *is continuous.*

PROOF.

1. This follows directly from the definition of $\mathfrak{T}'$.

2. If f is continuous, then so is $f \circ P$ by part 1 and composition. Conversely, suppose that $f \circ P$ is continuous, and let V be open in Y. Then $(f \circ P)^{-1}(V) = P^{-1}(f^{-1}(V))$ is open in X, and by definition of $\mathfrak{T}'$, $f^{-1}(V)$ must be open in $\mathfrak{D}$. ∎

EXAMPLES.

4. Consider the plane R^2 with the usual topology, let $Z = \{(n,0) : n$ is a positive integer$\}$, and let $\mathfrak{D} = \{Z\} \cup \{\{(x,y)\} : (x,y) \notin Z\}$. Then $\mathfrak{D}$ gives rise to a decomposition space of R^2. We will show that $\mathfrak{D}$ is not first countable and hence certainly not second countable or metrizable. Let $U_1, U_2, \ldots$ be any sequence of neighborhoods of the point Z of $\mathfrak{D}$. For each positive integer i there is a neighborhood V_i of $(i,0)$ such that $V_i \subset N((i,0), \frac{1}{3}) \cap P^{-1}(U_i)$ but $V_i \neq N((i,0), \frac{1}{3}) \cap P^{-1}(U_i)$. Let $V = V_1 \cup V_2 \cup \ldots$. Then V is a neighborhood of Z, and $P^{-1}P(V) = V$, so that $P(V)$ is a neighborhood of the point Z in $\mathfrak{D}$. If $P(V) \supset U_j$, then $V = P^{-1}P(V) \supset P^{-1}(U_j)$, so that $V \cap N((j,0), \frac{1}{3}) \supset P^{-1}(U_j) \cap N((j,0), \frac{1}{3})$. But $V \cap N((j,0), \frac{1}{3}) = V_j \cap N((j,0), \frac{1}{3})$, which does not contain $N((j,0), \frac{1}{3}) \cap P^{-1}(U_j)$. Hence $P(V)$ contains no U_j, and $\mathfrak{D}$ cannot be first countable at the point Z.

5. Let X be a Hausdorff space which is not normal, for example, the Sorgenfrey plane. Let A and B be disjoint closed subsets of X which do not have disjoint neighborhoods, and let $\mathfrak{D} = \{A, B\} \cup \{\{x\} : x \notin A \cup B\}$. Then $\mathfrak{D}$ gives rise to a decomposition space of X which we will show is not Hausdorff. Suppose that the points A and B of $\mathfrak{D}$ have disjoint neighborhoods U and V in $\mathfrak{D}$. Then $P^{-1}(U), P^{-1}(V)$ are disjoint neighborhoods of the sets A and B in X, a contradiction. Hence a decomposition space of a Hausdorff space need not be Hausdorff.

The above examples show that decomposition spaces do not preserve some important topological properties. We now turn to some theorems concerning properties which are preserved.

Theorem 3.5.7 *Let* $(\mathfrak{D}, \mathfrak{T}')$ *be a decomposition space of the space* $(X, \mathfrak{T})$.

1. *If* X *is compact, then so is* $\mathfrak{D}$.
2. *If* X *is connected, then so is* $\mathfrak{D}$.
3. *If* X *is separable, then so is* $\mathfrak{D}$.
4. *If* X *is locally connected, then so is* $\mathfrak{D}$.

PROOF. Parts 1–3 all follow since $\mathcal{D}$ is the continuous image of X under the projection map. Part 4 follows directly from Theorem 2.5.15. ∎

To ensure that a decomposition space preserves properties such as T_2 and second countable we must put some kind of restriction on the decomposition. The next definition introduces one such restriction, along with some other terminology which we will use to deal with such restrictions. There are many definitions of various kinds of decomposition spaces, but we must leave them for more detailed texts. It is probably true that ours is the most important.

Definition A decomposition $\mathcal{D}$ of a space $(X, \mathcal{T})$ is said to be *upper semicontinuous* if whenever $D \in \mathcal{D}$ and U is a neighborhood of D in X, then $\cup \{E \in \mathcal{D} : E \subset U\}$ is open in X. Also, a function f from a space $(X, \mathcal{T})$ to a space $(Y, \mathcal{U})$ is said to be *closed* if $f(C)$ is closed in Y whenever C is closed in X.

Theorem 3.5.8 *A decomposition $\mathcal{D}$ of a space $(X, \mathcal{T})$ is upper semicontinuous if and only if the projection map P is closed.*

PROOF. Suppose $\mathcal{D}$ is upper semicontinuous and let C be a closed set in X. Let D be an element of $\mathcal{D}$ not in $P(C)$. Then $D \cap C = \varnothing$ so that $X \setminus C$ is a neighborhood of D. Then $O = \cup \{E \in \mathcal{D} : E \subset X \setminus C\}$ is a neighborhood of D, and clearly $P^{-1}P(O) = O$. Thus $P(O)$ is a neighborhood of D missing $P(C)$. Hence $\mathcal{D} \setminus P(C)$ is open and $P(C)$ is closed, so that P is closed.

Conversely, suppose that P is closed, and let D be an element of $\mathcal{D}$ with neighborhood U in X. Then $X \setminus U$ is closed, so that $P(X \setminus U)$ is closed, and hence $P^{-1}P(X \setminus U)$ is closed. It is easy to check that $\cup \{E \in \mathcal{D} : E \subset U\} = X \setminus (P^{-1}P(X \setminus U))$, so that $\mathcal{D}$ is upper semicontinuous. ∎

The next two theorems are a partial justification for the introduction of upper semicontinuity. Again, more results are available along these lines, but our scope does not allow them to be included here.

Theorem 3.5.9 *Let $\mathcal{D}$ be an upper semicontinuous decomposition of a normal space $(X, \mathcal{T})$. Then $(\mathcal{D}, \mathcal{T}')$ is normal.*

PROOF. Let $\mathcal{A}$ and $\mathcal{B}$ be disjoint closed subsets of $\mathcal{D}$. Then $P^{-1}(\mathcal{A})$ and $P^{-1}(\mathcal{B})$ are disjoint closed subsets of X and so have disjoint neighborhoods U and V. Since $\mathcal{D}$ is upper semicontinuous, $U' = \cup \{E \in \mathcal{D} : E \subset U\}$ and $V' = \cup \{E \in \mathcal{D} : E \subset V\}$ are open, and as before $P(U')$ and $P(V')$ turn out to be disjoint neighborhoods of $\mathcal{A}$ and $\mathcal{B}$. ∎

Theorem 3.5.10 *Let $\mathcal{D}$ be an upper semicontinuous decomposition of a space X whose elements are compact sets.*

1. *If X is second countable, then so is $\mathcal{D}$.*
2. *If X is separable metrizable, then so is $\mathcal{D}$.*

PROOF.

1. Suppose that $\mathcal{U}$ is a countable base for X. Let $\mathcal{V}$ be the collection of unions of finite subcollections of U. Then $\mathcal{V}$ is also countable. For each $V \in \mathcal{V}$, let $V' = \bigcup \{ E \in \mathcal{D} : E \subset V \}$, and let $\mathcal{W} = \{ P(V') : V \in \mathcal{V} \}$. Since $\mathcal{D}$ is upper semicontinuous, $\mathcal{W}$ is a countable collection of open subsets of $\mathcal{D}$.

   Let $D \in \mathcal{D}$ have neighborhood σ in $\mathcal{D}$. Then D is a compact subset of $P^{-1}(\sigma)$ in X, and so there are elements $U_1, U_2, \ldots, U_n$ of $\mathcal{U}$ such that $D \subset U_1 \cup U_2 \cup \cdots \cup U_n \subset P^{-1}(\sigma)$. Letting $V = U_1 \cup U_2 \cup \cdots \cup U_n$, we see that $P(V')$ is an element of $\mathcal{W}$ satisfying $D \in P(V') \subset \sigma$. Hence $\mathcal{W}$ is a countable base for $\mathcal{D}$ and $\mathcal{D}$ is second countable.

2. If X is separable metrizable, then X is second countable, so part 1 implies that $\mathcal{D}$ is second countable. Theorem 3.5.9 says that $\mathcal{D}$ is normal. Finally, elements of $\mathcal{D}$ are compact and hence closed in X, so that their images, i.e., the points of $\mathcal{D}$, are closed in $\mathcal{D}$ by Theorem 3.5.8. Hence $\mathcal{D}$ is T_4 and second countable and so is separable metrizable by Urysohn's Metrization Theorem. ∎

It is often the case that a decomposition space of a space X is an easily recognizable space but in disguise. To deal with this situation, we introduce the following terminology.

Definition A function f from the space $(X, \mathcal{T})$ to the space $(Y, \mathcal{U})$ is a *quotient map* if f is continuous, onto, and has the property that U is open in Y whenever $f^{-1}(U)$ is open in X. Then $(Y, \mathcal{U})$ is said to be a *quotient space* of $(X, \mathcal{T})$.

The language suggests that quotient spaces and decomposition spaces should be intimately connected. Indeed they are, and in fact the two terms are often used interchangeably. The justification for this is the following theorem. It says essentially that a quotient space with quotient map f is really a decomposition space whose projection map is f.

Theorem 3.5.11 *Let f be a quotient map from the space $(X, \mathcal{T})$ to the space $(Y, \mathcal{U})$ and let $\mathcal{D} = \{ f^{-1}(y) : y \in Y \}$. Then there is a homeomorphism $\phi : \mathcal{D} \to Y$ such that $\phi \circ P = f$.*

PROOF. Define ϕ by $\phi(f^{-1}(y)) = y$. If $P(x) = f^{-1}(y)$, then $x \in f^{-1}(y)$ or

$f(x) = y$, so that $\phi(P(x)) = \phi(f^{-1}(y)) = y = f(x)$. Hence $\phi \circ P = f$. Theorem 3.5.6 implies that ϕ is continuous. It is easy to show that ϕ is one-to-one and onto. If U is open in $\mathfrak{D}$, then $f^{-1}(\phi(U)) = (\phi \circ P)^{-1}(\phi(U)) = P^{-1}(\phi^{-1}(\phi(U))) = P^{-1}(U)$ is open in X, so that $\phi(U)$ is open in Y. Hence $(\phi^{-1})^{-1} = \phi$ takes open sets to open sets and so ϕ^{-1} is continuous. ∎

Theorem 3.5.12

1. *A closed continuous function f from the space $(X, \mathfrak{I})$ onto the space $(Y, \mathfrak{U})$ is a quotient map.*
2. *A continuous function g from a compact space Z onto a Hausdorff space T is a quotient map.*

PROOF.
1. Let $f^{-1}(C)$ be open in X. Then $X \setminus f^{-1}(C)$ is closed, so that $f(X \setminus f^{-1}(C))$ is closed. But $f(X \setminus f^{-1}(C)) = Y \setminus C$, so that C is open.
2. Let K be closed in Z. Then K is compact, so that $g(K)$ is a compact subset of T. Hence $g(K)$ is closed in T, so that g is a closed function and thus a quotient map. ∎

The last two theorems often allow us to identify decomposition spaces by constructing the quotient map f. We use this technique to do some examples.

EXAMPLES.

6. Define $f : [0, 1] \to S^1$ by $f(t) = (\cos 2\pi t, \sin 2\pi t)$. Then f is continuous and onto and so is a quotient map by Theorem 3.5.12. Thus we may regard S^1 as the decomposition space of $[0, 1]$ obtained by identifying 0 and 1. This finally justifies our motivating example.
7. In this example we use the following notation. If $x = (x_1, x_2, \ldots, x_n) \in R^n$ and $t \in R$, then (x, t) denotes $(x_1, x_2, \ldots, x_n, t) \in R^{n+1}$. Note that $|(x_1, x_2, \ldots, x_n, t)| = \sqrt{|x|^2 + t^2}$. Let $B^n = \{x \in R^n : |x| \leq 1\}$ and define $f : B^n \to R^{n+1}$ by

$$f(x) = \begin{cases} \left(2x, -\sqrt{1 - |2x|^2}\right) & |x| \leq \frac{1}{2} \\ \left(\dfrac{2 - |2x|}{|x|} x, \sqrt{1 - (2 - |2x|)^2}\right) & |x| \geq \frac{1}{2}. \end{cases}$$

It is easy to see that f is a continuous function, and that $|f(x)| = 1$ for all x. Thus f takes B^n into S^n. If $z = (z_1, z_2, \ldots, z_{n+1}) \in S^n$, then let $z' = (z_1, z_2, \ldots, z_n)$. If $z_{n+1} \leq 0$, then $z = f(\frac{1}{2}z')$. If $0 < z_{n+1} < 1$, then

$$z = f((2 - |z'|)z'/2|z'|).$$

Finally, $f(x)=(0,0,\ldots,0,1)$ if $|x|=1$, and it is not hard to show that $f(x)=f(y)$ only if $x=y$ or $|x|=|y|=1$. Thus S^n is the decomposition space of B^n obtained by collapsing the boundary $\{x:|x|=1\}$ of B^n to a point.

8. Let X be any space. Define a decomposition of $X\times[0,1]$ by $\mathfrak{D}=\{X\times\{1\}\}\cup\{\{z\}:z\in(X\times[0,1])\backslash(X\times\{1\})\}$, that is, the top of $X\times[0,1]$ is collapsed to a point.

The following picture justifies the fact that $\mathfrak{D}$ is called the *cone* over X. If we let $\mathfrak{D}'=\{X\times\{1\}\}\cup\{X\times\{0\}\}\cup\{\{z\}:z\notin X\times\{0,1\}\}$, then $\mathfrak{D}'$ is called the *suspension* of X. The illustration supports the (true) conjecture that the suspension of S^n is homeomorphic to S^{n+1}.

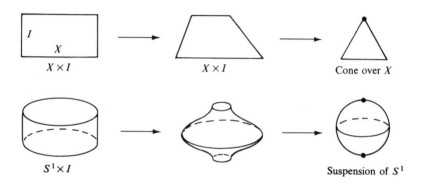

$X\times I$ $X\times I$ Cone over X

$S^1\times I$ Suspension of S^1

Exercises

1. Complete the proof of Theorem 3.5.4.

2. Complete the proof of Theorem 3.5.5.

3. Prove that if $(X,\mathfrak{T})$ is a topological space and $\mathfrak{D}$ a decomposition of X, then $\mathfrak{T}'=\{\sigma\subset\mathfrak{D}:P^{-1}(\sigma)$ is open in $X\}$ is a topology on $\mathfrak{D}$.

4. Supply all the details of Example 7.

5. Let $B^n=\{x\in R^n:|x|\leqslant1\}$. Prove that the cone over B^n is homeomorphic to B^{n+1}.

6. Prove that the suspension of S^n is S^{n+1}.

7. Prove that if X_i and Y_i are homeomorphic for each i in J, then the product spaces $\times\{X_i:i\in J\}$ and $\times\{Y_i:i\in J\}$ are homeomorphic.

8. Prove that a decomposition space is T_1 if and only if the elements of the decomposition are closed.

9. Prove that the product of indiscrete spaces is indiscrete.

10. Let $(X, \mathcal{T})$ be any space and let $\Delta = \{(x,x): x \in X\} \subset X \times X$. Prove that X and Δ are homeomorphic.

11. Prove that a sequence $[x_n]$ in a product space $\times \{X_i : i \in J\}$ converges to z if and only if $[\pi_i(x_n)]$ converges to $\pi_i(z)$ for each $i \in J$.

12. Prove that every Tychonoff space X can be embedded in a product of closed unit intervals, i.e., there is an index set J and a homeomorphism e from X onto a subset of $\times \{[0,1]_i : i \in J\}$. Hint: let $J = \{f : f$ is a continuous function from X to $[0,1]\}$, and define $e(x)_f = f(x)$. Follow the proof of Urysohn's Metrization Theorem.

13. Supply all the details in the proof of Theorem 3.5.11.

3.6 An adequate theory of convergence

In this section we introduce concepts which form a suitable generalization of the ideas surrounding sequences. Recall from Section 2.3 and Theorem 2.4.1 that sequences and their limits completely suffice to define topological concepts in metric spaces, but that in general sequences fail. This assertion is further supported by the relationship between compactness and sequences in metric spaces, which also fails to hold in general.

There are two generalizations of sequences which suffice in the general case, namely filters and nets. They are more or less equivalent, in that concepts from one can be translated to the other, but each has undeniable advantages in certain situations. Our choice of filters is dictated by the fact that they seem to be more useful in other topics in topology, for instance, in the study of collections of continuous functions. Readers interested in nets should consult other texts.

Our motivation lies as usual in a study of the already available case, namely sequences. Recall that a sequence $[x_n]$ in a space X converges to z if for each neighborhood U of z there is an integer P such that $x_n \in U$ for $n \geqslant P$. This is the same as saying that for some P, $\{x_n : n \geqslant P\} \subset U$. Thus the behavior of $[x_n]$ is governed by the behavior of the sets $\{x_n : n \geqslant P\}$ for various P's. Note that none of these sets are empty, and that the intersection of each pair is another such set. These considerations lead to the following definition.

Definition A *filter* $\mathcal{F}$ in a set X is a non-empty collection of non-empty subsets of X such that 1) $F_1 \cap F_2 \in \mathcal{F}$ whenever $F_1, F_2 \in \mathcal{F}$ and 2) $F_2 \in \mathcal{F}$ whenever $X \supset F_2 \supset F_1$ and $F_1 \in \mathcal{F}$.

EXAMPLES.

1. Let X be any set and let $x \in X$. Then $\mathcal{F} = \{F \subset X : x \in F\}$ is a filter in X.

2. Let x be a point of the topological space X, and let $\mathcal{U}_x = \{F \subset X : F$ contains a neighborhood of $x\}$. $\mathcal{U}_x$ is certainly a non-empty collection of non-empty subsets of X, and it is easily seen to satisfy part 2 of the definition. If F_1 contains the neighborhood V_1 of x and F_2 the neighborhood V_2, then $F_1 \cap F_2$ contains the neighborhood $V_1 \cap V_2$. Thus $\mathcal{U}_x$ is a filter on X which we will call the *neighborhood filter* of x.

In order to use filters to study topological concepts, we must relate them to the topology of a space. Again, our earlier remarks about sequences contain the motivation for the following.

Definition A filter $\mathcal{F}$ *converges* to the point x of a space X if every neighborhood of x contains some member of $\mathcal{F}$. We then write $\mathcal{F} \to x$.

EXAMPLE.

3. The neighborhood filter of a point x certainly converges to x, as does $\{F : x \in F\}$.

The next theorem already shows that filters and their convergence can be used to completely describe the topology of a space. Later theorems will add more support to the idea that filters are sufficient. Note the similarity with theorems in Section 2.3.

Theorem 3.6.1 *Let $(X, \mathcal{T})$ be a topological space and A a subset of X. Then,*

1. *The point x of X is a limit point of A if and only if there is a filter in $A \setminus \{x\}$ which converges to x.*
2. *A is closed if and only if the point y is in A whenever there is a filter in A converging to y.*

PROOF.

1. Suppose that x is a limit point of A. Then $U \cap (A \setminus \{x\}) \neq \varnothing$ for each neighborhood U of x, so we let $\mathcal{F} = \{F \subset A \setminus \{x\} : F \supset U \cap (A \setminus \{x\})$ for some neighborhood U of $x\}$. Then $\mathcal{F}$ is a non-empty collection of non-empty subsets of $A \setminus \{x\}$, and it is easy to show that $\mathcal{F}$ is a filter. Further, the neighborhood U of x contains the member $U \cap (A \setminus \{x\})$ of $\mathcal{F}$, so that $\mathcal{F} \to x$.

   Conversely, if $\mathcal{G}$ is a filter in $A \setminus \{x\}$ which converges to x, then each neighborhood V of x contains some element G of $\mathcal{G}$, so that $V \cap (A \setminus \{x\}) \supset G \neq \varnothing$. Hence x is a limit point of A.
2. We leave this as an exercise. ■

We now turn to the relationship between continuous functions and convergent filters. The image of a filter under a function f need not be a filter, since f may take every element to a single point. This makes the next definition slightly messier than the corresponding one for sequences. Again, the following theorem is almost identical to that for sequences.

Definition Let f be a function from X to Y and let $\mathscr{F}$ be a filter on X. The filter $f(\mathscr{F})$ is defined by $f(\mathscr{F}) = \{B \subset Y : B \supset f(F)$ for some $F \in \mathscr{F}\}$ (verification: an exercise).

Theorem 3.6.2 *Let f be a function from the space X to the space Y. The function f is continuous at x if and only if $f(\mathscr{F})$ converges to $f(x)$ whenever $\mathscr{F}$ is a filter in X converging to x.*

PROOF. Suppose that f is continuous at x and that $\mathscr{F} \to x$. If V is a neighborhood of $f(x)$, then $f^{-1}(V)$ is a neighborhood of x and so contains some element F of $\mathscr{F}$. But then $V \supset f(f^{-1}(V)) \supset f(F)$, so that V is actually an element of $f(\mathscr{F})$. Hence $f(\mathscr{F}) \to f(x)$.

To prove the converse, recall that the neighborhood filter $\mathscr{U}_x$ of x converges to x, so that $f(\mathscr{U}_x)$ converges to $f(x)$. Hence each neighborhood V of $f(x)$ contains $f(U')$ for some $U' \in \mathscr{U}_x$ and hence $f(U)$ for some neighborhood U of x. Thus f is continuous. ∎

This last proof illustrates the advantage that filters have over sequences, namely, the existence of neighborhood filters regardless of what kind of space we have. Sequences work well only when there is a *sequence* of sufficiently small neighborhoods, that is, only when the space is first countable.

Theorem 3.6.3 *Let X be the product of the spaces $\{X_i : i \in J\}$. A filter $\mathscr{F}$ on X converges to x if and only if $\pi_i(\mathscr{F})$ converges to $\pi_i(x)$ for each $i \in J$.*

PROOF. Each π_i is continuous, so that $\pi_i(\mathscr{F})$ converges to $\pi_i(x)$ when $\mathscr{F} \to x$ by Theorem 3.6.2. Conversely, suppose that $\pi_i(\mathscr{F}) \to \pi_i(x)$ for each $i \in J$. Any neighborhood of x contains a neighborhood of the form $\pi_{i_1}^{-1}(U_{i_1}) \cap \pi_{i_2}^{-1}(U_{i_2}) \cap \cdots \cap \pi_{i_n}^{-1}(U_{i_n})$, where $i_1, i_2, \ldots, i_n \in J$ and U_{i_r} is a neighborhood of $\pi_{i_r}(x)$ in X_{i_r}. Since $\pi_{i_r}(\mathscr{F}) \to \pi_{i_r}(x)$, $U_{i_r} \supset \pi_{i_r}(F_r)$ for some $F_r \in \mathscr{F}$. Thus $F_r \subset \pi_{i_r}^{-1}(U_{i_r})$, so that the element $F_1 \cap F_2 \cap \cdots \cap F_n$ of $\mathscr{F}$ lies in $\pi_{i_1}^{-1}(U_{i_1}) \cap \pi_{i_2}^{-1}(U_{i_2}) \cap \cdots \cap \pi_{i_n}^{-1}(U_{i_n})$. ∎

We now introduce a series of ideas designed to deal effectively with compactness. Their usefulness extends quite beyond that, but again we must leave further developments for other authors. Recall that compactness in metric spaces can be characterized by using sequences and subsequences. This leads to part 1 of the next definition, which then leads to part 2. Part 3 is a concept which is used to nicely link compactness with filters, as the succeeding theorems show.

Note that if $[x_{n_i}]$ is a subsequence of $[x_n]$, then $\{x_{n_i}: i \geqslant P\} \subset \{x_n: n \geqslant P\}$, so there are more sets which contain the "tails" of a subsequence than sets which contain the "tails" of the original sequence. The sets $\{x_n: n \geqslant P\}$ for sequences $[x_n]$ correspond to the sets in a filter, so we have part 1 of the following, in which finer filters correspond to subsequences.

Definition

1. A filter $\mathcal{G}$ is *finer* than a filter $\mathcal{F}$ if $\mathcal{G} \supset \mathcal{F}$.
2. A filter $\mathcal{U}$ is called an *ultrafilter* if $\mathcal{U}$ is properly contained in no other filter.
3. A family $\mathcal{C}$ of sets has the *finite intersection property* if the intersection of every finite subfamily of $\mathcal{C}$ is non-empty.

Note that the idea of an ultrafilter arises through the study of the relation *finer than*, since no filter is strictly finer than an ultrafilter. We next prove a theorem relating the finite intersection property with both compactness and filters, and then connect the latter two ideas.

Theorem 3.6.4

1. *A space X is compact if and only if every family of closed sets with the finite intersection property has non-empty intersection.*
2. *A non-empty family of sets is contained in a filter if and only if the family has the finite intersection property.*

PROOF.
1. Suppose that X is compact and that $\mathcal{C}$ is a family of closed sets with the finite intersection property. If $C_1, C_2, \ldots, C_n \in \mathcal{C}$, then

$$\varnothing \neq C_1 \cap C_2 \cap \cdots \cap C_n = X \setminus (X \setminus (C_1 \cap C_2 \cap \cdots \cap C_n))$$
$$= X \setminus [(X \setminus C_1) \cup (X \setminus C_2) \cup \cdots \cup (X \setminus C_n)],$$

so that no finite subfamily of $\{X \setminus C: C \in \mathcal{C}\}$ covers X. Hence the collection $\{X \setminus C: C \in \mathcal{C}\}$ of open sets does not cover X (recall that X is compact), so that $\varnothing \neq X \setminus (\cup \{X \setminus C: C \in \mathcal{C}\}) = \cap \{X \setminus (X \setminus C): C \in \mathcal{C}\} = \cap \{C: C \in \mathcal{C}\}$. The proof of the converse uses the same ideas and is left as an exercise.
2. Suppose the family $\mathcal{F}'$ is contained in a filter $\mathcal{F}$. Then by induction $F_1 \cap F_2 \cap \ldots \cap F_n \in \mathcal{F}$ whenever $F_1, F_2, \ldots, F_n \in \mathcal{F}'$, and since $\varnothing \notin \mathcal{F}$, $\mathcal{F}'$ has the finite intersection property.

Conversely, suppose $\mathcal{F}'$ is a non-empty family of sets with the finite intersection property. Let $\mathcal{F} = \{F : F \supset F_1 \cap F_2 \cap \ldots \cap F_n$ for some $F_1, F_2, \ldots, F_n$ in $\mathcal{F}'\}$. The proof that $\mathcal{F}$ is a filter is left as an exercise. ∎

We now know precisely which families are contained in filters, but as yet have no such information regarding ultrafilters. This is remedied by the next theorem, the proof of which uses the Axiom of Choice in the form of Zorn's Lemma (see the Appendix for relevant information).

Theorem 3.6.5 *Every filter is contained in an ultrafilter.*

PROOF.   Let $\mathcal{F}$ be a filter on X, and let S be the set of all filters on X which contain $\mathcal{F}$. The set S is a non-empty set which is partially ordered by set inclusion. Let $\{\mathcal{F}_\alpha : \alpha \in \mathcal{C}\}$ be a chain in S, and let $\mathcal{V} = \cup \{\mathcal{F}_\alpha : \alpha \in \mathcal{C}\}$. Each $\mathcal{F}_\alpha \neq \varnothing$, so $\mathcal{V} \neq \varnothing$. No $\mathcal{F}_\alpha$ contains $\varnothing$, so $\mathcal{V}$ does not contain $\varnothing$. If $G \supset F \in \mathcal{V}$, then $F \in \mathcal{F}_\beta$ for some $\beta \in \mathcal{C}$, so $G \in \mathcal{F}_\beta \subset \mathcal{V}$ since $\mathcal{F}_\beta$ is a filter. Finally, if $F_1 \in \mathcal{V}$ and $F_2 \in \mathcal{V}$, then for some $\alpha_1, \alpha_2 \in \mathcal{C}$ we have $F_1 \in \mathcal{F}_{\alpha_1}$ and $F_2 \in \mathcal{F}_{\alpha_2}$. Since $\{\mathcal{F}_\alpha : \alpha \in \mathcal{C}\}$ is a chain, either $\mathcal{F}_{\alpha_1} \subset \mathcal{F}_{\alpha_2}$ or $\mathcal{F}_{\alpha_2} \subset \mathcal{F}_{\alpha_1}$; we suppose the former. Thus $F_1, F_2 \in \mathcal{F}_{\alpha_2}$, so that $F_1 \cap F_2 \in \mathcal{F}_{\alpha_2} \subset \mathcal{V}$. Hence $\mathcal{V}$ is a filter on X certainly containing $\mathcal{F}$, so that the chain has the upper bound $\mathcal{V}$. Zorn's Lemma then implies that S has a maximal element, that is, a member $\mathcal{U}$ such that $\mathcal{U}$ is not properly contained in any other element of S. Hence $\mathcal{U}$ is an ultrafilter containing $\mathcal{F}$. ∎

EXAMPLE.

4. Consider R with the usual topology. The neighborhood filter of 0 is contained in the filter $\mathcal{U} = \{A \subset R : 0 \in A\}$. A set B not in $\mathcal{U}$ does not contain 0, so that $B \cap \{0\} = \varnothing$. Hence we cannot add any sets to $\mathcal{U}$ and still have a filter, so that $\mathcal{U}$ is an ultrafilter containing the neighborhood filter of 0. On the other hand, $\{(a, +\infty) : a \in R\}$ is contained in a filter $\mathcal{F}$ by Theorem 3.6.4, and $\mathcal{F}$ is contained in at least one ultrafilter $\mathcal{V}$, but $\mathcal{V}$ is not easily describable.

Theorem 3.6.6 *The following are equivalent for a space X:*

1. *X is compact;*
2. *Each filter on X has a finer filter which converges;*
3. *Every ultrafilter on X converges.*

PROOF.

(1)$\Rightarrow$(2). Let $\mathcal{F}$ be any filter on X. Then $\{\text{Cl}(F) : F \in \mathcal{F}\}$ has the finite intersection property, so by Theorem 3.6.4 there is a point x in $\cap \{\text{Cl}(F) : F \in \mathcal{F}\}$. Since $x \in \text{Cl}(F)$, each neighborhood of x meets F, so that $\{N \cap F : N$ a neighborhood of x, $F \in \mathcal{F}\}$ has the finite intersection property and hence is contained in a filter $\mathcal{G}$. Clearly $\mathcal{G} \supset \mathcal{F}$ and $\mathcal{G} \to x$.

(2)$\Rightarrow$(3). If $\mathcal{U}$ is an ultrafilter on X, then there is a finer filter $\mathcal{V}$ that converges. But no filter is strictly finer than $\mathcal{U}$ so that $\mathcal{U} = \mathcal{V}$ and $\mathcal{U}$ converges.

(3)$\Rightarrow$(1). Let $\mathcal{C}$ be a family of closed sets with the finite intersection property. Then $\mathcal{C}$ is contained in a filter, which is then contained in an ultrafilter $\mathcal{U}$. Let $\mathcal{U} \to x$. Each neighborhood of x contains some element of $\mathcal{U}$, and so must meet each element C of $\mathcal{C}$. Hence x must be in the closed set C, so that $\cap \{C : C \in \mathcal{C}\} \neq \varnothing$. ■

The next result gives us methods for recognizing and constructing ultrafilters. It is the last tool needed for the proof of Tychonoff's Theorem, which is the culmination of all the effort put into this section.

Theorem 3.6.7

1. A filter $\mathcal{U}$ on X is an ultrafilter if and only if either $A \in \mathcal{U}$ or $X \backslash A \in \mathcal{U}$ whenever $A \subset X$.
2. If $\mathcal{U}$ is an ultrafilter on X and f is a function from X to Y, then $f(\mathcal{U})$ is an ultrafilter on Y.

PROOF.

1. Suppose that $\mathcal{U}$ is an ultrafilter on X and that $A \subset X$ but $A \notin \mathcal{U}$. If $A \supset U$ for some $U \in \mathcal{U}$, then $A \in \mathcal{U}$, so that we must have $(X \backslash A) \cap U \neq \varnothing$ for each $U \in \mathcal{U}$. Hence $\mathcal{U} \cup \{X \backslash A\}$ has the finite intersection property and so is contained in a filter $\mathcal{V}$. But $\mathcal{U}$ is an ultrafilter, so that $\mathcal{U} = \mathcal{V}$ and $X \backslash A \in \mathcal{U}$.

   To prove the converse, suppose that $\mathcal{U}$ is contained in some filter $\mathcal{V}$. If $A \in \mathcal{V}$ but $A \notin \mathcal{U}$, then the hypothesis implies that $X \backslash A \in \mathcal{U} \subset \mathcal{V}$. But then the two elements A and $X \backslash A$ of $\mathcal{V}$ have empty intersection, a contradiction. Hence $\mathcal{U} = \mathcal{V}$ so that $\mathcal{U}$ must be an ultrafilter.

2. To prove that $f(\mathcal{U})$ is an ultrafilter we take any $B \subset Y$ and show that either $B \in f(\mathcal{U})$ or $Y \backslash B \in f(\mathcal{U})$. Since $\mathcal{U}$ is an ultrafilter, either $f^{-1}(B)$ or $X \backslash f^{-1}(B) = f^{-1}(Y \backslash B)$ is in $\mathcal{U}$. But then either $B \supset f(f^{-1}(B))$ is in $f(\mathcal{U})$ or $Y \backslash B \supset f(f^{-1}(Y \backslash B))$ is in $f(\mathcal{U})$. ■

The proof of the next theorem uses either directly or indirectly almost all of the results of this section. It is an extremely important result, perhaps the most important of all of general topology; its usefulness extends into almost every field of mathematics.

Theorem 3.6.8 (Tychonoff's Theorem) *The product of compact spaces is compact.*

PROOF. Let $\{X_j : j \in J\}$ be a collection of compact spaces, and let $X = \times \{X_j : j \in J\}$. Let $\mathcal{U}$ be an ultrafilter on X. Then $\pi_i(\mathcal{U})$ is an ultrafilter in X_i and so converges by Theorem 3.6.6. Hence $\mathcal{U}$ converges by Theorem 3.6.3 so that X is compact. ∎

Our scope does not allow us to delve into the consequences of Tychonoff's Theorem, but we do touch on some in the exercises. We conclude by noting that Tychonoff's Theorem is actually equivalent to the Axiom of Choice, and invite the reader to ascertain how the Axiom of Choice is used in its proof.

Exercises

1. Complete the proof of Theorem 3.6.1.

2. Complete the proof of Theorem 3.6.4, part 1.

3. Complete the proof of Theorem 3.6.4, part 2.

4. Describe the filters and ultrafilters on a finite set.

5. a. Prove that if X is a non-Hausdorff space, then there is a filter $\mathcal{F}$ on X and two distinct points x and y such that $\mathcal{F} \to x$ and $\mathcal{F} \to y$.
b. Show that (a) is not true if filters are replaced by sequences.

6. Prove that every filter is the intersection of all ultrafilters which contain it.

7. a. Prove that a space X is Tychonoff if and only if X is homeomorphic to a subspace of a compact Hausdorff space.
b. Prove that any Tychonoff space has a Hausdorff compactification.
c. Give an example of a subspace of a normal space which is not normal. Remarks: The results in this exercise depend on Exercise 12 of Section 3.5. The compactification thus obtained is called the *Stone—Cech compactification*, an extremely important object whose study we leave for other authors.

8. Prove that if A is a non-empty subset of X, then $\{F \subset X : A \subset F\}$ is a filter in X.

9. Provide the verification asked for in the definition of the image of a filter under a function.

4

Examples and pathologies

In this chapter we explore some interesting applications of the concepts introduced previously and look at some unusual and unexpected examples. Some of the applications are of greatest interest to topologists, while others will be of more interest to those who like analysis and differential equations. Although this chapter deals exclusively with metric spaces, we will freely use any of the ideas presented in Chapters 2 and 3.

4.1 Cantor sets

We begin an investigation of one of the more interesting spaces in topology, namely the *Cantor set*. This intriguing and important metric space was invented by Georg Cantor in 1883 and has since appeared in innumerable examples and theorems in topology. The reader should be warned that much important information will be unadorned by labels such as "theorem" or "definition," and that frequently proofs of statements will be intermingled with the statements themselves.

The Cantor middle-third set is constructed as follows. Define I_0 to be $[0, 1]$. Remove the open middle third of I_0 to obtain $I_1 = [0, \frac{1}{3}] \cup [\frac{2}{3}, 1]$. In general, remove the open middle third of each component of I_n to obtain I_{n+1}. The *Cantor middle-third set* is then $C = \cap_{i=1}^{\infty} I_i$.

We now list some of the properties of C. As an intersection of a decreasing sequence of non-empty compact sets, C is compact and non-empty by Theorem 3.6.4. Each component of C is contained in a single component of I_n for each n, and since the components of I_n have length $1/3^n$, the components of C are points. Note also that the end points of the components of I_n lie in each succeeding I_r and so lie in C, and it is then easy to conclude that every point of C is a limit point of C.

These last two properties of the Cantor middle-third set are important enough to deserve definitions. In fact, they are precisely the properties necessary to completely characterize the Cantor set, and our aim is to prove this fact.

Definition

1. A topological space is *totally disconnected* if each of its components consists of a single point.
2. A topological space is *perfect* if each of its points is a limit point of the space.

We need to investigate the Cantor middle-third set a bit more thoroughly before turning to its relationship with other metric spaces. To facilitate the discussion we make the following somewhat nonstandard definition.

Definition If J is a component of one of the sets I_n used to define the Cantor middle-third set C, then $J \cap C$ will be called a *sub-Cantor set*.

We note that there is a homeomorphism taking any component J of any I_n onto $[0,1]$ which carries $J \cap C$ onto C, so that a sub-Cantor set is in fact homeomorphic to C. Also, it is easy to see that a sub-Cantor set is an open and closed subset of C. These sub-Cantor sets can be used to decompose C in particularly nice ways, and this is the content of the next lemma.

Lemma 4.1.1 *If C' is any sub-Cantor set and n any positive integer then there are n pairwise disjoint sub-Cantor sets whose union is C'. If $n \geqslant 2$, then the diameters of these n sets do not exceed $\frac{1}{3}$ diam C' (see Exercise 5, Section 3.1, for a reminder about "diam").*

PROOF. Let j be such that $C' = J \cap C$, where J is a component of I_j, and let r be an integer such that $2^r \geqslant n > 2^{r-1}$. Use $2^r - n$ components $J_1, J_2, \ldots, J_{2^r - n}$ of $I_{j+r-1} \cap J$ and the components of $I_{j+r} \cap J$ not lying in $J_1 \cup J_2 \cup \cdots \cup J_{2^r - n}$ to form the desired n sub-Cantor sets.

Note that if $n \geqslant 2$, then $r \geqslant 1$, so each of the n sub-Cantor sets produced lies in a component of I_{j+1} and thus has diameter no larger than $\frac{1}{3}$ diam C'. ■

Our study of the relationship of the Cantor middle-third set with other metric spaces begins by investigating properties of metric spaces analogous to those of the Cantor set expressed in Lemma 4.1.1. Again we need some terminology.

Definition A *cover* of a space X is a collection of subsets of X whose union is X. A cover is *open* if it consists of open sets, *closed* if it consists of closed sets, and *finite* if it contains just finitely many sets. A cover is an *ε-cover* if each of its sets has diameter no larger than ε.

We streamline our work by studying totally disconnected compact metric spaces before we do the general case.

Lemma 4.1.2 *Let p be a point of a compact metric space X. Let $\mathcal{K} = \{K:$ $p \in K$ and K is open and closed in $X\}$ and $D = \cap\, \mathcal{K}$. Then D is connected.*

PROOF. Suppose that D is the union of two disjoint sets A and B, both closed in D, with $p \in A$. Clearly D is closed in X, so that A and B are closed subsets of X. Since X is normal, there are open sets U and V in X such that $A \subset U$, $B \subset V$, and $U \cap V = \varnothing$. Now $\{K \setminus (U \cup V): K \in \mathcal{K}\}$ is a family of compact sets, and if this family has the finite intersection property, then its intersection would be non-empty by Theorem 3.6.4. But $\cap\{K \setminus (U \cup V): K \in \mathcal{K}\} = (\cap\, \mathcal{K}) \setminus (U \cup V) = D \setminus (U \cup V) = \varnothing$. Hence there are sets $K_1, K_2, \ldots, K_n$ in $\mathcal{K}$ such that $(K_1 \cap K_2 \cap \cdots \cap K_n) \setminus (U \cup V) = \varnothing$, and $K = K_1 \cap K_2 \cap \cdots \cap K_n$ is an open-and-closed set containing p. Now, $\mathrm{Cl}(U) \cap V = \varnothing$ and $K \subset U \cup V$, so that $K \cap \mathrm{Cl}(U) = K \cap U$. Then $K \cap U$ is an open and closed set containing p, so that $D \subset K \cap U$ and B must be empty. Thus D is not the union of two disjoint non-empty closed sets and so must be connected. ◼

Lemma 4.1.3 *If p is a point of a compact totally disconnected metric space X and ε is positive, then there is an open and closed subset of X which contains p and has diameter less than ε.*

PROOF. As in Lemma 4.1.2 let $\mathcal{K} = \{K: p \in K$ and K is open and closed in $X\}$. By the preceding lemma $\cap\, \mathcal{K}$ is connected and so must be $\{p\}$ since X is totally disconnected. The finite intersection property argument in the proof of Lemma 4.1.2 can be used here to prove that some finite intersection K of elements of $\mathcal{K}$ must lie in $N(x, \varepsilon/3)$. It is easy to see that K is the desired subset of X. ◼

Theorem 4.1.4 *Let X be a compact metric space and ε a positive number. Then X has a finite closed ε-cover. Further, if X is also totally disconnected, then in addition the cover may be chosen to consist of pairwise disjoint sets.*

PROOF. Consider $\{N(x, \varepsilon/3): x \in X\}$. Since X is compact, this open cover of X has a finite subcover, and the closures of the sets in this finite subcover form the desired finite closed ε-cover.

If X is totally disconnected, then Lemma 4.1.3 delivers an open and closed ε-cover of X. From this extract a finite subcover $\{K_1, K_2, \ldots, K_n\}$. Then the reader can easily verify that $\{K_1, K_2 \backslash K_1, K_3 \backslash (K_1 \cup K_2), \ldots, K_n \backslash (\cup_{i=1}^{n-1} K_i)\}$ is a finite closed ε-cover of X consisting of pairwise disjoint sets. ∎

We now have the tools to prove the two most interesting facts about the Cantor middle-third set. Each is important enough to deserve the title "theorem", but their proofs are quite similar and are combined in the following.

Theorem 4.1.5 *Any compact metric space is the continuous image of the Cantor middle-third set.*

Theorem 4.1.6 *Any two compact totally disconnected perfect metric spaces are homeomorphic.*

PROOF. Let X be a compact metric space. The idea of the proof is to use Theorem 4.1.4 and Lemma 4.1.1 to construct sequences of covers of X and the Cantor middle-third set C which are as similar as possible, and then to use these covers to define a function h from C onto X.

We first construct a sequence of covers of X. Theorem 4.1.4 delivers a finite closed 1-cover $\mathcal{C}_1$ of X. Each element A of $\mathcal{C}_1$ is a compact metric space, and so has a finite closed $1/2$-cover $\mathcal{C}_A$, and then $\cup \{\mathcal{C}_A : A \in \mathcal{C}_1\}$ is a finite closed $1/2$-cover $\mathcal{C}_2$ of X. This procedure can be continued inductively to produce a sequence $\mathcal{C}_1, \mathcal{C}_2, \ldots$ where $\mathcal{C}_i$ is a finite closed $1/i$-cover of X. Further $\mathcal{C}_{i+1} = \cup \{\mathcal{C}_A : A \in \mathcal{C}_i\}$, where $\mathcal{C}_A$ is a cover of A for each A in $\mathcal{C}_i$.

If X is totally disconnected, then each of the covers $\mathcal{C}_i$ may be taken to consist of pairwise disjoint sets. Thus each element of $\mathcal{C}_i$ is both open and closed. Finally, if X is also perfect, then each element A of $\mathcal{C}_i$ must contain more than one point, since it is open, so that $\mathcal{C}_A$ may be taken to consist of two or more sets.

We now construct covers $\mathcal{C}_i$ of C. By Lemma 4.1.1 there is a cover $\mathcal{C}_1$ of C consisting of pairwise disjoint sub-Cantor sets and a one-to-one function ϕ_1 from $\mathcal{C}_1$ onto $\mathcal{C}_1$. For each $A \in \mathcal{C}_1$ there is a cover $\mathcal{C}_A$ of $\phi_1^{-1}(A)$ consisting of pairwise disjoint sub-Cantor sets and containing the same number of sets as does $\mathcal{C}_A$. Then let $\mathcal{C}_2 = \cup \{\mathcal{C}_A : A \in \mathcal{C}_1\}$. We can continue this procedure inductively to obtain covers $\mathcal{C}_1, \mathcal{C}_2, \ldots$ of C consisting of pairwise disjoint sub-Cantor sets and functions ϕ_i from $\mathcal{C}_i$ onto $\mathcal{C}_i$ such that $\phi_{i+1}(C_{i+1})\subset\phi_i(C_i)$ whenever C_{i+1} and C_i are elements of $\mathcal{C}_{i+1}$ and $\mathcal{C}_i$, respectively, and $C_{i+1}\subset C_i$.

Note that if X is totally disconnected, then each ϕ_i may be taken to be one-to-one, and if X is also perfect, then Lemma 4.1.1 guarantees that we may take diam $C'<1/3^i$ whenever $C'\in\mathcal{C}_i$.

We now define the function h. Fix a point p in C. Since $\mathcal{C}_i$ is a cover of C consisting of pairwise disjoint sets, there is a unique element C_i of $\mathcal{C}_i$ containing p. Certainly $C_1\supset C_2\supset C_3\supset\cdots$, so that $\phi_1(C_1)\supset\phi_2(C_2)\supset\phi_3(C_3)$ $\supset\cdots$. Theorem 3.6.4 says that $\cap_{i=1}^{\infty}\phi_i(C_i)$ is non-empty, and since $1/i>$ diam $\phi_i(C_i)$, the intersection must consist of a single point which we define to be $h(p)$. Note that h has the property that $h(C_i)\subset\phi_i(C_i)$ whenever $C_i\in\mathcal{C}_i$.

We show that h is continuous. Let p be in C and let ε be positive. There is an integer j such that diam $A<\varepsilon$ whenever A is in $\mathcal{C}_j$. If C_j is the element of $\mathcal{C}_j$ containing p, then $h(p)\in h(C_j)\subset\phi_j(C_j)$. Further, as an element of $\mathcal{C}_j$, $\phi_j(C_j)$ has diameter less than ε, so that $\phi_j(C_j)\subset N(h(p),\varepsilon)$. Thus C_j is an open set containing p which h maps into $N(h(p),\varepsilon)$, so that h is continuous.

We show that h is onto. Fix a point x in X. There is an element A_1 of $\mathcal{C}_1$ containing x. Then there is an element A_2 of $\mathcal{C}_{A_1}$ containing x. We inductively produce elements A_{i+1} of $\mathcal{C}_{A_i}$ which contain x. From our construction of the $\mathcal{C}_i$'s and ϕ_i's, we conclude that $\phi_1^{-1}(A_1)\supset\phi_2^{-1}(A_2)$ $\supset\cdots$. There is at least one point p in $\cap_{i=1}^{\infty}\phi_i^{-1}(A_i)$ by Theorem 3.6.4, and $h(p)\in\cap_{i=1}^{\infty}h(\phi_i^{-1}(A_i))\subset\cap_{i=1}^{\infty}\phi_i\phi_i^{-1}(A_i)=\cap_{i=1}^{\infty}A_i=\{x\}$. This concludes the proof of Theorem 4.1.5.

If X were totally disconnected, then the sets A_i in the last paragraph would be unique since the covers would consist of pairwise disjoint sets. Further, diam $\phi_i^{-1}(A_i)\leqslant 1/3^i$ if X were perfect, so that the argument would yield a unique point p such that $h(p)=x$. Thus h would also be one-to-one and hence a homeomorphism by Exercise 7 of Section 2.7, Part A. We have shown that any compact totally disconnected perfect metric space X is homeomorphic to the Cantor middle-third set, and Theorem 4.1.6 follows directly. ∎

These two theorems are really remarkable. Theorem 4.1.6 is the first time we have been able to characterize a space topologically and is responsible for the frequent appearance of the Cantor set in topology. Because of it we will use the term Cantor set to refer to any compact totally disconnected perfect metric space. We will see one application of Theorem 4.1.5 immediately and it will be used to prove a classic theorem in the next section.

The application we now make of Theorem 4.1.5 involves *decomposition spaces* and was discovered by Hurewicz in 1930. The study of decomposition spaces has been of a great deal of importance in topology. One would like to classify the possible decomposition spaces of the nice spaces like R^2 and R^3, at least when the elements of the decomposition are decent, e.g., compact and connected. This has in fact been done for R^2, but the next theorem shows that the situation for R^3 is exceedingly difficult.

Theorem 4.1.7 *There is an upper semicontinuous decomposition G of R^3 into compact connected sets such that the decomposition space G contains a copy of every separable metric space.*

PROOF. The proof of Theorem 3.3.3 shows that it is enough to construct a decomposition G such that the decomposition space contains a copy of the Hilbert cube I^∞. We will use Theorem 4.1.5 to produce G.

We need some notation, and we also assume familiarity with the vector operations in R^3 and the corresponding geometry. For points p and q in R^3, we let $[p,q]=\{tp+(1-t)q:0\leqslant t\leqslant 1\}$. Let $I=\{(x,y,z)\in R^3:x=y=0$ and $0\leqslant z\leqslant 1\}$ and $J=\{(x,y,z)\in R^3:z=0,x+y=1,$ and $0\leqslant x\leqslant 1\}$. Let C and C^1 be Cantor middle-third sets on J and I respectively. Define $\phi:C\to C^1$ by $\phi((x,y,z))=(0,0,x)$. It is easy to see that ϕ is a homeomorphism.

By Theorem 4.1.5 there is a continuous function f from the Cantor set C onto I^∞. For each x in I^∞ define g_x to be $\cup\{[p,\phi(q)]:p,q\in f^{-1}(x)\}$. If $g_x\cap g_y\neq\varnothing$, then $[p,\phi(q)]\cap[p',\phi(q')]\neq\varnothing$ for some $p,q\in f^{-1}(x)$ and $p',q'\in f^{-1}(y)$. The geometry of the situation implies that either $p=p'$ or $\phi(q)=\phi(q')$. In either case $f^{-1}(x)\cap f^{-1}(y)\neq\varnothing$, so that $x=y$. Let $K=\cup\{g_x:x\in I^\infty\}$. Then $G=\{g_x:x\in I^\infty\}\cup\{\{p\}:p\in R^3\backslash K\}$ is a decomposition of R^3. Further, a function h from K onto I^∞ is well defined by setting $h(p)=x$ when $p\in g_x$.

We now show that each g_x is connected. Fix a point p_0 in $f^{-1}(x)$. If p and q are points of $f^{-1}(x)$, then $[p_0,\phi(q)]\cup[p,\phi(q)]$ is a connected subset of g_x containing p_0 and $[p,\phi(q)]$. By Theorem 2.5.8 the set g_x is connected.

One could show directly that each g_x is compact and that G is upper semicontinuous, but it is easier to be a bit trickier. We begin by considering the set $A=\{(p,q)\in C\times C:f(p)=f(q)\}$. We show that A is closed in $C\times C$ by showing that its complement is open. If $(p_0,q_0)\in(C\times C)\backslash A$, then $f(p_0)\neq f(q_0)$. The points $f(p_0),f(q_0)$ have disjoint neighborhoods V_1, V_2 in I^∞ and p_0,q_0 then have neighborhoods U_1,U_2 in C such that $f(U_1)\subset V_1$ and $f(U_2)\subset V_2$. But then $f(x)\neq f(y)$ for $(x,y)\in U_1\times U_2$, so that $U_1\times U_2$ is a neighborhood of (p_0,q_0) which is disjoint from A. We can conclude that A is a compact set.

Now define a function $\tilde{f}:A\times[0,1]\to I^\infty$ by $\tilde{f}((p,q,t))=f(p)$ and a function $T:A\times[0,1]\to K$ by $T((p,q,t))=tp+(1-t)\phi(q)$. It is easy to verify that $\tilde{f}$ is continuous and onto as is T. Further, these functions satisfy $\tilde{f}=h\circ T$, where h is the function from K to I^∞ defined previously.

Conclusions now flow easily. First $K = T(A \times [0,1])$ is compact. Using the terminology and results of Section 3.5 concerning quotient maps and decomposition spaces, we note that T is a quotient map. Then since $\tilde{f} = h \circ T$, we conclude that h is continuous. Since $g_x = h^{-1}(x)$, each g_x is a closed subset of the compact set K and so is compact. Finally, K is compact so that h is a closed map and $\{ g_x : x \in I^\infty \}$ is thus an upper semicontinuous decomposition of K.

Suppose we are given a neighborhood U in R^3 of a set g_x. Then $\cup \{ g_y : g_y \subset U \}$ is open in K and so is $V \cap K$ for some open set V in R^3. Then $V \cap U$ is a neighborhood of g_x in R^3 which is contained in U and is a union of elements of G. Hence $\cup \{ g : g \subset U$ and $g \in G \}$ is open. A similar argument works when g_x is replaced by any element of G, so that G is an upper semicontinuous decomposition of R^3.

Finally, let $P : R^3 \to G$ be the decomposition map. From the construction and since h is a closed map, the function $\tilde{h} : P(K) \to I^\infty$ defined by $\tilde{h}(y) = h(P^{-1}(y))$ is a homeomorphism (see Theorem 3.5.11). Hence $P(K)$ is the desired copy of I^∞ contained in G. ∎

Exercises

1. Prove that a subspace of a totally disconnected space is totally disconnected.

2. Prove that a space if perfect if and only if each of its open sets contains at least two points.

3. Prove that an open subspace of a perfect space is perfect. Is this true for any subspace, not necessarily open?

4. Find an example of a countable perfect space.

5. Provide the verification asked for in the proof of Theorem 4.1.4.

6. Provide the details of the finite intersection argument used in the proof of Lemma 4.1.3.

7. Prove in complete detail that the decomposition G of Theorem 4.1.7 is upper semicontinuous.

8. Prove that C and $C \times C$ are homeomorphic.

9. Prove that if X is a totally disconnected compact metric space, then $X \times C$ is homeomorphic to C. Conclude that C has a subspace homeomorphic to X.

10. **a.** Prove that a countable metric space must be totally disconnected.
   b. Prove that a countable compact metric space cannot be perfect.

4.2 Peano spaces

During the nineteenth century mathematicians worked very hard at concocting precise and rigorous definitions of common mathematical concepts. One of the areas of concern at the time was the idea of a curve. The proper definition of a curve is rather elusive, and in this section we study one of the approaches which has been taken.

In calculus and other parts of analysis a *curve* is taken to be a function f from the unit interval $[0,1] = I$ into the plane or whatever space is appropriate. This mirrors the images we have of walking along a curve or of a particle traveling along a curve, since $f(t)$ can be taken to be the position of the walker or particle at time t. Without some restrictions on the function, however, any set at all would be the image of a curve. The most natural requirement would be that the function be continuous, i.e., that the walker or particle cannot instantaneously jump from point A to point B. This seemed to be a satisfactory definition until the Italian mathematician Peano in 1890 presented an example of such a function whose image covered the entire interior of a square in the plane.

This discovery led to both refinements in the definition of a curve and a study of just which spaces are the image of the unit interval under a continuous function. The latter culminated in the theorem due independently to Hahn (1914) and Mazurkiewicz (1920) which we will prove in this section. Before we state the result we need some terminology.

Definition A *Peano space* is a compact connected and locally connected metrizable space.

Theorem 4.2.1 (Hahn–Mazurkiewicz) *A Hausdorff space X is the continuous image of $[0,1]$ if and only if it is a Peano space.*

With this theorem examples become abundant. In the first place, the square $[0,1] \times [0,1]$ and in fact any product $[0,1] \times [0,1] \times \cdots \times [0,1]$ is a Peano space and thus the continuous image of $[0,1]$. Such curves are usually called *space-filling*. The reader can easily supply other examples of Peano spaces. Of course, any nonconnected space is not a Peano space. Also, the spaces pictured below fail to be locally connected and hence are not Peano spaces. The list of interesting examples is almost endless.

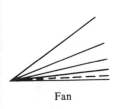

Fan

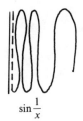

$\sin \dfrac{1}{x}$

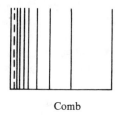

Comb

We now turn to a proof of the theorem. The one we present is not the most direct available, but it will lead us through several techniques and results that are of interest in themselves. The proof will consist of several theorems and their proofs; it should be easy for the reader to see that taken together they verify Theorem 4.2.1.

Theorem 4.2.2 *If X is Hausdorff and the continuous image of* $[0,1]$, *then X is a Peano space.*

PROOF. Theorems 3.5.11 and 3.5.12 say that X is homeomorphic to a decomposition space of $[0,1]$ whose elements are compact sets. Theorem 3.5.7 then implies that X is compact, connected and locally connected, and Theorem 3.5.10 says that X is metrizable. ∎

We have (easily) proved the necessity half of the Hahn–Mazurkiewicz Theorem. The sufficiency part is far harder. Our plan of attack is to use Theorem 4.1.5 to get a continuous function f from the Cantor middle-third set C onto X, and then to extend this function to the components of $[0,1]\backslash C$. It is the latter step which takes most of the work.

Suppose we have the function f mentioned above. Let (a,b) be a component of $[0,1]\backslash C$. We have the points $f(a)$ and $f(b)$ and need a continuous function from $[a,b]$ into X taking a to $f(a)$ and b to $f(b)$. In fact we will produce such a function which is also a homeomorphism from $[a,b]$ onto its image. As usual, we need definitions.

Definition An *arc* α is any space homeomorphic to $[0,1]$. The end points of α are the points a and b corresponding to 0 and 1 respectively, and we also say that α is an arc from a to b.

We note that if α is an arc, then there are many homeomorphisms from $[0,1]$ onto α. In order to show that the end points of α are well defined, we need to show that any such homeomorphism takes $\{0,1\}$ to the same set. After this build-up, we leave the problem as an exercise.

Our arc-building technique takes advantage of the order properties of $[0,1]$. The next collection of definitions and theorems is designed to produce similar orderings of points in a Peano space. We often omit terms such as "for each $i=1,2,\ldots,q$" for the sake of ease of expression and because it will never cause any confusion.

Definition A collection $\mathcal{O} = \{O_1, O_2, \ldots, O_q\}$ of sets is a *chain* from a to b if $a \in O_1 \backslash O_2$, $b \in O_q \backslash O_{q-1}$, and $O_i \cap O_j \neq \varnothing$ if and only if $|i-j| \leqslant 1$. We regard the sets of a chain as being ordered by their indices, so we can use terms such as "last," "precedes," etc. to refer to sets in a chain.

Definition A chain $\mathcal{P} = \{P_1, P_2, \ldots, P_m\}$ from a to b goes *straight through* a chain $\mathcal{O} = \{O_1, O_2, \ldots, O_q\}$ from a to b if there are integers $t_0, t_1, \ldots, t_q$ such that $0 = t_0 < t_1 < \cdots < t_q = m$, $P_i \subset O_j$ whenever $t_{j-1} \leqslant i < t_j$ and $P_m \subset$

O_q. We will call $P_{t_{j-1}}, \ldots, P_{t_j-1}$ the *block of sets* of $\mathcal{P}$ contained in O_j, with the obvious addition of P_m in case $j = q$.

Theorem 4.2.3 *Let a and b be distinct points of a connected space X and let $\mathcal{O}$ be an open cover of X. Then $\mathcal{O}$ contains a chain of sets from a to b.*

PROOF. Let $Z = \{x \in X: \text{there is a chain of sets in } \mathcal{O} \text{ from } a \text{ to } x\}$. Clearly Z is a union of sets in $\mathcal{O}$, so that Z is open. If y is in $\mathrm{Cl}(Z)$, then there is an element O_y of $\mathcal{O}$ containing y, and O_y contains some point x of Z. Suppose that $O_1, O_2, \ldots, O_t$ is a chain of sets in $\mathcal{O}$ from a to x. If O_s is the first set in the chain meeting O_y, then $O_1, O_2, \ldots, O_s, O_y$ is a chain of sets in $\mathcal{O}$ from a to y. Thus $\mathrm{Cl}(Z) \subset Z$, so that Z is closed. Certainly $a \in Z$, and since X is connected, Z must be X. ∎

Theorem 4.2.4 *Let $\mathcal{O} = \{O_1, O_2, \ldots, O_s\}$ be a chain of open connected sets in a space X from a to b. Let $\mathcal{P}$ be an open cover of $\cup \{O_i : i = 1, 2, \ldots, s\}$ such that each set in $\mathcal{O}$ is a union of elements of $\mathcal{P}$. Then there is a chain of sets in $\mathcal{P}$ from a to b going straight through $\mathcal{O}$.*

PROOF. Let $x_0 = a, x_s = b$ and x_i be a point of $O_i \cap O_{i+1}$ for $i = 1, 2, \ldots, s - 1$. For each j Theorem 4.2.3 delivers a chain $\mathcal{P}_j$ in $\mathcal{P}$ from x_{j-1} to x_j, each set of which is contained in O_j. We obtain the desired chain by amalgamating $\mathcal{P}_1, \mathcal{P}_2, \ldots, \mathcal{P}_s$ as follows. Let $\mathcal{P}_1 = \{P_{11}, P_{12}, \ldots, P_{1t}\}$, $\mathcal{P}_2 = \{P_{21}, P_{22}, \ldots, P_{2u}\}$, P_{1v} be the first set of $\mathcal{P}_1$ meeting a set of $\mathcal{P}_2$, and P_{2w} be the last set of $\mathcal{P}_2$ meeting P_{1v}. Then the desired amalgamation of $\mathcal{P}_1$ and $\mathcal{P}_2$ is $P_{11}, P_{12}, \ldots, P_{1v}, P_{2w}, \ldots, P_{2u}$. This chain is then amalgamated with $\mathcal{P}_3$, and the procedure is carried out inductively. The final amalgamation yields the desired chain. ∎

We now have the tools necessary to prove an important theorem about Peano spaces. The proof is difficult, as are all proofs in which a continuous function must be built from scratch. The reader is urged to compare our use of chains of sets here with our use of covers of a space in the proof of Theorem 4.1.5.

Theorem 4.2.5 (Arcwise Connectedness Theorem) *Let a and b be distinct points of a connected, locally connected, locally compact metric space X. Then there is an arc in X from a to b.*

PROOF. Since X is locally connected and locally compact, there is an open cover of X whose sets are connected, have compact closures and have diameters less than 1 (verification: an exercise). Theorem 4.2.3 then says that there is a chain $\mathcal{P}_1$ of such sets from a to b.

Now each set P in $\mathcal{P}_1$ is itself open and locally connected and so has a cover by connected open sets of diameter less than $\frac{1}{2}$ whose closures are

125

contained in P. Theorem 4.2.4 delivers a chain $\mathcal{P}_2$ of open connected sets of diameters less than $\frac{1}{2}$ which goes straight through $\mathcal{P}_1$. Note also that $\mathrm{Cl}(\cup \mathcal{P}_2) \subset \cup \mathcal{P}_1$.

Using this procedure inductively we construct chains $\mathcal{P}_1, \mathcal{P}_2, \mathcal{P}_3, \ldots$ from a to b which satisfy the following conditions:

1. The diameter of any set in $\mathcal{P}_i$ is less than $1/i$;
2. $\mathrm{Cl}(\cup \mathcal{P}_{i+1})$ is compact and contained in $\cup \mathcal{P}_i$;
3. Each set in $\mathcal{P}_i$ is connected;
4. $\mathcal{P}_{i+1}$ goes straight through $\mathcal{P}_i$.

The arc that we are after is $A = \cap \{\mathrm{Cl}(\cup \mathcal{P}_i): i = 1, 2, \ldots\}$, but it will take considerable work to prove this. We note that condition (2) implies that A is compact and also that $A = \cap \{\cup \mathcal{P}_i : i = 1, 2, \ldots\}$.

We define a relation $\prec$ between points of A which will have the same properties that the usual "less than" relation has for real numbers. If p and q are points of A, then $p \prec q$ means that there is a chain $\mathcal{P}_i$ in which the last set containing p precedes the first set containing q. We must first show that $p \prec q$ and $q \prec p$ cannot both be true.

Suppose that $\mathcal{P}_i = \{P_1, P_2, \ldots P_s\}$ is a chain in which P_l is the last set containing p, P_k the first set containing q and $l < k$. Let $\mathcal{P}_{i+1} = \{Q_1, Q_2, \ldots, Q_l\}$ and suppose that Q_i, Q_j are sets of $\mathcal{P}_{i+1}$ containing p and q respectively and that $j \leqslant i$. The block of sets of $\mathcal{P}_{i+1}$ contained in P_l cannot contain Q_j, for then q would be in P_l. Further, the chain $Q_1, Q_2, \ldots, Q_j$ must contain points of $P_l \backslash (P_{l-1} \cup P_{l+1})$ (see Exercise 1), so that the block of sets of $\mathcal{P}_{i+1}$ lying in P_l must come strictly before Q_j. Since $j \leqslant i$, the block of sets of $\mathcal{P}_{i+1}$ to which Q_i belongs must lie in P_s for $s > l$, so that $p \in Q_i \subset P_s$ for $s > l$. This contradiction establishes that if $\mathcal{P}_i$ can be used to show that $p \prec q$, then so can $\mathcal{P}_{i+1}$. Induction then verifies that 1) $p \prec q$ and $q \prec p$ cannot both be true and 2) if the last set of $\mathcal{P}_i$ containing p precedes the first set containing q, then this is also true of $\mathcal{P}_j$ for $j > i$.

It is easy to see that the relation $\prec$ is transitive and that $p \prec p$ is never true. We finish our investigation of $\prec$ by showing that distinct points p, q of A are always related. There is a positive integer m such that $1/m < d(p, q)$. In the chain $\mathcal{P}_m$ suppose that the sets Q_i and Q_k contain p, the set Q_j contains q and $i \leqslant j \leqslant k$. Since $p \in Q_i \cap Q_k$, we must have either $i = k$ or $i + 1 = k$, and hence either $j = i$ or $j = k$. In either case a single set of $\mathcal{P}_m$ contains both p and q, contradicting the fact that the diameter of such a set is less than $1/m$. Thus either each set of $\mathcal{P}_m$ containing p precedes each set containing q or vice versa, so that either $p \prec q$ or $q \prec p$. Note that since a always belongs to the first set of a chain $\mathcal{P}_m$ and b to the last, it is true that $a \prec x \prec b$ for any point x of A distinct from a and b.

We now turn to the connection between the relation $\prec$ and the topology of A. Let p and q be elements of A with $p \prec q$. We then define

$\langle p, q \rangle$ to be $\{z \in A : p \prec z \prec q\}$. There is a chain $\mathcal{P}_r$ with at least three sets between the last set containing p and the first containing q. Since each set of a chain $\mathcal{P}_r$ contains elements of A, $\langle p, q \rangle$ is never empty (verification: an exercise). If $z \in \langle p, q \rangle$, then let m be a positive integer such that $\frac{1}{m} < \frac{1}{4} \min\{d(p,z), d(p,q), d(q,z)\}$. Let Q_i be the last set of $\mathcal{P}_m$ containing p, Q_j any set of $\mathcal{P}_m$ containing z, and Q_k the first set of $\mathcal{P}_m$ containing q. Since the diameters of sets of $\mathcal{P}_m$ are less than $1/m$, we must have $i + 2 < j < k - 2$. If $y \in Q_j \cap A$, then the first set of $\mathcal{P}_m$ containing y is Q_{j-1} or Q_j while the last is Q_j or Q_{j+1}, so that $p \prec y \prec q$. Thus $z \in Q_j \cap A \subset \langle p, q \rangle$, and so $\langle p, q \rangle$ is an open subset of A.

We are now ready to define a function from A to $[0, 1]$. Let $D = \{p_i : i = 0, 1, 2, \dots\}$ be a countable dense subset of A such that $p_0 = a$ and $p_1 = b$, and let $D' = \{q_i : i = 0, 1, 2, \dots\}$ be a countable dense subset of $[0, 1]$ such that $q_0 = 0$ and $q_1 = 1$. We use induction to define an order-preserving function from D to D'.

Define $f(p_0) = q_0$ and $f(p_1) = q_1$. We induct as follows. If f has been defined for an even number of points, then let j be the smallest integer such that $q_j \neq f(p_i)$ for any p_i. Let $L = \max\{p_i : f(p_i) \text{ is defined and } f(p_i) < q_j\}$ and $R = \min\{p_i : f(p_i) \text{ is defined and } f(p_i) > q_j\}$. $\langle L, R \rangle$ is open and non-empty and so must contain p_r for some r. Define $f(p_r) = q_j$. If f has been defined for an odd number of points, then let j be the smallest integer such that $f(p_j)$ is not defined. In this case let $L = \max\{f(p_i) : f(p_i) \text{ is defined and } p_i < p_j\}$ and $R = \min\{f(p_i) : f(p_i) \text{ is defined and } p_i > p_j\}$. Define $f(p_j)$ to be any element of D' in (L, R). In this way we obtain a one-to-one order-preserving function f from D onto D'.

For any point x of A, let $\bar{f}(x) = \text{lub}\{f(p_i) : p_i \prec x \text{ or } p_i = x\}$. Since f is order-preserving, $\bar{f} | D = f$. If x and y are points of A with $x \prec y$, then there are points p_i, p_j of D satisfying $x \prec p_i \prec p_j \prec y$, so that $\bar{f}(x) \leqslant f(p_i) < f(p_j) \leqslant \bar{f}(y)$. Hence $\bar{f}$ is one-to-one and order-preserving.

We show that $\bar{f}$ is continuous. Let $x \in A$ and let U be a neighborhood of $\bar{f}(x)$ in $[0, 1]$. There are points q_i, q_j of D' such that $\bar{f}(x) \in [q_i, q_j] \subset U$ and $[q_i, q_j]$ contains a neighborhood of $\bar{f}(x)$. Since f is onto D', there are points p_r, p_s of D such that $f(p_r) = q_i$ and $f(p_s) = q_j$. Since $\bar{f}$ preserves order, $\bar{f}(\langle p_r, p_s \rangle) \subset U$, and $\langle p_r, p_s \rangle \cup \{p_r, p_s\}$ contains a neighborhood of x in A (verification: an exercise). Thus $\bar{f}$ is continuous. Since A is compact, $\bar{f}(A)$ is a compact subset of $[0, 1]$ which contains D', so that $\bar{f}$ is onto.

A one-to-one continuous function from a compact set onto $[0, 1]$ must be a homeomorphism, so that A must be an arc in X from a to b. ∎

There are several other proofs of the Arcwise Connectedness Theorem, some of which need less stringent hypotheses than ours. As usual, we urge the interested reader to pursue this subject elsewhere. For our purposes we need only the slight extension which is the next result.

Theorem 4.2.6 *A Peano space X is uniformly locally arcwise connected, i.e., for each positive ε there is a positive δ such that there is an arc in X from x to y of diameter less than ε whenever $d(x,y) < δ$.*

PROOF. Since X is locally connected, there is an open cover of X whose sets are connected and have diameters less than ε. Each set in this cover is a connected, locally compact, locally connected metric space and so contains an arc between each of its points. By Exercise 8 of Section 2.7, Part A, there is a positive number δ such that x and y both belong to a single set in the cover whenever $d(x,y) < δ$. ■

The next theorem completes the proof of the Hahn–Mazurkiewicz Theorem.

Theorem 4.2.7 *Any Peano space X is the continuous image of* $[0,1]$.

PROOF. Let C be the Cantor middle-third set in $I = [0,1]$. By Theorem 4.1.5, there is a continuous function f from C onto X. For $n = 1,2,3,\ldots$ let $δ_n$ be the positive number guaranteed by Theorem 4.2.6 for $ε = 1/n$, i.e., any two points of X within $δ_n$ can be joined by an arc of diameter less than $1/n$. We may assume that $δ_1 > δ_2 > \cdots$

If (a,b) is a component of $I \backslash C$ such that $d(f(a),f(b)) \geqslant δ_1$, then extend f to (a,b) by letting f be a homeomorphism from $[a,b]$ onto any arc in X from $f(a)$ to $f(b)$. If (c,d) is a component of $I \backslash C$ such that $d(f(c),f(d)) = 0$, then let $f(x) = f(c)$ for each x in (c,d). If (c,d) is a component of $I \backslash C$ such that $0 < d(f(c),f(d)) < δ_1$, then there is a j such that $δ_{j+1} \leqslant d(f(c),f(d)) < δ_j$. Extend f to (c,d) by letting f be a homeomorphism from $[c,d]$ onto an arc in X from $f(c)$ to $f(d)$ having diameter less than $1/j$. We thus have a function f from I onto X.

It remains to show that f is continuous. Since $I \backslash C$ is open and f is a homeomorphism or constant when restricted to any component of $I \backslash C$, f is continuous at each point of $I \backslash C$. Let $x \in C$ and let ε be positive. Let n be such that $1/n < ε/2$ and let U be a neighborhood of x in I such that $f(U \cap C) \subset N(f(x), \min\{δ_n/2, ε/2\})$. We do the case in which there is a $y > x$ such that $(x,y) \subset I \backslash C$; the other cases are similar and often easier. There is a point c of C such that $c < x$ and $[c,x] \subset U$ and since $f|[x,y]$ is continuous there is a point z such that $f([x,z]) \subset N(f(x), ε)$. If $t \in [c,x] \backslash C$, then the component (a,b) of $I \backslash C$ containing t satisfies $[a,b] \subset U$. Thus $d(f(a),f(b)) < δ_n$, so $f([a,b])$ has diameter less than $ε/2$. Since $d(f(a),f(x)) < ε/2$, $f([a,b]) \subset N(f(x), ε)$. Thus (c,z) is a neighborhood of x in I which f carries into $N(f(x), ε)$. ■

Exercises

1. Let $\mathcal{O} = \{O_1, O_2, \ldots, O_q\}$ be a chain of connected open sets from a to b.
   a. Show that $O_i \backslash (O_{i-1} \cup O_{i+1})$ is not empty for $i = 2, 3, \ldots, q-1$.
   b. Show that any chain from a to b whose sets are open and contained in $\cup \mathcal{O}$ must contain points of $O_i \backslash (O_{i-1} \cup O_{i+1})$ for $i = 2, 3, \ldots, q-1$.

2. Give an example of a chain $\mathcal{P} = \{P_1, P_2, \ldots, P_r\}$ from a to b and a chain $\mathcal{P}_1 = \{O_1, O_2, \ldots, O_s\}$ from b to c such that $\{P_1, P_2, \ldots, P_r, O_1, O_2, \ldots, O_s\}$ is not a chain from a to c.

3. Show that the end-points of an arc are well defined.

4. Provide the verifications asked for in the proof of Theorem 4.2.5.

5. List the cases mentioned in the proof of continuity of f in Theorem 4.2.7 and provide a proof for one other than that done in the text.

6. a. Prove that the one-point compactification of a locally compact locally connected noncompact Hausdorff space is locally connected. (*Hard.*)
   b. Prove that the one-point compactification of a connected, locally connected, locally compact noncompact separable metric space is a Peano space.
   c. Prove that a connected, locally connected, locally compact noncompact separable metric space contains a closed subspace homeomorphic to $[0, 1)$.

7. Prove that R^n is the continuous image of $[0, 1)$.

4.3 Embeddings

The relationships between a subspace and its containing space have been of interest to topologists almost since the time topology became a distinct field of study. Any topology text abounds in subspace theorems, and the area has been an extremely fruitful and active one right through the present day. In this section we will concentrate on geometric aspects of the subject, give some of the basic definitions, prove some elementary results and give some famous theorems and examples. First, we state the fundamental definition.

Definition Let X and Y be spaces. An *embedding* of X into Y is a homeomorphism from X onto a subspace of Y. If such a homeomorphism exists then we say that X *embeds* in Y. Two embeddings e_1 and e_2 of X into Y are *equivalent* if there is a homeomorphism h of Y onto itself such that $h \circ e_1 = e_2$.

It is an easy exercise to show that equivalence of embeddings is indeed an equivalence relation on the set of embeddings of a space X into a space Y. The basic problems arise when one tries to classify the equivalence classes in some reasonable way. Note that this includes the question of whether X has any embedding into Y at all.

EXAMPLES.

1. Let $X = \{n : n = 1, 2, \ldots\}$. Consider two embeddings of X into R, namely, e_1 defined by $e_1(n) = n$ and e_2 defined by $e_2(n) = 1/n$. Now $\mathrm{Cl}(e_2(X))$ is compact, so if h is any homeomorphism of R onto itself, then $h(e_2(X))$ must lie in $h(\mathrm{Cl}(e_2(X)))$ and so must be bounded. Since $e_1(X)$ is not bounded, $h \circ e_2$ cannot be e_1. Thus e_1 and e_2 are not equivalent embeddings.

2. Let $X = \{0\} \cup \{1/n : n = 1, 2, \ldots\}$. Define e_1 and e_2 by $e_1(x) = x$ for $x \in X$ and $e_2(0) = 0$, $e_2(1/n) = (-1)^n(1/n)$ for $n = 1, 2, \ldots$. Both e_1 and e_2 are embeddings of X into R. It is not hard to show that any homeomorphism of R either always preserves order or always reverses order. Since e_2 preserves the order of the points $1/2k$ and reverses the order of the points $1/(2k+1)$, the embeddings e_1 and e_2 cannot be equivalent. Equivalence of embeddings is a very subtle thing.

Before we look at more results we need some terminology and notation. The following material has been a subject of much activity among topologists during the past 20 years.

Definitions The *standard n-sphere* is $S^n = \{(x_1, x_2, \ldots, x_{n+1}) \in R^{n+1} : x_1^2 + x_2^2 + \cdots + x_{n+1}^2 = 1\}$ for $n = 0, 1, 2, \ldots$ and the *standard n-ball* is $B^n = \{(x_1, x_2, \ldots, x_n) \in R^n : x_1^2 + x_2^2 + \cdots + x_n^2 \leqslant 1\}$ for $n = 1, 2, \ldots$. An *n-sphere* or *n-ball* is any space homeomorphic to S^n or B^n, respectively. For $1 \leqslant k \leqslant n$ we define $J_{k,n}$ from R^k into R^n by $J_{k,n}((x_1, x_2, \ldots, x_k)) = (x_1, x_2, \ldots, x_k, 0, 0, \ldots, 0)$. An embedding of S^k into R^n is *flat* if it is equivalent to $J_{k+1,n}|S^k$, and an embedding of B^k into R^n is *flat* if it is equivalent to $J_{k,n}|B^k$.

Buried in this rather lengthy definition are some assumptions regarding the existence of embeddings of S^k and B^k into R^n. It seems eminently reasonable that B^k embeds in R^n only if $k \leqslant n$ and that S^k embeds in R^n only if $k \leqslant n - 1$. However, these facts are hard to prove. We will use the following classical result as our starting point; the proof of Theorem 4.3.1 is too difficult for this book.

Theorem 4.3.1 (Invariance of Domain) *Let U be an open subset of R^n and e an embedding of U into R^n. Then $e(U)$ is an open set.*

This theorem was first proved by L. E. J. Browwer in 1912. It has many important consequences, some of which we leave as exercises. We will be content with the following.

Theorem 4.3.2 *There is no embedding of B^k into R^n if $k > n$, and there is no embedding of S^k into R^n if $k \geqslant n$.*

PROOF. Suppose e is an embedding of S^k into R^n where $k \geqslant n$. $J_{n+1,k+1}|S^n$ embeds S^n in S^k, and $e \circ J_{n+1,k+1}|S^n$ is then an embedding of S^n in R^n. Thus if we get a contradiction assuming that $k=n$, we will be done. Now $e(S^n)$ is a compact subset of R^n and so is closed. We show that $e(S^n)$ is also open. If $(y_1,y_2,\ldots,y_{n+1})$ is a point of S^n, then y_j is not 0 for some j, and for notational purposes we assume that $j=n+1$. Suppose also that $y_{n+1}>0$. Define $T:B^n \to S^n$ by

$$T((x_1,x_2,\ldots,x_n)) = \left(x_1,x_2,\ldots,x_n,\sqrt{1-x_1^2-x_2^2-\cdots-x_n^2}\,\right).$$

It is not hard to see that T is a homeomorphism from B^n onto $T(B^n)$, so that $e \circ T$ is an embedding of B^n in R^n. Now $N((0,0,\ldots,0),1)$ is open in R^n, so by the Invariance of Domain Theorem, $e(T(N((0,0,\ldots,0),1)))$ is open in R^n, contains $e((y_1,y_2,\ldots,y_{n+1}))$ and is contained in $e(S^n)$. Thus $e(S^n)$ is an open and closed subset of R^n and so must be all of R^n. But $e(S^n)$ is compact and R^n is not.

We turn to the case of B^k. The same trick we used above suffices to show that we need only consider the case $k=n+1$. Also, the same argument used above shows that $e(J_{n,n+1}(N((0,0,\ldots,0),1)))$ is an open subset of R^n. In R^{n+1} the points $(0,0,\ldots,0,1/p)$, $p=1,2,\ldots$, form a sequence in B^{n+1} converging to $(0,0,\ldots,0)$ so the points $e((0,0,\ldots,0,1/p))$ converge to $e((0,0,\ldots,0))$. However, none of these points lie in $e(J_{n,n+1}(N((0,0,\ldots,0),1)))$. ∎

We now turn our attention to some positive results. Theorem 4.3.2 says that there are no embeddings of B^k or S^k into R^n for large k, so we must look at the other end of the spectrum and worry about the situation for small k. Although we did not define B^0, it is reasonable to take B^0 to be a point, so our first concern is the embedding of a point into R^n. It is trivial to prove that any two embeddings of a point in R^n are equivalent, but we will need more sophisticated results later, hence the following. We recall that for points p,q of R^n we set $[p,q]=\{tp+(1-t)q:0\leqslant t\leqslant 1\}$. We also let $(p,q]=\{tp+(1-t)q:0<t\leqslant 1\}$ and $(p,q)=\{tp+(1-t)q:0<t<1\}$.

Theorem 4.3.3 *Let p and q be distinct points of R^n and U an open set containing $(p,q]$. If z is any point of $(p,q]$, then there is a homeomorphism h of R^n onto itself such that $h(x)=x$ for $x \notin U$ and $h([p,q])=[p,z]$.*

PROOF. Choose points α and y such that $q \in (p,y)$, $(p,y] \subset U$, and $\alpha \in (p,z)$. Then $\phi(x)=(x-\alpha)/|y-\alpha|$ is a homeomorphism of R^n onto itself such that $\phi(\alpha)=(0,0,\ldots,0)$, $|\phi(y)|=1$ and $\phi(U)$ is an open set containing $[(0,0,\ldots,0),\phi(y)]$. We will be finished if we produce a homeomorphism h' of R^n onto itself such that $h'(x)=x$ for $x \notin \phi(U)$ and

$$h'\left(\left[(0,0,\ldots,0),\phi(q)\right]\right) = \left[(0,0,\ldots,0),\phi(z)\right],$$

for the desired homeomorphism will then be $\phi^{-1} \circ h' \circ \phi$.

Thus we change notation so that $(0,0,\ldots,0)\in(p,q), z\in[(0,0,\ldots,0),q]$, and there is a point y with $|y|=1, q\in((0,0,\ldots,0),y)$ and $[(0,0,\ldots,0),y]\subset U$. Now for $0\leqslant t\leqslant 1$, $ty\in U$, so there are neighborhoods U_t, V_t of t and y respectively such that $sx\in U$ whenever $s\in U_t$ and $x\in V_t$. Since $[0,1]$ is compact, we can find $U_{t_1}, U_{t_2},\ldots,U_{t_j}$ covering $[0,1]$. Then $V=V_{t_1}\cap V_{t_2}\cap\cdots\cap V_{t_j}$ is a neighborhood of y such that $tx\in U$ whenever $0\leqslant t\leqslant 1$ and $x\in V$. There is a positive number r such that $N(y,r)\subset V$.

The idea is to slide points along the segments $[(0,0,\ldots,0),\beta]$ for $|\beta|=1$ in such a way that we move them as desired along $[(0,0,\ldots,0),y]$ and move less and less as β approaches $R^n\setminus N(y,r)$. For this purpose we need a function k from $[0,1]\times[0,1]$ into $[0,1]$ such that $s\to k(s,0)$ takes 0 to 0, 1 to 1 and $|q|$ to $|z|$ and $s\to k(s,t)$ moves s less and less as t approaches 1. Some analytic geometry delivers

$$k(s,t) = \begin{cases} ts+(1-t)|z|\dfrac{1}{|q|}s & 0\leqslant s\leqslant|q| \\[2ex] ts+(1-t)\left[\dfrac{s-|q|}{1-|q|}(1-|z|)+|z|\right] & |q|\leqslant s\leqslant 1 \end{cases}.$$

Using the usual properties of real-valued functions it is easy to check that k is a continuous function from $[0,1]\times[0,1]$ into $[0,1]$. Further $k(0,t)=0, k(1,t)=1, k(s,1)=s$, for fixed t the map $s\to k(s,t)$ is a homeomorphism, and

$$k(s,0) = \begin{cases} \dfrac{|z|}{|q|}s & 0\leqslant s\leqslant|q| \\[2ex] \dfrac{s-|q|}{1-|q|}(1-|z|)+|z| & |q|\leqslant s\leqslant 1 \end{cases}.$$

Now define

$$h(x) = \begin{cases} k\left(|x|,\dfrac{1}{r}\left|\dfrac{x}{|x|}-y\right|\right)\dfrac{x}{|x|} & 0<|x|\leqslant 1 \quad\text{and}\quad \left|\dfrac{x}{|x|}-y\right|\leqslant r \\[2ex] x & \text{otherwise.} \end{cases}$$

Since $k(0,t)=0$ for each t, h is continuous at $(0,0,\ldots,0)$. Continuity of h then follows by the commonly used piecewise argument (see Exercise 6). The properties of k imply that h is a one-to-one function from R^n onto itself which is the identity outside a compact set, and so it is easy to check that h is a homeomorphism. Clearly $h(x)=x$ for $x\notin U$ and $h(q)=z$. ∎

The reader has undoubtedly noticed that some details are lacking in the last proof. If he has an appetite for analytic geometry, he is urged to satisfy it by supplying these missing details. The proof is a good example of the way in which a simple geometric idea becomes very complicated in its analytical details. We will not always use even this much care.

Note that if z and q are any two points of R^n both in $N(\alpha,r)$ for some α and r, then we can find p such that $z \in (p,q] \subset N(\alpha,r)$. We get a homeomorphism h of R^n onto itself such that $h(q)=z$ and $h(x)=x$ for $x \notin N(\alpha,r)$. This yields the following corollary as well as other more general results which we leave for the exercises.

Corollary 4.3.4 *Any two embeddings of a point into R^n are equivalent.*

The next case involves embeddings of B^1 into R^n. This turns out to be extremely difficult and interesting and will occupy a good part of the remainder of this section. The first result is almost trivial but also contains the germ of better ideas (see Exercise 15).

Theorem 4.3.5 *Every embedding of B^1 into R is flat.*

PROOF. Since $B^1 \subset R$, we must prove that any embedding e of B^1 into R is equivalent to the identity embedding Id. If $e(-1) < e(1)$, then define h by

$$h(x) = \begin{cases} x+1+e(-1) & x \leqslant -1 \\ e(x) & -1 \leqslant x \leqslant 1. \\ x-1+e(1) & 1 \leqslant x \end{cases}$$

It is easy to check that h is a homeomorphism of R onto itself such that $h \circ \mathrm{Id} = e$. The case in which $e(1) < e(-1)$ is similar. ∎

Theorem 4.3.2, Theorem 4.3.5, and Exercise 9 finish the study of embeddings of B^k or S^k into R. We now turn to R^2. One's first thought is that nothing bad can happen in R^2, and a few pictures usually strengthen this feeling. Our next result not only destroys this comfortable feeling but has intrinsic interest as well.

Theorem 4.3.6 *There is an arc α in R^2 which has positive area; in fact, if ε is positive then α can be taken to be an arc in $I^2 = [0,1] \times [0,1]$ which has area at least $1 - \varepsilon$.*

Some remarks are in order before we prove this theorem. The similarity between Theorem 4.3.6 and the space-filling curve results of Section 4.2 is striking. A continuous function from B^1 can cover the entire square I^2, but an arc cannot, since then B^1 and I^2 would be homeomorphic. However, this theorem says that in the sense of area an arc can cover all but the tiniest part of I^2. The American mathematician Osgood gave this example in 1903, and the reader can spend an enjoyable hour by looking up the original paper in the *Transactions of the American Mathematical Society*.

We need to develop some theory of area in the plane, so we give here some definitions and facts without proof. First, a *rectangle* is any set

$\mathcal{R} = \{(x,y) \in R^2 : a \leqslant x \leqslant b, c \leqslant y \leqslant d\}$. Its *area* is $A(\mathcal{R}) = (b-a)(d-c)$ and the *interior* of $\mathcal{R}$ is $\{(x,y) \in R^2 : a < x < b, c < y < d\}$. We use the term *figure* for a set which is the union of finitely many rectangles, no two of whose interiors intersect. The area of a figure $\mathcal{F}$ is defined to be the sum of the areas of the rectangles of which it is the union and is denoted by $A(\mathcal{F})$. If K is any compact set in R^2, then the area of K is defined to be $A(K) = \text{glb}\{A(\mathcal{F}) : \mathcal{F} \text{ is a figure with } K \subset \mathcal{F}\}$. Finally if $\mathcal{F}_1, \mathcal{F}_2, \ldots$ are figures with $\mathcal{F}_1 \supset \mathcal{F}_2 \supset \cdots$, then one can show that $A(\cap \{\mathcal{F}_i : i = 1, 2, \ldots\}) = \text{glb}\{A(\mathcal{F}_i) : i = 1, 2, \ldots\}$.

PROOF OF THEOREM 4.3.6   We obtain the arc α as the image of $[0, 1]$ under a function f which is the limit of embeddings $f_0, f_1, f_2, \ldots$ of $[0, 1]$ into R^2. We imagine that I^2 is an area of swampland surrounded on two sides by water (dashed area) and on two sides by dry land (dotted area). The picture of the situation at Stage 0 is as shown, and the function f_0 takes $[0, \frac{1}{2}]$ linearly onto the vertical black line segment and $[\frac{1}{2}, 1]$ linearly onto the horizontal black line segment.

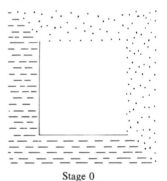

Stage 0

To get to Stage 1 from Stage 0 we dig canals and build dikes in the pattern shown. At Stage 0 the approximation $f_0([0, 1])$ to the desired arc runs along the water's edge. The next approximation $f_1([0, 1])$ continues to

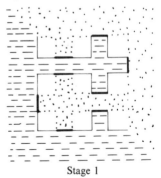

Stage 1

do so and is shown as a thin black line and a thick black line. Certainly there are numbers $0 = t_0 < t_1 < \cdots < t_{17} = 1$ equally spaced in $[0,1]$ and an embedding f_1 of $[0,1]$ into R^2 such that $f_1([t_i, t_{i+1}])$ is a thin black L-shaped arc in Stage 1 if i is even and a thick black line segment in Stage 1 if i is odd.

Note that at Stage 0 there was one square of swampland bordered on two adjacent sides by water and on two adjacent sides by dry land. At Stage 1 there are nine such squares. The approximation to the desired arc always runs along the water's edge, and the parts which form a border between water and dry land are drawn as thick black lines and will never again be adjusted.

Stage 2 is obtained from Stage 1 by doing to each of the nine squares of swampland what was done to the one square of swampland at Stage 0. Stage 2 thus has more canals and dikes and 81 squares of swampland. This procedure continues and creates Stage n for each nonnegative integer n.

We let f_2 be equal to f_1 on those subintervals of $[0,1]$ which f_1 takes to a thick black line segment. We divide each subinterval which f_1 takes to a thin black "L" into 17 subintervals of equal size, and define f_2 on these subintervals in exactly the same way we defined f_1. This procedure can also be continued to obtain the embeddings $f_0, f_1, f_2, \ldots$.

At Stage n there are 9^n squares of swampland each of which has side length less than $1/3^n$. If $f_n(x)$ is on a thick black line, then $f_n(x) = f_{n+r}(x)$ for $r = 1, 2, \ldots$; otherwise both $f_n(x)$ and $f_{n+r}(x)$ lie in the same square of Stage n swampland. Thus $d(f_n(x), f_{n+r}(x))$ is always less than $\sqrt{2}/3^n$, so that $f_0, f_1, f_2, \ldots$ is a uniformly convergent sequence of functions. Theorem 3.1.4 guarantees that this sequence converges to a continuous limit function f.

To show that f is a homeomorphism, it is enough to show that f is one-to-one. Let x and y be distinct points of $[0,1]$. If at any Stage n approximations $f_n(x)$ and $f_n(y)$ are separated by a thick line segment or are both in a thick line segment, then either $f_{n+r}(x)$ and $f_{n+r}(y)$ lie in different Stage n squares of swampland or $f_{n+r}(x) = f_n(x) \neq f_n(y) = f_{n+r}(y)$ for $r = 1, 2, \ldots$. Either way, $f(x) = \lim_{r \to \infty} f_{n+r}(x)$ and $f(y) = \lim_{r \to \infty} f_{n+r}(y)$ are distinct. The remaining case is that in which $f_n(x)$ and $f_n(y)$ are in the same thin black L-shaped arc for each n. By construction the subinterval of $[0,1]$, which f_n takes onto such an arc, has length no larger than $1/17^n$, so that $|x - y| \leqslant 1/17^n$ for $n = 1, 2, \ldots$. Thus $x = y$, so that this case cannot occur.

We have shown that $\alpha = f([0,1])$ is an arc. Note that α contains all the thick black arcs at each stage and that these arcs get arbitrarily close to the remaining swampland at any stage. Since α is compact and thus closed, α contains $\cap \{ S_n : S_n$ is the swampland at Stage $n \}$.

We have never required that the canals and dikes built at Stage n be of a specific thickness. Thus for any positive ε, we can make the canals and dikes constructed at Stage 1 so thin that their total area is less than $\varepsilon/2$, so the Stage 1 swampland has area larger than $1-\varepsilon/2$. At Stage 2 the added canals and dikes can be made so thin that the total canal/dike area is less than $\varepsilon/2+\varepsilon/4$. Thus the Stage 2 swampland has area larger than $1-(\varepsilon/2 +\varepsilon/4)$. We can continue in this way so that the swampland at Stage n has area larger than $1-(\varepsilon/2+\varepsilon/4+\cdots+\varepsilon/2^n)$. Our facts about area then imply that the area of the arc α is at least

$$\text{glb}\{1-(\varepsilon/2+\varepsilon/4+\cdots+\varepsilon/2^n):n=1,2,\ldots\} = 1-\varepsilon. \qquad \blacksquare$$

This example should destroy any satisfaction we may have had about the embedding of arcs or circles in the plane. It turns out to be difficult at best to prove that embeddings in the plane behave nicely, and we must leave such proofs for other authors. We will be content with the statements of the following theorems.

Theorem 4.3.7   (Schoenflies' Theorem) *Every embedding of S^1 into R^2 is flat.*

Theorem 4.3.8 *Every embedding of B^1 into R^2 is flat.*

Schoenflies' Theorem was first proved in 1906 by A. Schoenflies. A little thought shows that Theorem 4.3.8 follows from Schoenflies' Theorem as long as one can show that every arc in R^2 is contained in an embedded S^1 in R^2, but it turns out that this is definitely nontrivial. Also, Schoenflies' Theorem implies that every embedding of B^2 into R^2 is flat. Newman's book *Elements of the Topology of Plane Sets of Points* contains nice proofs of these and related results.

Our outline of the results on embeddings of S^k and B^k into R^2 is now complete. We turn our attention to R^3. One would like to prove an analogue of Schoenflies' Theorem for embeddings in R^3, i.e., show that every embedding of S^2 in R^3 is flat. In 1921 J. W. Alexander stated that he had done so. However, in 1924 he published an example to show that this cannot be done. There is also an example due to the French mathematician Antoine in 1921. Then in 1948 R. Fox and E. Artin gave several examples relating to embeddings in R^3.

As the reader may already have guessed, the proofs accompanying these examples are hard. We will draw some pictures and indicate the general idea of the proofs and hope that the reader will turn elsewhere for more information.

With the exception of Fox–Artin arc #2 one can prove that these embeddings are not flat by showing that the dashed circle cannot be slipped off the embedded arc or sphere. If these embeddings could be taken to the standard ones by a homeomorphism h of R^3 onto itself, then h would take the circle to one which could be slipped off the standard sphere

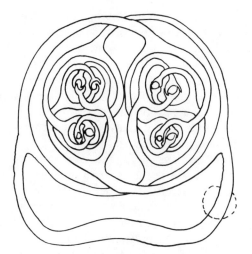

Alexander's horned sphere

Fox–Artin arc #1

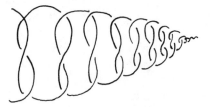

Fox–Artin arc #2

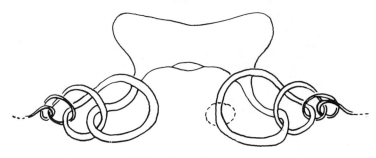

A Fox–Artin sphere

or arc, and h^{-1} would carry this slipping-off process back to the badly embedded cases. Making this argument rigorous requires the construction of a lot of mathematical machinery, some of which we will do in Chapter 7, and this machinery can also be used to deal with Fox–Artin arc #2.

These examples show that there are embeddings of B^1 and S^2 into R^3 which are not flat. The bad embedding of B^1 can easily be extended to an embedding of S^1, and removal of a disk from the badly embedded S^2 leaves a badly embedded B^2. Finally, similar techniques can be used to produce nonflat embeddings of B^3 into R^3.

Since not all embeddings in R^3 are nice as they are in R^2, several questions arise. One is whether there are any properties of embeddings of balls or spheres that generalize from R^2 to R^n. The following theorem is the most important such result. For $n=2$ the theorem is called the *Jordan Curve Theorem* and was proved about 1900. The general case was done by L. E. J. Brouwer in 1912. We must omit the proof.

Theorem 4.3.9 **(Jordan–Brouwer Separation Theorem)** *Let e be any embedding of S^{n-1} into R^n. Then $R^n \backslash e(S^{n-1})$ has exactly two components A and B, and $\mathrm{Cl}(A) \cap \mathrm{Cl}(B) = e(S^{n-1})$.*

Another problem that arises since not all embeddings are flat is to determine conditions under which an embedding is flat. There are lots of these, but we must concentrate on the simplest and most classical. We need some terminology, but in order not to go too far afield, we restrict ourselves to R^3 and to a slightly nonrigorous approach. These ideas will be encountered in more polished form in Chapter 6.

Definitions A *line segment* is a set of the form $\{tp + (1-t)q : 0 \leqslant t \leqslant 1\}$ for distinct points p and q of R^3. The term *triangle* will refer to a planar triangle plus its interior. A *tetrahedron* is a bounded region in R^3 enclosed by four planes no three of which meet except at a single point. Finally, a *polyhedron* in R^3 is any set which is the union of finitely many points, line segments, triangles and tetrahedra.

We now use polyhedra in our study of embeddings. Though we restricted ourselves to R^3, the reader should be able to obtain a good idea of how these ideas generalize to R^n. A fundamental type of embedding is the following.

Definition Let X be a space homeomorphic to a polyhedron in R^3. An embedding e of X into R^3 is *tame* if there is a homeomorphism h of R^3 onto itself such that $h(e(X))$ is a polyhedron; otherwise e is said to be *wild*.

The next theorem shows the usefulness of the idea of tameness. Hopefully the reader's appetite for geometric detail has been satisfied by the proof of Theorem 4.3.3, so we will give only the main ideas of the proof. We also use the natural generalization of the preceding definitions to R^n.

Theorem 4.3.10 *A tame embedding of B^1 into R^n is flat.*

PROOF. Let e be a tame embedding of B^1 into R^n. Then there is a homeomorphism h of R^n onto itself such that $h(e(B^1))$ is a polyhedron. This means that there are points $p_0, p_1, \ldots, p_r$ in R^n such that $h(e(B^1)) = \bigcup_{i=1}^{r}[p_{i-1}, p_i]$. Use Theorem 4.3.3 to pull $[p_{r-1}, p_r]$ very close to p_{r-1} without disturbing the rest of $h(e(B^1))$. Then rotate the shortened $[p_{r-1}, p_r]$ so that the part of $h(e(B^1))$ from p_{r-2} to the moved p_r is straight, again without disturbing the rest of $h(e(B^1))$. Continue this procedure inductively to finally move $h(e(B^1))$ onto $[p, q]$ for some $p, q \in R^n$ and then slide and rotate $[p, q]$ onto $[(-1, 0, \ldots, 0), (1, 0, \ldots, 0)]$. ∎

We note that this proof does not work for tame embeddings of S^1 into R^3, since S^1 has no "free end" at which to start the moving procedure. In fact, there are tame embeddings of S^1 in R^3 which are not flat, and these embeddings are called *knots*. An example is shown below. Knot theory is a large and thriving part of topology.

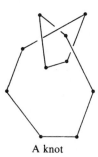

A knot

The next theorem was proved by J. W. Alexander in 1924 and shows that Theorem 4.3.10 extends to embeddings of S^2 into R^3. It is a somewhat surprising fact that it does not extend to higher dimensions, i.e., there are tame embeddings of S^{n-1} into R^n which are not flat when $n \geqslant 4$. Again, the proof is too hard for this book.

Theorem 4.3.11 *A tame embedding of S^2 into R^3 is flat.*

We have given only a glimpse of the subject of embedding problems but must reluctantly conclude our study with a few more comments. We note that many of the results in Chapter 3 can be viewed as embedding theorems, e.g., Urysohn's Metrization Theorem, completions, and compactifications. We have barely touched the whole problem of when space X embeds in space Y, which has led to a great deal of beautiful mathematics. Hopefully the reader will pursue these problems elsewhere.

Exercises

1. Show that equivalence of embeddings is indeed an equivalence relation on the set of embeddings of a space X into space Y.

2. Show that if h is a homeomorphism of R onto itself, then either $h(x)<h(y)$ whenever $x<y$ or $h(x)>h(y)$ whenever $x<y$.

3. Prove that R^n and R^k are not homeomorphic if $n \neq k$.

4. Let U be an open subset of R and e an embedding of U into R.
   a. If J is a component of U, then $e|J$ either preserves order or reverses order.
   b. If J is a component of U, then $e(J)$ is open.
   c. $e(U)$ is open.

5. Supply all the details of the proof of Theorem 4.3.2 for B^k.

6. Prove that if C_1 and C_2 are closed subsets of a space X whose union is X and f_1, f_2 are continuous functions from C_1, C_2 respectively into a space Y such that $f_1(x)=f_2(x)$ for $x \in C_1 \cap C_2$, then $f: X \to Y$ defined by

$$f(x) = \begin{cases} f_1(x) & x \in C_1 \\ f_2(x) & x \in C_2 \end{cases}$$

   is continuous.

7. Prove that a continuous function from R^n onto itself which is one-to-one and is the identity outside a compact set is a homeomorphism.

8. Complete the proof of Theorem 4.3.5.

9. Prove that any embedding of S^0 into R is flat.

10. These exercises refer to the material on area.
   a. If $\mathcal{F}$ is any figure and ε is positive, then there is a figure $\mathcal{F}'$ and an open set O such that $A(\mathcal{F}')<A(\mathcal{F})+\varepsilon$ and $\mathcal{F} \subset O \subset \mathcal{F}'$.
   b. If $\mathcal{F}_1, \mathcal{F}_2, \ldots$ are figures with $\mathcal{F}_1 \supset \mathcal{F}_2 \supset \ldots$, then $A(\cap\{\mathcal{F}_i : i=1,2,\ldots\})=$ glb $\{A(\mathcal{F}_i): i=1,2,\ldots\}$.

11. Use Schoenflies' Theorem to prove that every embedding of B^2 into R^2 is flat.

12. Supply all the details of the proof of Theorem 4.3.10.

13. A *manifold M* is a separable metric space each point of which lies in an open set whose closure is homeomorphic to B^n for some n. The *interior* of M is Int $M = \{x \in M : x$ lies in an open set homeomorphic to R^n for some $n\}$ and the *boundary* of M is Bd $M = M \setminus$ Int M.
   a. Prove that if M is connected, then the integer n is unique.
   b. Prove that if h is a homeomorphism of M onto itself, then $h(\text{Int } M)=\text{Int } M$ and $h(\text{Bd } M)=\text{Bd } M$.

c. Give examples of manifolds where $n = 1$, $n = 2$ and $n = 3$.

d. Prove that any two embeddings of a point into a connected manifold with empty boundary are equivalent.

Feel free to use the Invariance of Domain Theorem in these exercises.

14. Use the Schoenflies' Theorem to prove the Jordan Curve Theorem.

15. a. Prove that any embedding e of S^n into R^{n+1} is flat if $e(S^n) = S^n$.

   b. Prove that any embedding e of B^n into R^n is flat if $e(B^n) = B^n$.

4.4 The continuous real-valued functions on [0, 1]

Topological ideas play a major role in that branch of mathematics called *analysis*, which includes the detailed study of real-valued functions of a real variable. In this section we deal with this subject by applying results we have obtained earlier concerning complete metric spaces.

Recall that $C([0,1])$ denotes the set of continuous functions from $[0,1]$ into R endowed with the metric $\rho(f,g) = \max\{|f(x) - g(x)| : x \in [0,1]\}$. Theorem 3.1.4 implies that this space is a complete metric space, so that we can apply other results from Section 3.1 to it. An examination of our previous work on $C([0,1])$ shows that $[0,1]$ plays no special role and that we can deal with $C([a,b]) = \{f : f \text{ is a continuous function from } [a,b] \text{ into } R\}$ in exactly the same way.

Our first project is to prove an existence and uniqueness theorem for differential equations via the application of a fixed point theorem for complete metric spaces. This technique has generated many results dealing with the existence of fixed points in various settings, some of which we will see in Chapter 5. We need some definitions to clarify these remarks.

Definition Let f be a function from a set X to itself. A point x_0 satisfying $f(x_0) = x_0$ is called a *fixed point* of f. Further, we define $f^0(x) = x$ and $f^{n+1}(x) = f(f^n(x))$ for $n = 0, 1, 2, \ldots$. Finally, a *contraction mapping* on a metric space (X, d) is a function $T : X \to X$ for which there is a constant $k < 1$ such that $d(T(x), T(y)) \leqslant kd(x,y)$ for $x, y \in X$.

Theorem 4.4.1 **(Banach Fixed-Point Theorem)** *Let X be a complete metric space, x any point of X, and T a contraction mapping on X. Then T has a unique fixed point z_0 and the sequence $[T^n(x)]$ converges to z_0.*

PROOF. Consider the sequence $[T^n(x)]$. We have $d(T(x), T^2(x)) = d(T(x), T(T(x))) \leqslant kd(x, T(x))$. If

$$d(T^n(x), T^{n+1}(x)) \leqslant k^n d(x, T(x)),$$

then

$$d(T^{n+1}(x), T^{n+2}(x)) = d(T(T^n(x)), T(T^{n+1}(x)))$$
$$\leqslant kd(T^n(x), T^{n+1}(x)) \leqslant k^{n+1} d(x, T(x)).$$

By induction we have $d(T^n(x), T^{n+1}(x)) \leqslant k^n d(x, T(x))$ for all positive integers n.

Now the triangle inequality implies that

$$d(T^n(x), T^{n+r}(x)) \leqslant d(T^n(x), T^{n+1}(x)) + d(T^{n+1}(x), T^{n+2}(x))$$
$$+ \cdots + d(T^{n+r-1}(x), T^{n+r}(x))$$
$$\leqslant k^n d(x, T(x)) + k^{n+1} d(x, T(x))$$
$$+ \cdots + k^{n+r-1} d(x, T(x))$$
$$= [d(x, T(x))][k^n + k^{n+1} + \cdots + k^{n+r-1}].$$

The familiar method of summing a geometric series shows that

$$k^n + k^{n+1} + \cdots + k^{n+r-1} = k^n \frac{1-k^r}{1-k} \leqslant \frac{k^n}{1-k},$$

thus

$$d(T^n(x), T^{n+r}(x)) \leqslant \frac{k^n}{1-k} d(x, T(x)).$$

Since $k < 1$, there is an integer N such that

$$\frac{k^N}{1-k} d(x, T(x)) < \varepsilon$$

for any given positive ε, and then $d(T^n(x), T^m(x)) < \varepsilon$ when $n, m \geqslant N$. Hence $[T^n(x)]$ is a Cauchy sequence and so converges to some point z_0 of X.

Now $[T^n(x)]$ converges to z_0 and T is clearly continuous (an exercise), so $[T(T^n(x))]$ converges to $T(z_0)$. But $[T(T^n(x))]$ is a subsequence of $[T^n(x)]$ and so must converge to z_0. Thus $T(z_0) = z_0$, so that z_0 is a fixed point of T.

If we also have $T(y) = y$, then $d(z_0, y) = d(T(z_0), T(y)) \leqslant k d(z_0, y)$. Since $k < 1$, this implies that $d(z_0, y) = 0$, so that z_0 is the unique fixed point of T. ∎

Our application of this result to differential equations is typical of a very useful method of proof in the theory of functions. In general, it consists of the following steps: (a) pick or construct a nice (usually complete) space of functions, (b) rephrase the problem in terms of properties of that space, and (c) apply known results to verify these properties. The reader will be able to pick out these steps in the next proof without any difficulty and will be asked to carry them out himself in the exercises.

Theorem 4.4.2 (Picard's Existence Theorem for Differential Equations)
Let $f(x, y)$ be a continuous function from an open subset U of R^2 into R satisfying $|f(x, y_1) - f(x, y_2)| \leqslant L|y_1 - y_2|$ for a fixed number L whenever $(x, y_1), (x, y_2)$ are in U. Let (x_0, y_0) be any point of U. Then there is an interval $(x_0 - a, x_0 + a)$ and a unique real-valued function $y(x)$ defined on $(x_0 - a, x_0 + a)$ satisfying $y(x_0) = y_0$ and $y'(x) = f(x, y(x))$ for $x_0 - a < x < x_0 + a$.

PROOF. Our first step is to pick a nice set of functions. We must insure that $(x, g(x))$ lies in U for x's near x_0 and g in this set, and other restrictions will be seen to be necessary as we go through the proof. First, since U is open, there is a positive r such that $\{z \in R^2 : d(z, (x_0, y_0)) \leqslant r\} \subset U$. This set is closed and bounded in R^2, so let $M - 1 = \max\{f(z) : d(z, (x_0, y_0)) \leqslant r\}$. Choose a positive number a such that $[x_0 - a, x_0 + a] \times [y_0 - Ma, y_0 + Ma] \subset N((x_0, y_0), r)$ and $La < 1$. The space we need is $C([x_0 - a, x_0 + a], [y_0 - Ma, y_0 + Ma])$, which we will denote here by just C. Note that Theorem 3.1.4 says that it is complete under the metric $\rho(f, g) = \max\{|f(x) - g(x)| : x \in [x_0 - a, x_0 + a]\}$.

Our next step is to show that any function $y(x)$ satisfying $y(x_0) = y_0$ and $y'(x) = f(x, y(x))$ for $|x - x_0| \leqslant a$ must lie in C. If $|y(x) - y_0| > Ma$ for some x with $|x - x_0| \leqslant a$, then the Intermediate Value Theorem says that $\{x : |y(x) - y_0| = Ma\}$ is not empty. Since this set is closed in $[x_0 - a, x_0 + a]$, there is an $\bar{x}$ in $[x_0 - a, x_0 + a]$ such that $|y(\bar{x}) - y_0| = Ma$ but $|y(s) - y_0| < Ma$ for s between x_0 and $\bar{x}$. The Mean Value Theorem implies that $|y(\bar{x}) - y_0| = |y(\bar{x}) - y(x_0)| = |y'(s)(\bar{x} - x_0)| \leqslant |y'(s)|a$ for some s between x_0 and $\bar{x}$. But $|y'(s)| = |f(s, y(s))| < M$, since $(s, y(s))$ lies in $\{z : d((x_0, y_0), z) \leqslant r\}$. Hence $|y(\bar{x}) - y_0| < Ma$. This contradiction shows that $|y(x) - y_0| \leqslant Ma$ for all x in $[x_0 - a, x_0 + a]$, so that y belongs to C.

We want to apply the Banach Fixed Point Theorem to C to produce the desired $y(x)$, so we need a contraction mapping on C whose fixed point is precisely the $y(x)$ we are after. So, if $g \in C$, then define $T(g)$ by $T(g)(x) = y_0 + \int_{x_0}^x f(t, g(t)) dt$ for $|x - x_0| \leqslant a$. Note first that since f and g are continuous, the integral exists. Further, if $T(g) = g$, then $g(x) = y_0 + \int_{x_0}^x f(t, g(t)) dt$, so that $g(x_0) = y_0$ and $g'(x) = f(x, g(x))$ by the Fundamental Theorem of Calculus. It is easy to check that the converse is also true, so that the fixed points of T (if there are any) are exactly the functions we want. Finally, note that

$$|T(g)(x) - y_0| = \left| \int_{x_0}^x f(t, g(t)) dt \right| \leqslant \left| \int_{x_0}^x |f(t, g(t))| dt \right| \leqslant Ma$$

since $(t, g(t)) \in N((x_0, y_0), r)$ and $|x - x_0| \leqslant a$. Thus $T(g)$ is in C when g is.

We now show that T is a contraction mapping on C. Let g and h be in C and x satisfy $|x - x_0| \leqslant a$. Then

$$|T(g)(x) - T(h)(x)| = \left| \int_{x_0}^x f(t, g(t)) dt - \int_{x_0}^x f(t, h(t)) dt \right|$$

$$\leqslant \left| \int_{x_0}^x |f(t, g(t)) - f(t, h(t))| dt \right|$$

$$\leqslant \left| \int_{x_0}^x L|g(t) - h(t)| dt \right|$$

$$\leqslant \left| \int_{x_0}^x L\rho(g, h) dt \right| \leqslant La\rho(g, h).$$

Thus we have $\rho(T(g), T(h)) = \max\{|T(g)(x) - T(h)(x)| : |x - x_0| \leqslant a\} \leqslant La\rho(g, h)$, and since $La < 1$, T is a contraction mapping.

The Banach Fixed Point Theorem now says that T has a unique fixed point y in C, i.e., there is a unique function $y(x)$ satisfying $y(x_0) = y_0$ and $y'(x) = f(x, y(x))$ for $|x - x_0| \leqslant a$. ∎

Some remarks concerning Theorem 4.4.2 and its proof are in order. In the first place, Banach's Fixed Point Theorem not only certifies the existence of the solution but gives a method for finding it. In fact, one can start with any function $h(x)$ in C, find $T(h)$ either numerically or otherwise, then $T^2(h)$, $T^3(h)$, etc, and this sequence will converge to the desired solution. Secondly, questions regarding the weakening of conditions on the function f and the size of the interval $(x_0 - a, x_0 + a)$ naturally arise. We leave their investigation for the differential equations specialist.

We now change direction rather drastically and show the existence of a continuous nowhere-differentiable function on $[0, 1]$. Such a function was first constructed via an infinite series of functions by K. W. T. Weierstrass in the 1800's. Our approach uses the Baire Category Theorem and thus is more indirect, but it also shows that such functions are plentiful rather than rare.

Theorem 4.4.3 *There is a function from $[0, 1]$ into the real numbers which is continuous on $[0, 1]$ but not differentiable anywhere in $(0, 1)$.*

PROOF. We apply the Baire Category Theorem to the space $C([0, 1])$ by finding a sequence of suitable dense open sets with the property that a function in their intersection cannot be differentiable anywhere. Note that this technique not only shows the existence of the desired function but also proves that these functions are dense in $C([0, 1])$.

For $n = 2, 3, \ldots$ let

$$\mathcal{O}_n = \left\{ g \in C([0, 1]): \text{ for some } h \text{ with } 0 < h \leqslant 1/n, \right.$$

$$\text{either } \left| \frac{g(x - h) - g(x)}{h} \right| > n \quad \text{or} \quad \left| \frac{g(x + h) - g(x)}{h} \right| > n$$

$$\left. \text{for each } x \text{ in } \left[\frac{1}{n}, 1 - \frac{1}{n} \right] \right\}.$$

If f is a function which is differentiable at some point x_0 in $(0, 1)$, then there is an integer n such that x_0 is in $[1/n, 1 - 1/n]$ and $|f'(x_0)| < n$. There is a positive number S such that

$$\left| \frac{f(x_0 + h) - f(x_0)}{h} \right| < n \quad \text{when } 0 < |h| < S.$$

If N is an integer satisfying $N \geq n$ and $1/N < S$, then f cannot be in $\mathcal{O}_N$. Thus $\cap \{\mathcal{O}_n : n = 2, 3, \ldots\}$ consists entirely of continuous nowhere differentiable functions.

In order to apply the Baire Category Theorem to $\{\mathcal{O}_n : n = 2, 3, \ldots\}$ we must show that each $\mathcal{O}_n$ is open and dense in $C([0, 1])$. To attack the first problem, we take any g in $\mathcal{O}_n$. Then for some h_0 in $(0, 1/n]$, either

$$\left| \frac{g(x - h_0) - g(x)}{h_0} \right| > n \quad \text{or} \quad \left| \frac{g(x + h_0) - g(x)}{h_0} \right| > n$$

for each x in $[1/n, 1 - 1/n]$. The function defined for x in $[1/n, 1 - 1/n]$ by

$$M(x) = \max \left\{ \left| \frac{g(x - h_0) - g(x)}{h_0} \right|, \left| \frac{g(x + h_0) - g(x)}{h_0} \right| \right\}$$

is continuous and so has a minimum value, so that there is a positive number γ such that $M(x) > n + \gamma$ for each x in $[1/n, 1 - 1/n]$.

Suppose that $\rho(f, g) < \frac{1}{2} \gamma h_0$. If

$$M(x) = \left| \frac{g(x + h_0) - g(x)}{h_0} \right|,$$

then $|f(x + h_0) - f(x)| = |f(x + h_0) - g(x + h_0) + g(x + h_0) - g(x) + g(x) - f(x)| \geq |g(x + h_0) - g(x)| - |f(x + h_0) - g(x + h_0)| - |g(x) - f(x)| > (n + \gamma) h_0 - \frac{1}{2} \gamma h_0 - \frac{1}{2} \gamma h_0 = n h_0$. Thus

$$\left| \frac{f(x + h_0) - f(x)}{h_0} \right| > n.$$

The same argument works when

$$M(x) = \left| \frac{g(x - h_0) - g(x)}{h_0} \right|,$$

so that either

$$\left| \frac{f(x + h_0) - f(x)}{h_0} \right| > n \quad \text{or} \quad \left| \frac{f(x - h_0) - f(x)}{h_0} \right| > n,$$

so that f belongs to $\mathcal{O}_n$. Since $\mathcal{O}_n$ contains a neighborhood of each of its points, it must be open.

We now show that $\mathcal{O}_n$ is dense in $C([0, 1])$ by constructing a function g which lies in $\mathcal{O}_n$ and in $N(f, \varepsilon)$ for any f in $C([0, 1])$ and positive ε. Since f is continuous on the compact space $[0, 1]$, it is uniformly continuous there, so there is a positive S such that $|f(x) - f(y)| < \varepsilon/4$ whenever $|x - y| < S$. Let m be a positive integer such that $1/m < S$ and $\frac{1}{2} m \varepsilon > n$. Define a function g as follows. Let $g(k/m) = f(k/m)$ and $g((k + \frac{1}{2})/m) = f(k/m) + \varepsilon/2$ for $k = 0, 1, 2, \ldots, m$. Extend g linearly on the intervals $[k/m, (k + \frac{1}{2})/m]$ and

$[(k + \frac{1}{2})/m, (k+1)/m]$. On $[k/m, (k + \frac{1}{2})/m]$ the function g is linear with slope $(\varepsilon/2)/(1/2m) = m\varepsilon > n$. On $[(k + \frac{1}{2})/m, (k+1)/m]$ the function g is linear with slope $[f((k+1)/m) - f(k/m) - \varepsilon/2]/(1/2m)$. Now

$$|f((k+1)/m) - f(k/m)| < \varepsilon/4,$$

so in absolute value this slope exceeds $(\varepsilon/4)/(1/2m) = m\varepsilon/2 > n$. The usual piecewise argument shows that g is continuous. Further, taking $h = 1/5m$ shows that g belongs to $\mathcal{O}_n$.

Suppose that x belongs to $[k/m, (k+1)/m]$. By linearity, $g(x)$ lies in the interval

$$\left[\min\left\{ f\left(\frac{k}{m}\right), f\left(\frac{k+1}{m}\right), f\left(\frac{k}{m}\right) + \frac{\varepsilon}{2} \right\}, \max\left\{ f\left(\frac{k}{m}\right), f\left(\frac{k+1}{m}\right), f\left(\frac{k}{m}\right) + \frac{\varepsilon}{2} \right\} \right],$$

as does $f(k/m)$. Since $|f(k/m) - f((k+1)/m)| \leqslant \varepsilon/4$, this interval has length less than $3\varepsilon/4$. Thus $|g(x) - f(x)| = |g(x) - f(k/m) + f(k/m) - f(x)| \leqslant |g(x) - f(k/m)| + |f(k/m) - f(x)| < 3\varepsilon/4 + \varepsilon/4 = \varepsilon$. Hence g is in $N(f, \varepsilon)$, so that $\mathcal{O}_n$ is dense in $C([0,1])$.

The Baire Category Theorem now says that $D = \cap\{\mathcal{O}_n : n = 2, 3, \dots\}$ is dense in $C([0,1])$, so that $C([0,1])$ contains a dense set of functions with derivatives at no point x in $(0,1)$. ■

There are many similar applications of the Baire Category Theorem elsewhere in topology and/or analysis, some of which appear here as exercises. It is a favorite technique for showing the existence of objects with certain properties. Note also that by following the proof of the Baire Category Theorem itself one can obtain the desired object (in the above case, a continuous nowhere differentiable function) as a limit of usually directly constructible objects.

Exercises

1. Prove that a contraction mapping is continuous.

2. a. The *irrational punch* is a device which when centered at the point (a, b) of R^2 and struck, punches out or destroys all points of R^2 at irrational distance from (a, b). How many times must we use the irrational punch in order to destroy the entire plane? Justify your answer.

  b. Define a *rational punch*. How many times must we use the rational punch in order to destroy the entire plane? Justify your answer.

3. *The Uniform Boundedness Theorem*: Let $\mathcal{F}$ be a collection of continuous real-valued functions on a complete metric space X with the property that for each $x \in X$ there is a number M_x such that $|f(x)| \leqslant M_x$ for each $f \in \mathcal{F}$. Then there is a non-empty open subset of O of X and a number M such that $|f(x)| \leqslant M$ for each $f \in \mathcal{F}$ and each $x \in O$. Hint: apply Theorem 3.1.6 to $N_i = \{x \in X : |f(x)| \leqslant i$ for each $f \in \mathcal{F}\}$.

4. Let $K(x,y,z)$ be a continuous real-valued function defined on $[0,1]\times[0,1]\times[-1,1]$ and satisfying $|K(x,y,z)-K(x,y,z')|\leqslant c|z-z'|$ for some constant c. Prove that there is a positive number δ such that for each $\lambda, 0\leqslant\lambda\leqslant\delta$, there is a function $u(x)$ satisfying $u(x)=\lambda\int_0^1 K(x,t,u(t))dt$ for $0\leqslant x\leqslant 1$. Hint: apply the techniques of the proof of Theorem 4.4.2 to T_λ, where $T_\lambda(u)(x)=\lambda\int_0^1 K(x,t,u(t))dt$.

5. This exercise consists of a step-by-step proof of the following version of the Implicit Function Theorem. Let $F(x,y)$ be a continuous real-valued function defined on $[x_0-a,x_0+a]\times[y_0-b,y_0+b]$ such that $F(x_0,y_0)=0$ and $|F(x,y)-F(x,y')|\leqslant k|y-y'|$ for a fixed $k<1$. Then there is a positive S and a unique continuous function h from $[x_0-S,x_0+S]$ to $[y_0-b,y_0+b]$ such that $h(x_0)=y_0$ and $h(x)=y_0+F(x,h(x))$ for $|x-x_0|\leqslant S$.
a. Prove that there is a positive S such that $|F(x,y_0)|\leqslant b(1-k)$ for $|x-x_0|\leqslant S$.
b. Define T by $T(\phi)(x)=y_0+F(x,\phi(x))$. Prove that $|y_0-T(\phi)(x)|\leqslant b$ for $|x-x_0|\leqslant S$.
c. Prove that T is a contraction mapping on $C([x_0-S,x_0+S],[y_0-b,y_0+b])$.
d. Prove the version of the Implicit Function Theorem given above.

6. In this exercise we give a proof of the following version of the Implicit Function Theorem: Let $G(x,y)$ be a continuous real-valued function on $\mathcal{R}=[x_0-A,x_0+A]\times[y_0-B,y_0+B]$ such that $G(x_0,y_0)=0$ and $\dfrac{\partial G}{\partial y}(x,y)=G_y(x,y)$ exists on $\mathcal{R}$ and is continuous with $G_y(x_0,y_0)\neq0$. Then there is a positive S and a unique continuous function h from $[x_0-S,x_0+S]$ to $[y_0-B,y_0+B]$ such that $h(x_0)=y_0$ and $G(x,h(x))=0$ for $|x-x_0|\leqslant S$.
a. Prove that there are positive numbers a and b such that

$$\left|1-\frac{G_y(x,y)}{2G_y(x_0,y_0)}\right|\leqslant\frac{3}{4}\quad\text{for}\quad|x-x_0|\leqslant a\quad\text{and}\quad|y-y_0|\leqslant b.$$

b. Use the Mean Value Theorem to prove that $F(x,y)=y-y_0-G(x,y)/2G_y(x_0,y_0)$ satisfies the hypotheses of the version of the Implicit Function Theorem in Exercise 5.
c. Complete the proof of this version of the Implicit Function Theorem.

5

Winding numbers and their applications

In this chapter we will use some of the tools we developed in Chapter 2 to investigate properties of continuous functions from the circle or the unit interval [0, 1] into the plane. Our treatment will be as rigorous as possible, but maintaining complete mathematical precision would in places lead us very far afield. Hence we will sometimes rely on intuition and pictures. All theorems are true as stated, regardless of how much hand-waving is done in the proof.

5.1 Definition of winding number and the fundamental theorem

The basic question that we wish to consider can be phrased intuitively as follows. If f is a continuous function from the circle into the plane R^2, then how many times does f wrap the circle around a given point p? The answer to this question will be called the *winding number* of f. It is clear that the question is meaningless if p happens to be in the image of the circle under f. It also turns out that in most applications the origin $(0,0)$ of R^2 plays an important role. Thus we will require that the image of the circle under f miss the origin $(0,0)$, and we will ask how many times f wraps the circle around $(0,0)$.

To fix these ideas we have drawn several images of a circle under a continuous function in the following examples, and have stated what the winding numbers are in each case.

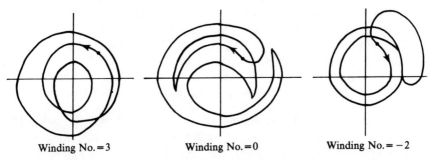

Winding No. = 3   Winding No. = 0   Winding No. = −2

Consideration of the space-filling curves of Chapter 4 shows that defining the winding number of a function may not be easy. There are several approaches that may be taken; we have chosen one that relies as much as possible on topological tools.

The motivation for our definition of winding number derives from the following picture, in which is shown the image of the unit circle under a function *f* from the circle into the plane.

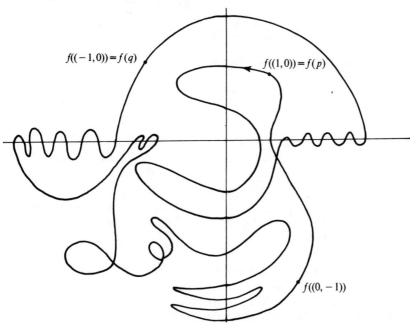

Since the image of the part of the circle from $(1,0)$ to $(-1,0)$ does not meet the negative x-axis, it contributes only the angle subtended by the line segment from $f(p)$ to $f(q)$ to the winding around $(0,0)$. If it had hit the negative x-axis, then it may have contributed this amount plus a non-zero multiple of 2π. Similar remarks hold for the parts of the circle from $(-1,0)$ to $(0,-1)$ and from $(0,-1)$ to $(1,0)$. We can thus find the winding number of f by adding the three angles thus obtained and then dividing by 2π. It is this procedure which we will carry out in the general case.

It turns out to be somewhat easier technically to define and use winding numbers for functions from a square into the plane. The exercises will contain an outline of how to make our definitions and theorems more general. To facilitate the discussion we introduce some notation.

Definition We use D to denote the square $\{(x,y)\in R^2:\max\{|x|,|y|\}\leqslant 1\}$ and Σ to denote its boundary, i.e., $\Sigma=\{(x,y)\in R^2:\max\{|x|,|y|\}=1\}$. We let $R^+=\{(x,y)\in R^2:y=0$ and $x\geqslant 0\}$ and $R^-=\{(x,y)\in R^2:y=0$ and $x\leqslant 0\}$. The *punctured plane* is the set $\tilde{R}^2=R^2\backslash\{(0,0)\}$. We define the function P from $[0,1]$ into Σ by

$$
P(t) = \begin{cases}
(1,8t-1) & 0\leqslant t\leqslant \frac{1}{4} \\
(3-8t,1) & \frac{1}{4}\leqslant t\leqslant \frac{1}{2} \\
(-1,5-8t) & \frac{1}{2}\leqslant t\leqslant \frac{3}{4} \\
(8t-7,-1) & \frac{3}{4}\leqslant t\leqslant 1.
\end{cases}
$$

Finally, a *subdivision* of $[0,1]$ is a list of numbers $x_0,x_1,x_2,\ldots,x_n$ such that $0=x_0<x_1<x_2<\cdots<x_n=1$. The interval $[x_{i-1},x_i]$, $i=1,2,\ldots,n$, is called a *subinterval* of the subdivision.

Theorem 5.1.1 *Let f be a continuous function from Σ into the punctured plane. Then there is a subdivision of $[0,1]$ such that the image under $f\circ P$ of any of its subintervals misses either R^+ or R^-.*

PROOF. Suppose no such subdivision exists. Then in particular a subdivision of $[0,1]$ into n congruent intervals does not work, so there is an interval $[p,q]$ of length $1/n$ such that $f(P([p,q]))$ meets both R^+ and R^-. Thus for each positive integer n there are points x_n,y_n in $[0,1]$ such that $f(P(x_n))\in R^-$, $f(P(y_n))\in R^+$, and $d(x_n,y_n)<1/n$. Since $[0,1]$ is compact, there is a subsequence $[x_{n_j}]$ of $[x_n]$ that converges to the point x_0 of $[0,1]$. Since $d(x_n,y_n)<1/n$, it is easy to show that the subsequence $[y_{n_j}]$ of $[y_n]$ also converges to x_0.

The function $f\circ P$ is continuous, so that $f(P(x_{n_j}))\to f(P(x_0))$ and $f(P(Y_{n_j}))\to f(P(x_0))$. Now R^- is closed and $f(P(x_{n_j}))\in R^-$ for all i, so $f(P(x_0))\in R^-$. Similarly, $f(P(x_0))\in R^+$, and hence $f(P(x_0))\in R^+\cap R^-=\{(0,0)\}$, that is, $f(P(x_0))=(0,0)$. This contradicts the fact that f is a function into the punctured plane and hence establishes the theorem. ∎

We are now in a position to define the winding number of a continuous function from Σ into the punctured plane.

Definition Let f be a continuous function from Σ into the punctured plane. Let $x_0,x_1,\ldots,x_r$ be a subdivision of $[0,1]$ having the properties set forth in the last theorem. Let α_i be the radian measure of the angle obtained by rotating the line segment $[(0,0),f(P(x_{i-1}))]$ to the line segment $[(0,0),f(P(x_i))]$ while missing that one of R^+, R^- missed by $f(P([x_{i-1},x_i]))$, where as usual α_i is positive if this rotation is counterclockwise and negative otherwise. The *winding number of f* is then $w(f)=(1/2\pi)\Sigma^r_{i=1}\alpha_i$.

Some comments are in order before examples. First, since $f(P(0))=f(P(1))$, $\Sigma^r_{i=1}\alpha_i$ will be a multiple of 2π, so that $w(f)$ is always an integer. Second, suppose that we form a new subdivision of $[0,1]$ by inserting a point t between x_{i-1} and x_i, and use this new subdivision to compute the winding number of f. This new computation differs from the old only in that the angle α_i is replaced by angles formed by $f(P(x_{i-1}))$, $(0,0)$, $f(P(t))$ and $f(P(t))$, $(0,0)$, $f(P(x_i))$. The sum of the latter two angles is clearly α_i, so that both computations yield the same $w(f)$. By induction any subdivision formed in this way by adding more subdividing points yields the same $w(f)$. Since any two subdivisions of $[0,1]$ have a common "sub-subdivision" formed by taking all the points in either subdivision, we see that any two subdivisions (satisfying the conditions in the last theorem, of course) yield the same $w(f)$.

EXAMPLES.

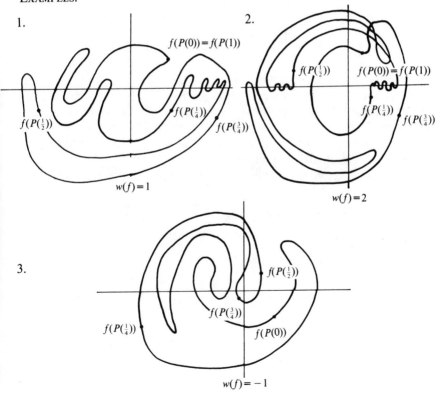

151

Notice that the *direction of traversal* or *orientation* of $f(\Sigma)$ is important. Changing the orientation clearly changes the sign of $w(f)$.

We are now ready to prove the Fundamental Winding Number Theorem, which is the result we will use in all the applications. Some of the techniques are very similar to those used in the proof of Theorem 5.1.1, so the details will be left as exercises.

Theorem 5.1.2 **(Fundamental Winding Number Theorem)** *If f is a continuous function from the square D into the punctured plane, then the winding number of f on Σ, i.e., of $f|\Sigma$, is zero.*

PROOF. The illustration shows a subdivision of D such that the image of any pair of adjacent small squares under f misses either R^+ or R^-.

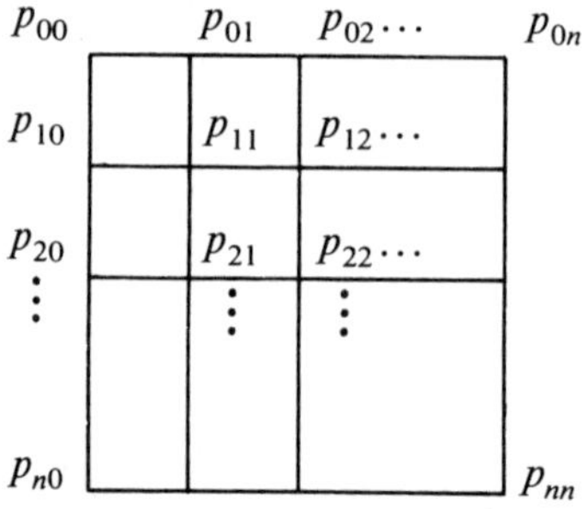

The existence of such a subdivision is guaranteed by methods similar to those in the proof of Theorem 5.1.1 (see Exercise 5). If p_{ij} and p_{rk} are adjacent corner points, then by $\alpha(p_{ij},p_{rk})$ we denote the radian measure of the angle formed by rotating the line segment $[(0,0),f(p_{ij})]$ to the line segment $[(0,0),f(p_{rk})]$ while missing that one of R^+, R^- missed by the image of all the squares containing both p_{ij} and p_{rk}.

Since the image of any small square under f misses either R^+ or R^-, it is easy to see that

$$\alpha(p_{ij},p_{i+1,j}) + \alpha(p_{i+1,j},p_{i+1,j+1}) + \alpha(p_{i+1,j+1},p_{i,j+1}) + \alpha(p_{i,j+1},p_{ij})$$

must be zero. Thus we have, in particular, that

$$\alpha(p_{00},p_{10}) + \alpha(p_{10},p_{11}) + \alpha(p_{11},p_{01}) + \alpha(p_{01},p_{00}) = 0$$

and

$$\alpha(p_{01},p_{11}) + \alpha(p_{11},p_{12}) + \alpha(p_{12},p_{02}) + \alpha(p_{02},p_{01}) = 0.$$

Now $\alpha(p_{11},p_{01}) = -\alpha(p_{01},p_{11})$, so taking the sum yields

$$\alpha(p_{00},p_{10}) + \alpha(p_{10},p_{11}) + \alpha(p_{11},p_{12}) + \alpha(p_{12},p_{02}) +$$
$$\alpha(p_{02},p_{01}) + \alpha(p_{01},p_{00}) = 0.$$

We can now add in a third square sharing a side with one of the first two, then a fourth sharing a side with one of the first three, etc. The angular contributions of the "inner" line segments all cancel, just as did $\alpha(p_{11}, p_{01})$ and $\alpha(p_{01}, p_{11})$ in the first step. Thus the sum of the angular contributions of the "outer" line segments is zero. The images under P^{-1} of the outer corner points clearly form a suitable subdivision of $[0, 1]$, and the sum of the angles involved in computing $w(f)$ is clearly zero. Thus $w(f) = 0$. ∎

Exercises

1. Compute the winding numbers of the following functions from Σ into $\tilde{R}^2$:
   a. A constant function
   b. The function f such that $f(P(t)) = (\cos 2\pi n t, \sin 2\pi n t)$, where n is an integer
   c. The identity function on Σ.

2. Supply all the details for the proof that any two subdivisions of $[0, 1]$ satisfying the conclusion of Theorem 5.1.1 for a function f yield the same winding number for f.

3. Prove that if $f(\Sigma)$ misses either R^+ or R^-, then $w(f) = 0$.

4. Let S be any 1-sphere, i.e., any space homeomorphic to Σ, and f a continuous function from S into the punctured plane.
   a. Prove that if h_1, h_2 are any two homeomorphisms of Σ onto S, then $|w(f \circ h_1)| = |w(f \circ h_2)|$, so that $w(f)$ is well defined up to sign.
   b. Following (a), give an example to show that $w(f \circ h_1)$ may not equal $w(f \circ h_2)$.

5. a. Prove that if f is a continuous function from D into the punctured plane, then there is a positive ε such that $f(A)$ misses either R^+ or R^- whenever $A \subset D$ and diam $A < \varepsilon$.
   b. Define what is to be meant by a subdivision of D, and prove that one exists satisfying the requirement stated in the proof of Theorem 5.1.2.

6. Prove that the function h defined by

$$h((x,y)) = \begin{cases} \dfrac{\max\{|x|, |y|\}}{\sqrt{x^2 + y^2}}(x,y) & (x,y) \neq (0,0) \\ (0,0) & (x,y) = (0,0) \end{cases}$$

is a homeomorphism taking D onto $B^2 = \{(x,y) \in R^2 : x^2 + y^2 \leq 1\}$ and Σ onto $S^1 = \{(x,y) \in R^2 : x^2 + y^2 = 1\}$.

5.2 Retracts and fixed points

In this section we use winding numbers to prove the two-dimensional versions of some classical theorems. Some of the ideas presented here have appeared earlier in this text, but for convenience we repeat the definitions.

Definition A subspace A of a space X is a *retract* of X if there is a continuous function $r : X \to A$ such that $r(a) = a$ for each $a \in A$. The function r is called a *retraction*.

Definition Let f be a function from a set X to itself. The point x is called a *fixed point* of f if $f(x) = x$. A space X is said to have the *fixed point property* if every continuous function from X to itself has a fixed point.

It is not hard to show that the fixed point property is a topological property of the space X. The *retraction property* can be thought of as a property of the pair of spaces X, A, but simple examples show that of two homeomorphic subspaces of a space X, it may happen that exactly one is a retract of X. We leave proofs for the exercises and refer the reader to Section 3.3 for more information.

It may be surprising that there is a close connection between retractions and the fixed point property. The next theorem is the first indication of this, and the other results in this section support the point.

Theorem 5.2.1 *If A is a retract of X and X has the fixed point property, then so does A.*

PROOF. Let f be a continuous function from A to itself and r a retraction from X to A. Then $f \circ r$ is a continuous function from X to itself and so has a fixed point x. Thus $f(r(x)) = x$. Now $r(x)$ is in A, so that $x = f(r(x))$ is in A. Since r is a retraction, $r(x) = x$, so that $x = f(r(x)) = f(x)$. ∎

As we have done before, we now investigate the relationships between these ideas and our familiar spaces, the n-balls and n-spheres (see Section 4.3 for definitions). One can use properties of connectedness to prove that S^0 is not a retract of B^1 and also that B^1 has the fixed point property (see the exercises). Our next project is to verify these results for S^1 and B^2.

Exercise 6 from Section 5.1 shows that we can deal with D and Σ rather than B^2 and S^1, so that the theory of winding numbers is directly applicable. Our first result was formulated by the Polish topologist K. Borsuk in 1931, although his work was considerably more general.

Theorem 5.2.2 **(Borsuk Nonretraction Theorem)** Σ *is not a retract of D.*

PROOF. Suppose that the theorem is false and that r is a retraction from D onto Σ. Then r is a continuous function from D into the punctured plane, so that the Fundamental Winding Number Theorem says that the winding number of $r|\Sigma$ is zero. But r is the identity function on Σ, so that Exercise 1 of Section 5.1 says that its winding number is 1. This contradiction establishes the theorem. ∎

Some comments are pertinent here. First, the S^0, B^1 case of this theorem is proved using connectedness, which leads us to regard winding numbers as a higher-dimensional version of connectedness. Further study would lend support to this point of view. In fact, the Borsuk Nonretraction Theorem holds in all dimensions, and it is precisely the higher dimensional versions of connectedness that are used in most proofs. Also, we should emphasize that our statement of the Borsuk Nonretraction Theorem immediately implies that the same property holds for S^1 and B^2.

We now turn to the fixed point property and its relationship with the existence or nonexistence of retractions. The next theorem was first proved by Brouwer in 1910 for balls of arbitrary finite dimension. Our machinery is restricted to dimension 2.

Theorem 5.2.3 (Brouwer Fixed Point Theorem) *The two-dimensional ball* B^2 *has the fixed point property.*

PROOF. Suppose that f is a continuous function from B^2 to itself which does not have a fixed point. We will use f to define a retraction from B^2 to S^1. Since $f(p) \neq p$ for all p in B^2, we can always define $r(p)$ by drawing the ray from $f(p)$ through p and letting $r(p)$ be the point at which this ray meets S^1. It is intuitively clear that this r is a retraction from B^2 to S^1. However, to be more precise, some analytic geometry shows that there is a continuous function α of p such that $\alpha(p)p + (1 - \alpha(p))f(p)$ lies on S^1 for each p and $\alpha(p) = 1$ when p lies on S^1. If we define $\alpha(p)p + (1 - \alpha(p))f(p)$ to be $r(p)$, then r will be a retraction from B^2 to S^1. This contradiction shows that f must have a fixed point. We leave the analytical details for the exercises. ∎

There is the following nonmathematical version of the Brouwer Fixed Point Theorem which is interesting to consider.

Crumpled Map Theorem *Trace a map. Crumple the copy and drop it back inside the original. Then some point on the copy is directly above the corresponding point on the original.*

PROOF. Regard the map as a disk. The function which takes a point of the original map to the copy, then crumpled, then directly down to the original is a continuous function, and so has a fixed point. By construction of the function this fixed point lies directly below its corresponding point on the copy. ∎

Before we leave the subject of fixed points, we state an old unsolved problem of topology. Perhaps a lucky reader will someday find the solution.

Problem

Does every compact connected set in R^2 which does not disconnect R^2 have the fixed point property?

Exercises

1. Prove that S^0 is not a retract of B^1.

2. Prove that B^1 has the fixed point property.

3. Prove that the fixed point property is topological.

4. Supply all the details in the proof of the Brouwer Fixed Point Theorem.

5. Prove that the Brouwer Fixed Point Theorem and the Borsuk Nonretraction Theorem are equivalent.

6. Prove that R^n does not have the fixed point property.

7. Prove that S^n does not have the fixed point property.

8. Prove that B^n is a retract of R^n.

9. An *n-od* is any space homeomorphic to the planar set $\cup\{[(0,0),(1,1/i)]:i= 1,2,\ldots,n\}$. Prove that an n-od has the fixed point property.

10. Find an example of a space X and two subspaces A and B such that A and B are homeomorphic but A is a retract of X while B is not.

11. Repeat Exercise 10 with the added condition that X and A both be connected.

12. Prove that if A is a retract of X and h is a homeomorphism of X onto Y such that $h(A)=B$, then B is a retract of Y.

5.3 Vector fields

This section furnishes us with a peek at a wide and important area of mathematics lying between topology and analysis. It has very close ties to differential equations, in fact, the whole theory of differential equations can be formulated in terms of the following concept.

Definition A *continuous vector field* on the k-sphere S^k is a continuous function $f:S^k \rightarrow R^{k+1}$ such that $f(x) \cdot x = 0$ for all $x \in S^k$. The vector space structure of R^{k+1} is used here, and "$\cdot$" represents inner product.

The reader should recall that two vectors having inner product zero are said to be perpendicular or orthogonal. Further, pictures or some several-variable calculus show that if f is a continuous vector field on S^k then $f(x)+x$ lies in the tangent plane to S^k at x. Thus a continuous vector field f should be thought of as a function which attaches a tangent vector $f(x)$ to S^k at the point x, and this tangent vector varies continuously in length and direction with x. This idea easily generalizes to spaces other than S^k, though the analytical details are a bit formidable and would lead us far astray from the main course of this book.

The alert reader will remark that *angle, perpendicular* and *tangent* are not topological properties. He is absolutely correct. These are differential properties rather than topological properties, and this fact forces us to do some hand-waving in this section in order to avoid a long digression into the study of "differential" ideas. However, be assured that our results and techniques can be made rigorous, and that enough topology enters the picture to justify the inclusion of this material in a topology text like this. Note that every sphere S^k has a continuous vector field, namely, the vector field $f(x) = \theta$ (throughout this section θ will denote the zero vector) for all x in S^k. However, this is certainly not of much interest. A more interesting question arises when we ask if there is a continuous vector field on S^k with no zeros whatsoever, that is, no points x in S^k for which $f(x) = \theta$.

EXAMPLE

4. For $(r,s) \in S^1$, define $f((r,s)) = (s, -r)$. Then $(r,s) \cdot f((r,s)) = (r,s) \cdot (s, -r)$ $= rs + (-rs) = 0$. Further, since (r,s) is never $(0,0)$ when $(r,s) \in S^1$, neither is $(s, -r)$, so that f is a continuous vector field on S^1 without zeros.

Theorem 5.3.1 (Vector Field Theorem for S^2) *There is no continuous vector field on S^2 without zeros.*

PROOF. Let f be a continuous vector field on S^2 such that there is a point $p \in S^2$ with $f(p) \neq \theta$. Since f is continuous, there is a small curved disk on S^2 with center p such that $|f(x) - f(p)| < \min\{0.0000001, |f(p)|/2\}$ for all x in the disk. Flatten this small curved disk, at the same time carrying along the tangent vectors that f attaches. The small disk plus attached vectors then looks like this:

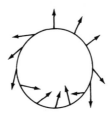

Now peel off the remainder of the sphere and deform it into a large disk, again at the same time carrying along the tangent vectors that f attaches. By using the small disk to check the part of the sphere into which the vectors point, we can construct the following picture of the large disk:

157

If these vectors are translated so that their tails are at the origin, we see that the image under f of the circle which is the boundary of the large disk is

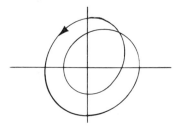

so that the winding number of f on the boundary of the large disk is 2. If f had no zero in the large disk, then by the Fundamental Winding Number Theorem the winding number would be zero. Hence f has a zero and we have established the theorem. ∎

The Vector Field Theorem for S^2 has the following nice corollaries.

Corollary 5.3.2 *The wind cannot blow everywhere at once.*

Corollary 5.3.3 *You cannot comb the hair on a coconut without a cowlick.*

In Corollary 1 the surface of the earth is regarded as S^2, and the wind velocity at point x yields a continuous vector field which must have a zero. Then this zero is a point at which the wind is not blowing. In Corollary 2 the surface of a coconut is regarded as S^2, and we suppose that each point on the surface has hair attached. If these hairs could be combed without a cowlick, then the hairs would form a continuous vector field without a zero.

The "differential" ideas which lie behind the proper formulation of the results in this section do not apply to all spaces. In essence, they apply only to spaces which are manifolds, that is, which are locally like R^n (see the exercises for Section 4.3). These ideas can be tied very closely to topological concepts; in fact, a pretty result called Hopf's Theorem tells precisely which spaces have continuous vector fields without zeros, and does this in terms of the higher-dimensional connectedness properties that winding number expresses in dimension two. Unfortunately, this theorem is well beyond the scope of this book.

We conclude this section by stating without proof a further result concerning vector fields on spheres. If $f_1, f_2, \ldots, f_r$ are continuous vector fields on S^n then we say that $f_1, f_2, \ldots, f_r$ are *linearly independent* if for each x the vectors $f_1(x), f_2(x), \ldots, f_r(x)$ are linearly independent. It is of some interest to determine the maximum number of linearly independent vector fields on S^n for each n. In 1962 work was finally completed on the following composite result. The numbers involved are somewhat surprising.

Theorem 5.3.4

1. If n is even, then every continuous vector field on S^n has a zero.
2. If n is odd, then find integers a, c and d such that $n + 1 = (2a + 1)$ (2^{c+4d}), where $0 \leqslant c \leqslant 3$. Then the maximum number of linearly independent continuous vector fields on S^n is $2^c + 8d - 1$.

Exercises

1. Prove that if n is odd, then S^n has a continuous vector field without a zero.

2. Explain where the proof of the Vector Field Theorem for S^2 uses nontopological methods.

3. Tell what the maximum number of linearly independent continuous vector fields is for
   a. S^1
   b. S^3
   c. S^{20}
   d. S^{27}
   e. S^{2^q-1}.

4. a. Does the surface of an inner tube (more precisely, $S^1 \times S^1$) have a continuous vector field without a zero?
   b. What is the maximum number of linearly independent continuous vector fields on the surface of an inner tube?

5.4 The Borsuk–Ulam Theorem and the Ham Sandwich Theorem

In this section we use winding numbers to prove the Borsuk–Ulam Theorem, which was first established in 1933. As has been the case with other results in this chapter, an analogous theorem holds in all dimensions. We then use the Borsuk–Ulam Theorem to prove the Ham Sandwich Theorem, which again generalizes to higher dimensions. The reason for the terminology will be evident! Neither of these theorems is strictly topological, but we leave it to the reader to ascertain why. As we have consistently in this chapter, we use vector space notation and terminology.

Theorem 5.4.1 (Borsuk–Ulam Theorem) Let f and g be two continuous real-valued functions on the 2-sphere S^2. There is a point x_0 of S^2 such that $f(x_0) = f(-x_0)$ and $g(x_0) = g(-x_0)$.

PROOF. In order to use winding numbers, we need a function into the plane. Not only that, but we must make $(0,0)$ a point of significance. Thus we define a function G from S^2 into R^2 by $G(x)=(f(x),g(x))-(f(-x),g(-x))$. Results from Section 2.4, in particular, Theorem 2.4.4 and Exercise 6, imply that G is continuous. If we can find a point x_0 such that $G(x_0)=(0,0)$, then we will be done, since $G(x_0)=(0,0)$ implies that $f(x)-f(-x_0)=0=g(x_0)-g(-x_0)$, i.e., $f(x_0)=f(-x_0)$ and $g(x_0)=g(-x_0)$.

Let h be the function from Exercise 6 of Section 5.1 which takes D homeomorphically onto $B^2=\{(x,y)\in R^2:x^2+y^2\leqslant 1\}$, and let $k((x,y))=(x,y,\sqrt{1-x^2-y^2}\,)$. It is easy to check that $k\circ h$ is a homeomorphism from D onto the northern hemisphere of S^2, so that $G'=G\circ k\circ h$ is a continuous function from D into R^2. Suppose that the theorem is false, so that G and hence G' never takes the value $(0,0)$. Then G' is a continuous function into the punctured plane so we can consider the winding number of G' on Σ. By the Fundamental Winding Number Theorem this must be zero.

We now calculate $w(G'|\Sigma)$. First note that if $(x,y)\in\Sigma$, then $(-x,-y)\in\Sigma$, $h((x,y))$, $h((-x,-y))$ are both points of S^1, and $h((x,y))=-h((-x,-y))$. An easy calculation then shows that $G'((-x,-y))=-G'((x,y))$. To calculate $w(G'|\Sigma)$, we use a subdivision of $[0,1]$ which P (remember that P is the function from $[0,1]$ onto Σ defined in Section 5.1) carries into a set on Σ which is symmetric with respect to the origin and contains $(1,0)$.

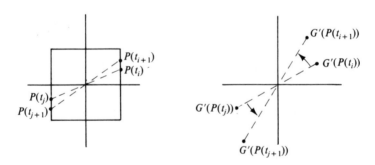

The accompanying diagram illustrates the fact that since $G'((-x,-y))=-G'((x,y))$, the same angular change occurs on any two subintervals which P carries into subsets of Σ which are symmetric with respect to $(0,0)$. Since $G'((1,0))=-G'((-1,0))$, the net angular change of G' on the upper half of Σ is an odd number of π's. The net angular change of G' on the lower half of Σ is the same odd number of π's, so the total net angular change of G' on Σ is an odd number of 2π's. Hence the winding number of G' on Σ is odd and cannot be zero. This contradiction establishes the theorem. ∎

Before we turn to more substantive matters, we continue the study of meteorology which we began in Section 5.3. We remind the reader that *antipodal points* on a standard sphere are points which are symmetric with respect to the center of the sphere.

Corollary 5.4.2 *At any given time there are two antipodal points on the earth with the same temperature and relative humidity.*

PROOF. Regard the earth as S^2. Then temperature and relative humidity are two continuous real-valued functions on S^2. The Borsuk–Ulam Theorem now delivers the two antipodal points. ∎

Our next application is the result which is popularly (among mathematicians) called the Ham Sandwich Theorem. It deals with subsets of R^3 and their volumes, so we state here without proof some of the facts regarding the volume function. If the volume of a set K is defined (it isn't for every set, but we needn't worry about that here), then we will denote it by $V(K)$. The function V has the properties that a volume function should have, in particular:

1. If $K \subset L$ and $V(K)$, $V(L)$ are defined, then $V(K) \leqslant V(L)$;
2. The volume of a rectangular solid is always defined;
3. If $V(K)$ and $V(L)$ are defined, then so are $V(K \cap L)$ and $V(K \cup L)$;
4. If M is a planar set with area $A(M)$, then $V(M \times [a,b]) = (b-a)A(M)$.

With this background we can state our result. Its proof consists primarily of the several lemmas which follow.

Theorem 5.4.3 (Ham Sandwich Theorem) *Let B_1, B_2, and H be three bounded subsets of R^3 whose volumes are defined. Then there is a plane which simultaneously divides each of the regions B_1, B_2, and H into two regions of equal volume.*

The lemmas we need deal with the relationships between volume, planes, and half-spaces. The reader needs a small knowledge of the analytic and vector geometry of R^3.

To emphasize the vector aspects of our statements, we use $\bar{x}$ to distinguish the vector $\bar{x}$ from a real number like t. Further, when $\bar{x}$ is a non-zero vector and t is any number, then $H(\bar{x},t)$ denotes the half-space of R^3 on the side of the plane perpendicular to $\bar{x}$ through $t\bar{x}$ into which $\bar{x}$ points. *The boundary plane of* $H(\bar{x},t)$ *is the plane perpendicular to* $\bar{x}$ through $t\bar{x}$. Analytically, $H(\bar{x},t) = \{\bar{z} \in R^3 : \bar{z} \cdot \bar{x} \geqslant t\}$.

Lemma 5.4.4 *Let K be a bounded set in R^3 whose volume is defined. Define the function $f: S^2 \times R \to R$ by $f(\bar{x},t) = V(K \cap H(\bar{x},t))$. Then f is continuous.*

PROOF. Since K is bounded, $K \cap H(\bar{x},t)$ is the same as the intersection of K with some rectangular solid, so that $V(K \cap H(\bar{x},t))$ is defined. We want to make $|f(\bar{x},t) - f(\bar{y},s)|$ small. Note that $|f(\bar{x},t) - f(\bar{y},s)| \leqslant |f(\bar{x},t) - f(\bar{x},s)| + |f(\bar{x},s) - f(\bar{y},s)|$. Since K is bounded, there is an M such that $|\bar{z}| \leqslant M$ for each $\bar{z}$ in K. Hence the circular cylinder with radius M and axis any line through $(0,0,0)$ contains K, so that $|f(\bar{x},t) - f(\bar{x},s)| \leqslant \pi M^2 |t - s|$.

We now consider $|f(\bar{x},s) - f(\bar{y},s)|$. If $s \geqslant M$, then $f(\bar{x},s) = f(\bar{y},s) = 0$ and if $s \leqslant -M$, then $f(\bar{x},s) = f(\bar{y},s) = V(K)$. Thus we need to worry about the case in which $|s| < M$. We illustrate the case in which $s > 0$, but the other cases are almost identical.

We can make $d(\bar{x},\bar{y})$ so small that the following figure indicates the cross section of the situation in the plane containing $\bar{x}$ and $\bar{y}$. We use the notation established in the figure, and note that all angles denoted by α can be shown to be congruent.

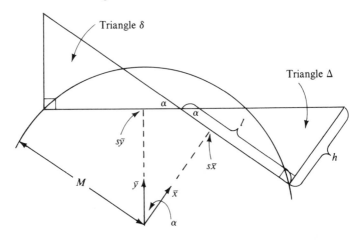

Now, $l \leqslant 2M$ so that $h \leqslant 2M \tan\alpha$, and the area of triangle Δ is no larger than $2M^2 \tan\alpha$. Similarly the area of triangle δ is no larger than $2M^2 \tan\alpha$. The definition of f implies that $f(\bar{x},s)$ and $f(\bar{y},s)$ can differ by at most twice the volume of a prism with height $2M$ and base that one of the triangles Δ and δ with larger area, so that $|f(\bar{x},s) - f(\bar{y},s)|$ is less than $8M^3 \tan\alpha$.

Thus $|f(\bar{x},t) - f(\bar{y},s)| \leqslant \pi M^2 |t - s| + 8M^3 \tan\alpha$. As $(\bar{y},s)$ approaches $(\bar{x},t)$, s approaches t and the angle α approaches 0, so that $|f(\bar{x},t) - f(\bar{y},s)|$ approaches 0. Hence f is continuous. ∎

We now use Lemma 5.4.4 with $K = H$, where H is one of the regions in Theorem 5.4.3. Again let M be such that $|\bar{p}| \leqslant M$ for each $\bar{p} \in H$. Fix a point $\bar{x}$ in S^2. Now $f(\bar{x},t) = V(H \cap H(\bar{x},t))$ is a continuous function of t, $f(\bar{x}, -M) = V(H)$, and $f(\bar{x},M) = 0$. An application of the Intermediate Value Theorem shows that $\{t : f(\bar{x},t) = \frac{1}{2}V(H)\}$ is not empty. Hence we can let $r(\bar{x})$ be that number t for which $|t| = \min\{|s| : s \in [-M, M]$ and $f(\bar{x}, s) = \frac{1}{2} V(H)\}$ and $f(\bar{x}, t) = \frac{1}{2} V(H)$.

It is not hard to see that the set of s's for which $f(\bar{x}, s) = \frac{1}{2} V(H)$ is a closed interval, so that $r(\bar{x})$ is unique. The geometric interpretation of $r(\bar{x})$ is that the plane through $r(\bar{x})\bar{x}$ perpendicular to $\bar{x}$ is the one nearest the origin among all planes perpendicular to $\bar{x}$ which bisect H. It will be well to keep this interpretation in mind.

Lemma 5.4.5 *The function r defined above is continuous.*

PROOF. Consider the picture. Using the geometric interpretation of $r(\bar{x})$ one sees that $r(\bar{y}) \leqslant r(\bar{x}) + W_2$ and $r(\bar{y}) \geqslant r(\bar{x}) - W_1$. Geometry shows that $W_2 \leqslant 2M \tan \alpha$ and $W_1 \leqslant 2M \sin \alpha$. As $\bar{y}$ approaches $\bar{x}$, the angle α approaches 0, so that $\tan \alpha$ and $\sin \alpha$ approach zero and $r(\bar{y})$ approaches $r(\bar{x})$. ∎

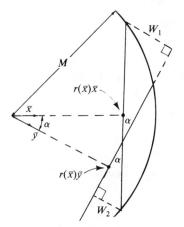

PROOF OF THEOREM 5.4.3. For $i = 1$ and 2 let $V_i(x) = V(B_i \cap H(\bar{x}, r(\bar{x})))$. By Lemmas 5.4.4 and 5.4.5, V_1 and V_2 are continuous functions so that we can apply the Borsuk–Ulam Theorem to them. Thus there is a point $\bar{x}_0$ such that $V_1(\bar{x}_0) = V_1(-\bar{x}_0)$ and $V_2(\bar{x}_0) = V_2(-\bar{x}_0)$.

We concentrate on B_1. The boundary plane of $H(\bar{x}_0, r(\bar{x}_0))$ is the one nearest the origin among those perpendicular to $\bar{x}_0$ which bisect H. But the planes perpendicular to $\bar{x}_0$ are the same as those perpendicular to $-\bar{x}_0$, so the boundary planes of $H(\bar{x}_0, r(\bar{x}_0))$ and $H(-\bar{x}_0, r(-\bar{x}_0))$ are the same. However, $\bar{x}_0$, $-\bar{x}_0$ point into different half-spaces, so that $V(B_1 \cap H(\bar{x}_0, r(\bar{x}_0))) + V(B_1 \cap H(-\bar{x}_0, r(-\bar{x}_0))) = V(B_1)$. Since $V_1(\bar{x}_0) = V_1(-\bar{x}_0)$, we have $V(B_1 \cap H(\bar{x}_0, r(\bar{x}_0))) = V(B_1 \cap H(-\bar{x}_0, r(-\bar{x}_0)))$. Thus the plane through $r(\bar{x}_0)\bar{x}_0$ perpendicular to $\bar{x}_0$ bisects B_1.

The same argument works for B_2, so that this plane is the one required by the theorem. ∎

The following corollary is the reason for the name of the Ham Sandwich Theorem.

Corollary 5.4.6 *Any ham sandwich made with bread, butter, and a piece of ham can be divided into equal parts with one knife slice.*

PROOF. Let the regions B_1, B_2, and H in the Ham Sandwich Theorem be the bread, butter, and ham, respectively. Slice along the plane guaranteed by the theorem. ∎

Exercises

1. Explain what is nontopological about the Borsuk–Ulam Theorem and the Ham Sandwich Theorem.

2. Furnish the details necessary to show that $G'((-x, -y)) = -G'(x,y))$ in the proof of the Borsuk–Ulam Theorem.

3. Verify the assertions made about $\{s : f(\bar{x},s) = \frac{1}{2} V(H)\}$ in the proof of results leading up to the Ham Sandwich Theorem.

4. Let f be a continuous function from B^2 to S^1. Prove that there is a point $\bar{y}_0$ of S^1 such that $f(\bar{y}_0) = f(-\bar{y}_0)$. Hint: adapt the proof of the Borsuk–Ulam Theorem.

5.5   Kakutani's Theorem

Our next application of the theory of winding numbers was proved by Kakutani in 1940. It is related to the Borsuk–Ulam Theorem, in a way, but Kakutani has only one function and produces three special points rather than just two. We must omit some of the geometric details in the proof.

Theorem 5.5.1   (Kakutani's Theorem) *If f is a continuous real-valued function on S^2, then there are three mutually perpendicular points $\overline{U}_1$, $\overline{U}_2$, and $\overline{U}_3$ on S^2 such that $f(\overline{U}_1) = f(\overline{U}_2) = f(\overline{U}_3)$.*

PROOF. Recall that a great circle on S^2 is the intersection of S^2 with a plane through the origin. Further, geometry on S^2 is done by using arcs of great circles as straight line segments. Thus we can talk about *spherical equilateral triangles* and *medians of triangles*, i.e., line segments from a triangle's vertex to the midpoint of the opposite side. Further, the *geometric centroid* of a spherical triangle is the point at which the three medians of the triangle meet.

Since f is a continuous real-valued function on the compact set S^2, f attains a maximum at a point we will call N (for North Pole) and f also has a minimum. To make things more intuitive later, we assume that the minimum of f is positive. If not, we can add a constant to f to make it so.

Now let ABC be any spherical equilateral triangle. We will prove that ABC can be so placed on S^2 that $f(A)=f(B)=f(C)$, and Kakutani's Theorem then follows by taking ABC to be a triangle each side of which has length $\pi/2$.

Suppose ABC has been placed on S^2. We can view $f(A), f(B)$, and $f(C)$ as weights attached to the vertices A, B, and C, respectively. The *weighted centroid* of the triangle ABC is then the point at which the triangle balances. This can be obtained by balancing the weighted line segment AB at X and the weighted line segment BC at Y, and the weighted centroid is then the intersection of the line segments CX and AY. From this construction it is clear that the weighted centroid coincides with the geometric centroid if and only if $f(A)=f(B)=f(C)$.

For simplicity assume that N actually is the North Pole $(0,0,1)$ of S^2. Further assume that we always place the spherical triangle ABC so that it is contained in the northern hemisphere. Finally, suppose the theorem is not true and that the weighted centroid and geometric centroid never coincide regardless of how we place ABC. Then there is always a non-zero vector from the geometric centroid to the weighted centroid. We can project this vector vertically into the equatorial plane and it will always be non-zero there as well.

Place the triangle ABC so that its geometric centroid is N. The illustration shows the view of the northern hemisphere of S^2 seen by an observer looking down. The angle θ is defined by the illustration. We define a function F from $[0,1]$ into the punctured plane as follows. Define $F(t)$ to be the projection in the equatorial plane of the vector from the geometric centroid of ABC to the weighted centroid of ABC when ABC is placed so that $\theta=2\pi t$. Since f is continuous, a small change in t will cause only a small change in F, so that F is continuous.

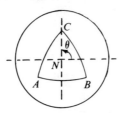

Now one-third of a revolution of the triangle does nothing but permute the vertices, so that $F(t)=F(t+\frac{1}{3})$ for $0\leqslant t\leqslant\frac{2}{3}$. In particular, $F(0)=F(\frac{1}{3})$ $=F(\frac{2}{3})=F(1)$ and F does the same thing on each of the subintervals $[0,\frac{1}{3}]$, $[\frac{1}{3},\frac{2}{3}]$, and $[\frac{2}{3},1]$. Since F is a function into the punctured plane, we can talk about the total angular change of F as in the development of winding numbers, and the above discussion implies that the total angular change on each of $[0,\frac{1}{3}]$, $[\frac{1}{3},\frac{2}{3}]$, $[\frac{2}{3},1]$ is the same and a multiple of 2π. Hence the total angular change of F on $[0,1]$ is a multiple of 6π.

We now define a function on the square I^2 line by line from the bottom up. On the bottom line put F. We define a function F_k along the horizontal line a distance k up the square as follows. Slide the triangle in the illustration down until N lies k of the way from the geometric centroid of ABC to the vertex C along the median from C to AB. Rotate ABC about N and define F_k just as F was defined. F_k may not be periodic as F was, but it certainly is continuous and $F_k(0) = F_k(1)$. This procedure defines a continuous function on the entire square I^2.

Now $f(N) \geqslant f(\bar{x})$ for all $\bar{x} \in S^2$. Hence $F_1(t)$ never points in the direction opposite $(\cos 2\pi t, \sin 2\pi t)$. Exercise 3 then implies that the net angular change of F_1 is the same as that of $(\cos 2\pi t, \sin 2\pi t)$ and so must be 2π.

In the proof of the Fundamental Winding Number Theorem we actually showed that a function from a square into the punctured plane must have total angular change zero on the boundary. The function defined above on I^2 has the property that the angular changes on the vertical sides are equal and opposite, and so they cancel out. Hence the net angular change of F_1 must equal the net angular change of F. But the former is 2π and the latter is divisible by 6π. This contradiction establishes the theorem. ∎

The application we wish to make of Kakutani's Theorem requires that we develop the notion of the width of a compact set. So let B be a compact set in R^3. Let $M(\bar{x}) = \max\{\bar{h}\cdot\bar{x} : \bar{h} \in B\}$. For fixed $\bar{x}$ in S^2 the function $g(\bar{h}) = \bar{h}\cdot\bar{x}$ is continuous and so has a maximum on the compact set B, so that $M(\bar{x})$ is well defined. It is the unique number such that the plane through $M(\bar{x})\bar{x}$ perpendicular to $\bar{x}$ meets B but for $S > M(\bar{x})$ the plane through $S\bar{x}$ perpendicular to $\bar{x}$ misses B.

Similarly define $m(\bar{x}) = \min\{\bar{h}\cdot\bar{x} : \bar{h} \in B\}$. Then $m(\bar{x})$ is the unique number such that the plane through $m(\bar{x})\bar{x}$ perpendicular to $\bar{x}$ meets B but for $S < m(\bar{x})$ the plane through $S\bar{x}$ perpendicular to $\bar{x}$ misses B. Now

$$m(\bar{x}) = \min\{\bar{h}\cdot\bar{x} : h \in B\} = -\max\{-(\bar{h}\cdot\bar{x}) : \bar{h} \in B\}$$
$$= -\max\{h\cdot(-\bar{x}) : \bar{h} \in B\} = -M(-\bar{x}).$$

We define the width of B in the direction $\bar{x}$ to be $W(\bar{x}) = M(\bar{x}) - m(\bar{x}) = M(\bar{x}) + M(-\bar{x})$. The following illustration shows the correctness of this definition.

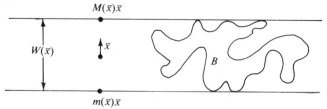

Lemma 5.5.2 *The function M defined above is continuous, and hence W is continuous.*

PROOF. We leave the proof as an exercise. The continuity of M follows by an argument almost identical to that used in the proof of Lemma 5.4.5. The continuity of W then follows from properties of continuous functions. ∎

Theorem 5.5.3 (Cubing-the-Blob Theorem) *Let B be any blob, i.e., any compact set in R^3. Then a cube C can be placed such that C contains B and B touches each face of C.*

PROOF. We use the width function W for B. It is a continuous function on S^2 and so by Kakutani's Theorem there are three mutually perpendicular points $\overline{U}_1$, $\overline{U}_2$, $\overline{U}_3$ on S^2 such that $W(\overline{U}_1) = W(\overline{U}_2) = W(\overline{U}_3)$. For each $\overline{U}_i$ there is a pair of planes as illustrated above for the point $\bar{x}$. Since $\overline{U}_1$, $\overline{U}_2$, $\overline{U}_3$ are mutually orthogonal and $W(\overline{U}_1) = W(\overline{U}_2) = W(\overline{U}_3)$ these three pairs of planes cut off a cube C which must contain B. The blob B must touch each face of C, for otherwise a pair of planes for some $\overline{U}_i$ would be incorrectly given. ∎

Exercises

1. Prove that for each continuous function $\hat{f}$ from $[0,1]$ into a space X which satisfies $\hat{f}(0) = \hat{f}(1)$ there is a continuous function f from Σ into X such that $\hat{f} = P \circ f$, and conversely. Recall that P is the function from $[0,1]$ onto Σ defined in Section 5.1. Thus the theories of these two classes of functions are essentially equivalent.

2. Prove that if Kakutani's Theorem is true for a function f, then it is also true for $f \pm c$, where c is any constant, and thus that the assumption made about the minimum of f in the proof does not cause a loss of generality.

3. Prove that if f and g are continuous functions from Σ into the punctured plane such that $f(\bar{x})$ and $g(\bar{x})$ are never opposite, i.e., $f(\bar{x})$ never equals $kg(\bar{x})$ for $k < 0$, then $w(f) = w(g) = w(f + g)$. Hint: use Exercise 1 to replace f, g by $\hat{f}$, $\hat{g}$, fill in squares as shown below, and use the arguments in the proof of Kakutani's Theorem.

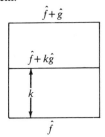

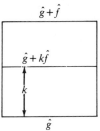

167

4. Prove that if f and g are continuous functions from Σ into the punctured plane such that $|f(\bar{x})| > |g(\bar{x})|$ for all $\bar{x}$, then $w(f) = w(f+g)$. Hint: see the hint for Exercise 3.

5. Let f be a continuous function from Σ to Σ with odd winding number. Prove that f takes some pair of antipodal points to antipodal points, i.e., $f(-\bar{x}) = -f(\bar{x})$ for some $\bar{x}$. Hint: let $G(\bar{x}) = f(\bar{x}) + f(-\bar{x})$. Use Exercise 3 to compute $w(G)$, then use techniques like those in the proof of the Borsuk—Ulam Theorem to compute $w(G)$.

6. Prove Lemma 5.5.2.

7. This exercise requires some knowledge of complex numbers.
  a. Let $P(x) = a_n x^n + a_{n-1} x^{n-1} + \cdots + a_1 x + a_0$, where x is a complex number, $a_n, a_{n-1}, \ldots, a_0$ are complex numbers, n is an integer greater than 0, and $a_n \neq 0$. Prove that there is an R such that $|a_n z^n| > |a_{n-1} z^{n-1} + \cdots + a_1 z + a_0|$ whenever $|z| = R$.
  b. Prove that the naturally defined winding number of P on $\{z : |z| = R\}$ is n.
  c. Prove that $P(z)$ has a root, i.e., that $P(z_0) = 0$ for some complex number z_0. This result is called the Fundamental Theorem of Algebra but no purely algebraic proof has ever been found.

6

Topics in combinatorial topology

Any student of topology is quickly convinced that the class of all topological spaces or even the class of all metric spaces contains an inconceivable number of strange and exotic objects. This is a blessing, in that general theorems then apply to a myriad of situations, but it is also a hindrance, in that one often cannot prove what he would like to and cannot even hope to make any reasonable classification of such spaces.

One way to eliminate these defects of generality is to restrict the class of spaces under study. In this chapter we investigate one such restricted class that has turned out to be extremely important in almost every aspect of topology. It is general enough to include a large number of the most important examples of topological objects, while at the same time the restrictions placed on this class allow us to bring very powerful mathematical tools to bear on its study. Perhaps the more important of these tools arise because of a certain "finiteness" in the construction of these special spaces. One of the aims of this chapter is to illustrate the meaning and usefulness of this "finiteness" idea.

We cannot go further without some concrete definitions and examples. The topics in this chapter are different in spirit from those of previous chapters. In order to make this chapter essentially independent, we will relegate to the exercises many of the connections with ideas introduced earlier.

6 Topics in combinatorial topology

6.1 Simplicial complexes

The spaces we want to deal with are obtained by starting with a collection of nice building blocks and pasting them together in a suitable way. This pasting process will be inherently finite, so that we can count and induct in our study of these spaces. Much of this chapter is devoted to results and proofs which illustrate these combinatorial techniques. However, in this section we must do some rather detailed work in order to properly define the building blocks and pasting process. The reader should always keep low-dimensional examples at hand.

Our building blocks will be points, line segments, triangular regions, solid tetrahedra, and the corresponding higher-dimensional objects. However, we want to place these objects in Euclidean spaces with any sort of orientation, so we must introduce some linear ideas to distinguish between the concepts collinear and noncollinear, etc. We use $\bar{x}$ to denote vectors of R^n when the vector space properties are important. Also, $\bar{0}$ denotes the zero vector.

Definition The set of points $\{\bar{x}_0, \bar{x}_1, \ldots, \bar{x}_p\}$ of R^n is *affinely independent* if $\lambda_0 = \lambda_1 = \cdots = \lambda_p = 0$ whenever $\sum_{i=0}^{p} \lambda_i \bar{x}_i = \bar{0}$ and $\sum_{i=0}^{p} \lambda_i = 0$.

EXAMPLE.

1. Let $\bar{x}_1$, $\bar{x}_2$ and $\bar{x}_3$ be points of R^n. Suppose that $\lambda_1 \bar{x}_1 + \lambda_2 \bar{x}_2 + \lambda_3 \bar{x}_3 = 0$, $\lambda_1 + \lambda_2 + \lambda_3 = 0$ and $\lambda_1 \neq 0$. Then $\bar{x}_1 = -\lambda_2/\lambda_1 \bar{x}_2 - \lambda_3/\lambda_1 \bar{x}_3$ and since $\lambda_3 = -\lambda_1 - \lambda_2$, we have $\bar{x}_1 = -\lambda_2/\lambda_1 \bar{x}_2 + (1 - (-\lambda_2/\lambda_1))\bar{x}_3$, so that $\bar{x}_1, \bar{x}_2, \bar{x}_3$ are collinear. The converse is also easy to check; hence a set of three points is affinely independent if and only if the points are not collinear.

Theorem 6.1.1 *A subset of an affinely independent set of points of R^n is affinely independent.*

PROOF. Since the indexing is clearly immaterial, we can consider the subset $\{\bar{x}_0, \bar{x}_1, \ldots, \bar{x}_q\}$ of the affinely independent set $\{\bar{x}_0, \bar{x}_1, \ldots, \bar{x}_p\}$. If $\sum_{i=1}^{q} \lambda_i \bar{x}_i = \bar{0}$ and $\sum_{i=1}^{q} \lambda_i = 0$, then putting $\lambda_{q+1} = \cdots = \lambda_p = 0$ we have $\sum_{i=1}^{p} \lambda_i \bar{x}_i = \bar{0}$ and $\sum_{i=1}^{p} \lambda_i = 0$. Hence $\lambda_1 = \lambda_2 = \cdots = \lambda_q = \cdots = \lambda_p = 0$, and $\{\bar{x}_0, \bar{x}_1, \ldots, \bar{x}_q\}$ is affinely independent. ∎

We are now ready to define our building blocks and the building procedure. This process can be done very generally, but we will stick to a thoroughly geometric and concrete approach. We will try to use simple terminology in keeping with this approach. Consequently, the reader should be careful to be aware of the definitions and conventions when reading other material on this subject.

Definition A *p-dimensional simplex* or *p-simplex* s^p is a subset of R^n of the form $s^p = \{\Sigma_{i=0}^p \lambda_i \bar{x}_i : \Sigma_{i=0}^p \lambda_i = 1\}$, where $\{\bar{x}_0, \bar{x}_1, \ldots, \bar{x}_p\}$ is an affinely independent subset of R^n. The points $\bar{x}_0, \bar{x}_1, \ldots, \bar{x}_p$ are called the *vertexes* of s^p, the sets of the form $\{\Sigma_{i=0}^p \lambda_i \bar{x}_i : \Sigma_{i=0}^p \lambda_i = 1$ and $\lambda_{i_1} = \lambda_{i_2} = \cdots = \lambda_{i_r} = 0\}$ are $(p-r)$-simplexes which are called *faces* of s^p. We also say that the empty set and s^p itself are faces of s^p. We may denote s^p by $[\bar{x}_0, \bar{x}_1, \ldots, \bar{x}_p]$.

EXAMPLES.

2. The triangular region is a 2-simplex in R^2. Its faces are the empty set, the region itself, the line segments $[\bar{x}_0, \bar{x}_1]$, $[\bar{x}_1, \bar{x}_2]$, $[\bar{x}_2, \bar{x}_0]$ and the vertexes $\bar{x}_0, \bar{x}_1, \bar{x}_2$.

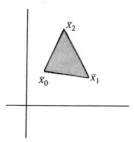

3. Here $\{\bar{x}_0\}$ is a 0-simplex and $[\bar{y}_0, \bar{y}_1]$ is a 1-simplex.

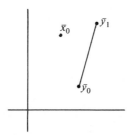

We leave the examination of properties of simplexes for the exercises. It is worth mentioning, however, that any p-simplex is homeomorphic to the p-ball $B^p = \{\bar{z} \in R^p : |\bar{z}| \leq 1\}$, and hence is compact and connected. We note also that the vector space structure of R^n implies that there is no p-simplex in R^n if $p > n$.

We now have our bricks and are ready to define the building or pasting procedure. We do not use even as much generality as we provide except in a few isolated (but important) instances, so the reader is urged to furnish himself with several simple examples.

Definition A *locally finite simplicial complex* (or just *simplicial complex*) is a set $\mathcal{K}$ of simplexes of any dimension in a Euclidean space R^n which satisfies the following conditions: (1) a face of a simplex of $\mathcal{K}$ is also a simplex of $\mathcal{K}$, (2) any two simplexes of $\mathcal{K}$ meet in a face of each, and (3) each point p of R^n has a neighborhood $N(p,\delta_p)$ which meets just finitely many simplexes of $\mathcal{K}$. The maximum of the dimensions of the simplexes in $\mathcal{K}$ is called the *dimension of* $\mathcal{K}$. A simplicial complex is *finite* if it contains just finitely many simplexes. The subspace of R^n underlying a locally finite simplicial complex $\mathcal{K}$, that is, $\cup \mathcal{K}$, is called *a polyhedron* and is denoted by $|\mathcal{K}|$. Finally, a *triangulation of a space X* consists of a polyhedron $|\mathcal{K}|$ and a homeomorphism from $|\mathcal{K}|$ onto X. The space X is then said to be *triangulable*.

EXAMPLES.

4.

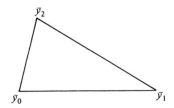

5.

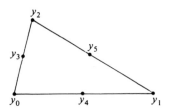

6.

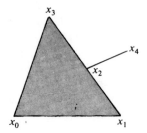

7.

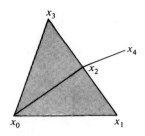

8.

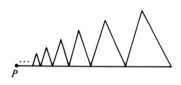

9.

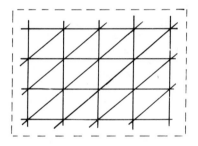

Example 4 shows a 1-dimensional simplicial complex consisting of three 1-simplexes and three 0-simplexes. The simplicial complex in Example 5 contains six 1-simplexes and six 0-simplexes but has the same underlying space. Thus the same polyhedron may arise from many different simplicial complexes. This is an important fact in a thorough study of polyhedra, but we will not go deeply enough for it to cause us much concern.

Example 6 shows a collection consisting of a 2-simplex, five 1-simplexes and five 0-simplexes. It is not a simplicial complex, since $[x_2, x_4]$ and $[x_0, x_1, x_3]$ do not meet in a common face. In addition, the face $[x_1, x_3]$ of $[x_0, x_1, x_3]$ does not belong to the collection. Example 7 shows a collection consisting of two 2-simplexes, six 1-simplexes, and five 0-simplexes which is a simplicial complex and which has the same underlying space as does Example 6.

Example 8 shows a collection of 0- and 1-simplexes which is not a simplicial complex because it fails to satisfy the locally finite condition. In particular, no neighborhood of the point P meets just finitely many simplexes of the collection. This condition is designed to make the topology of the underlying space agree nicely with the topologies of each simplex.

Finally, Example 9 shows how to cover the entire plane with a locally finite simplicial complex. The exercises will show why one cannot get by with a finite simplicial complex. The desire to include the Euclidean spaces among the polyhedra thus forces us to deal with nonfinite simplicial complexes.

Exercises

1. Prove that the set $\{\bar{x}_0, \bar{x}_1, \ldots, \bar{x}_p\}$ of points of R^n is affinely independent if and only if $\{\bar{x}_1 - \bar{x}_0, \bar{x}_2 - \bar{x}_0, \ldots, \bar{x}_p - \bar{x}_0\}$ is linearly independent.

2. Prove that a p-simplex is homeomorphic to the p-ball.

3. Prove that the underlying space of a simplicial complex is compact if and only if the simplicial complex is finite.

4. A simplicial complex $\mathcal{K}$ is said to be *connected* if whenever s and t are simplexes of $\mathcal{K}$, then there are simplexes $q_0, q_1, q_2, \ldots, q_n$ of $\mathcal{K}$ such that $s = q_0$, $t = q_n$, and $q_i \cap q_{i+1}$ is not empty for $i = 0, 1, 2, \ldots, n-1$. Prove that $\mathcal{K}$ is connected if and only if its underlying space $|\mathcal{K}|$ is connected.

5. The *r-skeleton of a simplicial complex* $\mathcal{K}$ is defined to be $\mathcal{K}^r = \{s : s$ is a simplex of $\mathcal{K}$ and the dimension of s is no larger than $r\}$.
   a. Prove that the r-skeleton of a simplicial complex is a simplicial complex.
   b. Prove that a simplicial complex is connected if and only if its 1-skeleton is.

6. Prove that the n-sphere S^n is triangulable.

7. Prove that R^n is triangulable.

8. Two simplicial complexes $\mathcal{K}$ and $\mathcal{L}$ are said to be *isomorphic* if there is a one-to-one function ϕ from $\mathcal{K}$ onto $\mathcal{L}$ (called an *isomorphism*) such that the dimension of $\phi(s)$ is the same as the dimension of s and $\phi(s)$ is a face of $\phi(t)$ whenever s is a face of t for all simplexes s, t of $\mathcal{K}$.
   a. Prove that if ϕ is an isomorphism from $\mathcal{K}$ to $\mathcal{L}$, then s is a face of t whenever $\phi(s)$ is a face of $\phi(t)$.
   b. Prove that if two simplicial complexes $\mathcal{K}$ and $\mathcal{L}$ are isomorphic, then their underlying spaces are homeomorphic.
   c. Prove that the converse of (b) is not true.

9. a. Prove that a simplicial complex has at most countably many simplexes.
   b. Prove that there is a countably infinite set $P = \{p_i : i = 1, 2, \ldots\}$ of points of R^n such that every subset of $n+1$ points is affinely independent and P has no limit points.
   c. Prove that if $\mathcal{K}$ is an r-dimensional simplicial complex, then there is a simplicial complex $\mathcal{L}$ in R^{2r+1} isomorphic to $\mathcal{K}$. Hint: map the vertexes of $\mathcal{K}$ into the set P of part (b) in R^{2r+1}, then build the simplexes of $\mathcal{L}$.

6.2 Graphs

Our study of simplicial complexes will be limited to low dimensions, and in this section we deal with the lowest dimensional case of interest, namely, dimension one. The theory of graphs is a large and well-developed area of mathematics in its own right, and we can give only a brief view of some of its more topological aspects. In so doing we will furnish excellent illustrations of the power of the restrictions involved in defining polyhedra.

Definition A *graph* is a space homeomorphic to the underlying space of a finite 1-dimensional simplicial complex together with the simplicial structure carried from the simplicial complex by the homeomorphism. The images under the homeomorphism of the vertexes and 1-simplexes of the simplicial complex are called the *vertexes* and *arcs* or *edges of the graph*.

We should emphasize that a graph has some structure besides just that of a topological space and that because of this, different graphs may in fact be homeomorphic. This point has already been made in the previous section, but the following examples show its effect in the case of graphs.

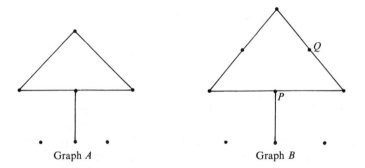

Graph *A*   Graph *B*

The two graphs shown are clearly homeomorphic as spaces, but graph *B* has more vertexes and edges than graph *A*. We note that vertexes may always be added in the middle of edges, thereby also increasing the number of edges. We also note that some vertexes can be suppressed, that is, their status as vertexes can be removed, without changing the fact that the space is a graph, but that others cannot. For example, vertex *Q* can be suppressed in graph *B* but vertex *P* cannot.

The different status of various vertexes discussed above suggests the following definition. We leave some topological considerations for the exercises and go on to our first theorem about graphs, which clearly exemplifies the counting aspects of the theory.

Definition   The *order of a vertex V* in a graph G is the number of arcs that have V as a face. A vertex is said to be *odd* if its order is odd and *even* otherwise.

Theorem 6.2.1   *The number of odd vertexes in a graph G is even.*

PROOF.   Suppose $2k + 1$ is at least as large as the highest order of a vertex in G. Let $V_0, V_1, V_2, \ldots, V_{2k+1}$ denote the number of vertexes of G of orders $0, 1, 2, \ldots, 2k + 1$ respectively. Now each vertex of order i accounts for i arc ends, so the total number of arc ends must be

$$M = 0V_0 + 1V_1 + 2V_2 + \cdots + (2k+1)V_{2k+1}.$$

This is even, since it is twice the number of arcs in G. Hence

$$N = 1V_1 + 3V_3 + 5V_5 + \cdots + (2k+1)V_{2k+1}$$

is also even, since it is $M - (0V_0 + 2V_2 + 4V_4 + \cdots + 2kV_k)$. But

$$N = (V_1 + V_3 + V_5 + \cdots + V_{2k+1}) + (2V_3 + \cdots + 2kV_{2k+1}),$$

so $V_1 + V_3 + V_5 + \cdots + V_{2k+1}$ must also be even.   ∎

We now introduce a way of thinking about graphs which is not strictly topological but which has wide application in graph theory. Again, we leave relationships with topological ideas for the exercises. The basic idea is that one can regard a graph as a picture of a road network in which the edges are roads and the vertexes are cities. Then questions arise concerning routes from city to city (vertex to vertex) and whether there is a route passing through every city. We must make these ideas more rigorous.

Definition   A *path* in a graph G is a finite sequence of arcs $a_1, a_2, \ldots, a_n$ in G such that a_i and a_{i+1} have a common vertex but $a_i \neq a_{i+1}$ for $i = 1, 2, \ldots, n-1$. The vertex of a_1 not shared by a_2 is the *initial vertex* of the path, and the vertex of a_n not shared by a_{n-1} is the *terminal vertex* of the path. A *closed path* is one whose initial vertex is the same as its terminal vertex.

EXAMPLE.

1. Here $a_1 a_2 a_6 a_5 a_4 a_3 a_2 a_1$ is a path but $a_1 a_{10} a_{11}$ is not, since a_1 and a_{10} do

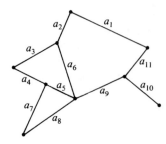

not have a common vertex. Also, $a_{11}a_{10}a_{10}$ is not a path, though our first example shows that arcs may be repeated in a path, but not immediately. Also, $a_1a_2a_6a_5a_4a_3a_2a_1$ is a closed path, but $a_1a_2a_6a_5a_4a_3a_2$ is not.

We now investigate a special kind of path first studied by one of the most prolific mathematicians in history, Leonhard Euler. He introduced and studied such paths in order to solve the *Königsberg Bridge Problem*. In 1736 the city of Königsberg (now Russian, then East Prussian) looked like this:

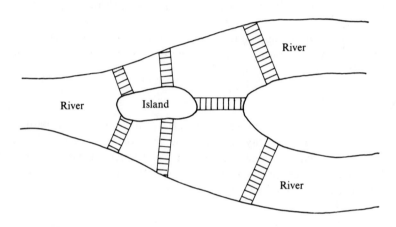

For some time the citizens had wondered whether one could take a walk and cross each bridge exactly once. Euler realized that this was equivalent to asking whether the graph shown has a path which used each arc exactly once (we have had to add two "unnatural" vertexes in order to form a graph) and solved the problem through the following sequence of theorems. We first make a definition.

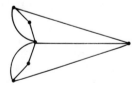

Definition An *Eulerian path* in a graph G is a path in G which uses each arc of G exactly once.

Theorem 6.2.2 *A graph having an Eulerian path can have at most two odd vertexes.*

PROOF. Suppose that $a_1, a_2, \ldots, a_n$ is an Eulerian path in the graph G, and let V be a vertex of G other than the initial and terminal vertexes of the path. Since V is not the initial vertex, either the path does not pass through V at all, in which case V has order 0, or the path has an arc entering V. But since V is not the terminal vertex of the path, each time the path enters V it must also leave, and so uses up arc ends at V in pairs. Since the path uses each arc exactly once, V must have even order. Thus the only possible odd vertexes in G are the initial and terminal vertexes of the Eulerian path. ∎

We note that this already solves the Königsberg Bridge Problem in the negative, since the graph has four odd vertexes. However, we can go further. The natural conjecture is that a graph with at most two odd vertexes has an Eulerian path. That something more is required is shown by the following.

EXAMPLE.

2. This graph has no odd vertexes, but clearly has no Eulerian path, since a path must always stay in the same part of the graph in which it started. The required idea is clearly that of connectedness, and our next definition phrases this concept in graph theory terms. It is the same as topological connectedness (see the exercises).

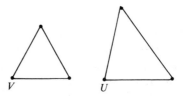

Definition   A graph G is said to be *connected* if whenever V and U are two distinct vertexes of G then there is a path in G with initial vertex V and terminal vertex U.

The above example is not connected, since there is no path from V to U, which suggests that being connected is a necessary condition for a graph to have an Eulerian path. This is not strictly true, but we leave further investigation for the exercises. Theorem 6.2.1 also implies that a graph having an Eulerian path must have either zero or two odd vertexes. We first prove the converse under the strongest conditions.

Theorem 6.2.3   *Let G be a connected graph with no odd vertexes and let a_1 be any arc of G. Then there is an Eulerian path in G whose first arc is a_1.*

PROOF. We proceed to build a path by induction. We have a one-arc path, namely, a_1. Suppose $a_1, a_2, \ldots, a_k$ is a path in which each arc appears at most once. If we have used all arcs of G already, then we are done. Otherwise, consider the terminal vertex U of $a_1, a_2, \ldots, a_k$. Suppose $a_1, a_2, \ldots, a_k$ is not a closed path. Then when the path enters U, say via arc a_i for $i < k$, it also leaves via a_{i+1}, so that the arc ends at U are used up in pairs except for the last entry via a_k. Hence the path uses up an odd number of arc ends at U. Since U is an even vertex, there is an arc a_{k+1} which can be added to form the path $a_1 a_2 \ldots a_{k+1}$.

Now suppose that $a_1 a_2 \ldots a_k$ is a closed path but does not use all the arcs of G. Since G is connected, we can form a path P starting with an unused arc and leading to a vertex of the path $a_1 a_2 \ldots a_k$. Let b_1 be any arc of P that shares a vertex with some arc a_i but is not one of the arcs $a_1, a_2, \ldots, a_k$. Since $a_1 a_2 \ldots a_k$ uses up an even number of arc ends at each vertex of G, an argument like that in the first paragraph shows that we can build a closed path $b_1 b_2 \ldots b_r$ using only arcs that do not appear in $a_1 a_2 \ldots a_k$. Since the initial vertex lies on the path $a_1 a_2 \ldots a_k$ and is also the terminal vertex of $b_1 b_2 \ldots b_r$, the latter can be spliced into the path $a_1 a_2 \ldots a_k$ to form a longer path $a_1 a_2 \ldots a_i b_1 b_2 \ldots b_r a_{i+1} \ldots a_k$.

If we still have not used all the arcs of G, we can repeat the above procedure. Since G has only finitely many arcs, after finitely many repetitions we will have constructed an Eulerian path for G. ∎

We now characterize those connected graphs which have Eulerian paths. The technique used to prove the following theorem is one of any mathematician's favorites, namely, reduction to a previously solved problem.

Theorem 6.2.4 *A connected graph G has an Eulerian path if and only if G has at most two odd vertexes.*

PROOF. We have already proved in Theorem 6.2.2 that a graph with an Eulerian path can have at most two odd vertexes. We now prove the converse.

By Theorems 6.2.1 and 6.2.3 we only have to worry about a graph G with two odd vertexes U and V. If each vertex of G were even, we would be done, so we add an arc a_1 to G joining the vertexes U and V. In the new graph G' every vertex is even, so by Theorem 6.2.3 there is an Eulerian path in G' starting with a_1, say $a_1 a_2 \ldots a_n$. Then clearly $a_2 a_3 \ldots a_n$ is an Eulerian path for G. ∎

This is a very pleasant theorem which can be used to solve many mathematical puzzles, some of which are exercises. To make its beauty even more apparent, we change the problem slightly.

Definition   A *Hamiltonian path* in a graph G is a closed path which passes
through each vertex of G exactly once, with the natural convention for
the initial vertex.

EXAMPLES.

3. $a_1a_2a_3a_4a_5a_6a_7a_8$ is a Hamiltonian path.

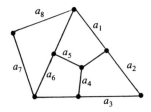

4. This graph has a Hamiltonian path.

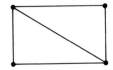

5. This graph does not have a Hamiltonian path.

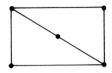

A Hamiltonian path might also be called a *salesman's path*, since the
graph can be viewed as a road map in which the vertexes are cities. A
salesman would want a route which takes him to each city exactly once
and ends again in his home town.

In contrast to the simple theorem characterizing graphs having Eulerian
paths, there is no known reasonable, computable characterization of
graphs having a Hamiltonian path. We leave the problem to those readers
who will grow up to become graph theorists.

We now turn to the relationship between graphs and the spaces which
contain them. This is really a continuation of the subject begun in Section
4.3 and some of the ideas introduced there will be repeated here. Also,
some of the concepts we will see here in their infancy will mature, though
not completely, in the next section.

The first question we want to discuss is that of which spaces can contain which graphs. So far all examples of graphs have been drawn in the plane, though we have seen nothing very complicated. Can *all* graphs be drawn in the plane?

We give an example generated by the fairly well-known *Utilities Problem*. In this problem the gas, water, and electricity companies (*G*, *W*, and *E*) want to run lines to factories *A*, *B*, and *C* in such a way that no two of their lines cross. This leads to the following graph, where the line from *E* to *B* "hops over" the line from *G* to *C* without touching it.

We will call this graph the *GWE* graph. We have *not* drawn it in the plane because of the "hopping over." A few more tries will quickly convince the reader that it is probably impossible to draw the *GWE* graph on a sheet of paper.

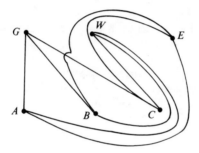

For another example, we turn to the graph we will call K_5. It consists of five vertexes and all possible arcs, and is pictured as

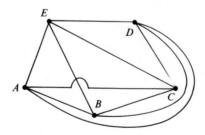

We have again been forced to hop over, and again some experimentation will quickly convince the reader that it is impossible to draw K_5 in the plane.

These examples raise a host of questions. How can you tell whether a graph can be drawn in the plane? Are there graphs so complicated that they cannot be drawn in a three-dimensional space? Is there a two-dimensional space, e.g., the surface of an inner tube, on which all graphs can be drawn? Note also that we used curved arcs in our representations of K_5 and the GWE graph. Is this necessary, or can we always get by with straight arcs?

Results from Section 6.1 imply that every graph can be embedded in three-dimensional space in such a way that every arc of the graph is straight. Thus the interesting problems arise when we restrict ourselves to the plane. The following theorem, which we state but do not prove, answers the "straightness" problem.

Theorem 6.2.5 *If a graph can be embedded in the plane, then it can be embedded in the plane in such a way that all its arcs are straight.*

The reader should have recognized that this is not a topological theorem at all. Further, we do not need straightness of all the arcs in order to apply the tools associated with simplicial complexes. Our next result shows that we can always use simplicial tools, though the proof does not contain all the analytical details. Rigorous proofs of the results we will state are difficult and beyond our scope.

Definition Recall that an *arc* is a space homeomorphic to [0, 1]. A *polygonal arc* is an arc which is also a polyhedron, i.e., is the union of finitely many straight line segments.

EXAMPLE.

6. Even though it is much more complicated, the arc on the left is polygonal while the arc on the right is not.

Theorem 6.2.6 *If G is a graph in the plane, then G may be placed in the plane in such a way that each of its arcs is polygonal.*

PROOF. The proof consists of straightening each of the arcs of G. Care must be exercised in order to insure that the straightening procedure does not introduce new intersections among the arcs. It is clear that if two arcs are disjoint, then there is room enough to straighten each and still keep them from meeting. Hence the trouble comes around the vertexes of G.

We take care of this as follows. Around each vertex V draw a small circle which contains no other vertex and meets no arc of G which does not end at V. Do this in such a way that no two of these circles meet. Draw straight line segments from each vertex to the last point of each arc on the vertex's circle. Then straighten the remainder of each arc using the fact that the remainders do not meet. ■

The ambitious reader who has waded through Chapter 2 should be able to supply the missing details of this proof. However, note that in making the arcs of G polygonal we may have destroyed some of the relationships between G and the plane, for example, the number of pieces into which G divides R^2. That all of this can also be preserved is true but even more difficult to prove.

We now return to the problem of graphs which cannot be drawn in the plane. We note a common characteristic of the attempts shown for K_5 and the GWE graph. In the latter vertex E is cut off from vertex B by what is essentially a circle, namely, the closed path from A to W to C to G to A. In the former vertex A is cut off from vertex C by the "circle" formed by the path from E to B to D to E.

These examples highlight a fundamental property of the plane, namely, that every circle in the plane cuts the plane into two pieces. This property has already been studied a bit in Section 4.3. However, in order to keep this chapter almost self-contained and to maintain the proper spirit, we recall some definitions and restate the result in an equivalent way.

Definition A *simple closed curve* is a space which is homeomorphic to a circle. A *polygonal simple closed curve* is one which is also a polyhedron, i.e., is made up of finitely many straight line segments.

EXAMPLE.

7. The simple closed curve on the left is polygonal; that on the right is not.

Theorem 6.2.7 (**Jordan Curve Theorem**) *A simple closed curve J in the plane divides the plane into two non-empty sets A and B, neither meeting J, such that any two points in A or B can be joined by a polygonal arc in A or B respectively and any polygonal arc joining a point of A with a point of B meets J.*

Before we proceed to a proof of a special case of this theorem, a few comments are in order. First, the following examples show that the theorem expresses a property of the plane.

EXAMPLES.

8. Here the simple closed curve *J* cuts a disk into four, not two, pieces.

9. Here the simple closed curve *J* does not cut the surface of an inner tube into pieces at all.

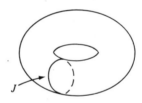

Second, the sets *A* and *B* are intuitively the inside and the outside of the simple closed curve. If the reader has not already studied the arc with positive area in Section 4.3, he should do so now in order to be convinced that the Jordan Curve Theorem is a highly nontrivial result.

We now present a proof of the Jordan Curve Theorem for the special case in which the simple closed curve is polygonal. This will illustrate the usefulness of polyhedra and besides, the proof of the general result is beyond our scope.

PROOF OF JORDAN CURVE THEOREM FOR POLYGONAL CURVES. Let *J* be a polygonal simple closed curve in the plane. Choose a direction in the plane which is not parallel to any line joining two vertexes of J, and for each point x, let H_x be the ray starting at x and pointing in the chosen direction. Let A be the set of points x not on J for which H_x meets J an even number of times, and let B be the set of points y not on J for which H_y meets J an odd number of times. An intersection at a vertex of J counts once if J and the ray cross at the vertex, but does not count at all otherwise.

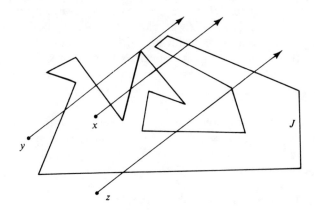

As a point x moves along a line segment missing J, the number of times H_x meets J changes only when H_x passes a vertex of J. The only possible cases are

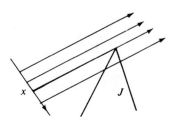

and

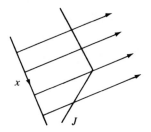

185

In each case the number of times H_x meets J remains either even or odd. Hence no polygonal arc can join a point of A to a point of B without meeting J, since all points along such an arc belong to the same one of A or B to which the first point of the arc belongs.

It remains to show that two points of A or B can be joined by a polygonal arc lying in A or B respectively. We do the case involving A, that for B being similar. So let p and q be two points of A. If the line segment from p to q misses J, we are done. Otherwise, follow the line segment pq from p to J, and then go along the line segments close to but not meeting J until you hit pq again near the last point of J on pq, say at the point r. If rq hits J, it hits it only once by "lastness" of r, so that r would be in B. But a polygonal arc not meeting J joins p and r, so that r is in A. Hence rq misses J and we have joined p to q. ∎

We develop some terminology to help us deal with graphs in the plane. This terminology arises from yet another way of looking at such graphs, namely, as the boundaries of countries. The restriction to the plane will be eased in the next section.

Definition A *planar map* is a graph in the plane. The portions into which the graph divides the plane are called the *faces of the map*, and F denotes the number of these faces. The vertexes and arcs of the graph are respectively called the *vertexes* and *edges of the map*. The number of vertexes is denoted by V and the number of edges by E. A planar map is *connected* if its graph is.

It is worth emphasizing that the part of the plane outside the graph is also a face. With this in mind, we look at some examples.

EXAMPLES.

10.

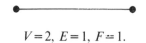

$V = 2,\ E = 1,\ F = 1.$

11.

$V = 7,\ E = 10,\ F = 5.$

12.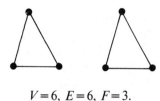

$$V = 6, \ E = 6, \ F = 3.$$

We note that the maps in Examples 10 and 11 are connected, whereas that in Example 12 is not. We note further that in both Examples 10 and 11, $V - E + F = 2$. The conjecture to which this leads is a remarkable fact which appears again and again in various branches of topology with various degrees of generalization. We will use it in several applications and generalize it in the next section.

Theorem 6.2.8 **(Euler's Formula for the Plane)** *For any connected planar map, $V - E + F = 2$.*

PROOF. The proof is somewhat similar to a proof by mathematical induction. We note that the formula is true for the simplest planar map, namely, a vertex. For in this case $V = 1$, $E = 0$, and $F = 1$, so that $V - E + F = 2$. We now state two operations that can be performed on planar maps and note that they do not alter $V - E + F$. This is analogous to the induction step. The operations are as follows:

1. Add an edge joined at one end only together with its other vertex. In this case we have added one vertex and one edge, leaving $V - E + F$ unchanged.
2. Add an edge joined at both ends. If the original graph is connected this forms a new simple closed curve in the graph and the Jordan Curve Theorem says that this new simple closed curve separates the plane. Since points on either side of and close to the new edge used to belong to a single face and now belong to two different ones, we see that we have added one face. We have also added one edge, so that $V - E + F$ is unchanged.

It remains only to show that any connected planar graph N can be built starting from a single vertex and applying operations 1 and 2. Note that these operations keep a connected graph connected so the analysis of operation 2 remains valid. Since $V - E + F = 2$ for a single vertex and the operations do not change $V - E + F$, we will have $V - E + F = 2$ for N.

So, begin with any vertex of N and apply operations 1 and 2 in any order, always adding parts of N. Since N is finite, we must arrive at a stage at which we can no longer perform either 1 or 2 with parts of N. Let M be the graph we have built. If M contains all the vertexes of N, then it contains all the edges of N, otherwise operation 2 could be performed.

Suppose P is a vertex of N which is not in M. Since N is connected there is a path from a vertex of M to P made up of arcs of N. The first arc of this path which does not belong to M can be used to perform operation 1 or 2.

We have shown that if $M \neq N$, then we can perform either operation 1 or operation 2. Since we had obtained M precisely at the stage at which we could no longer perform one of these operations, we see that $M = N$, and we are done. ∎

We now use Euler's Formula to prove facts that we guessed by trial and error earlier, namely that the graph K_5 and the GWE graph are not planar. The following metamathematical points should be contemplated. First, the trial and error method did *not* deliver a proof. Second, what we are doing is *proving* that something is impossible, which is not even remotely the same as not yet having found a way to do it.

Theorem 6.2.9   *The K_5 graph and the GWE graph are not planar.*

PROOF.   We will do the proof for K_5 and leave the remainder as an exercise. Suppose K_5 is embeddable in the plane. Each face of the resulting planar map has a simple closed curve for a boundary. By inspecting K_5 we see that a simple closed curve in K_5 must have at least three arcs, so the sum of the edges of the faces is at least $3F$. But each edge is counted twice in this sum, so that $2E \geqslant 3F$, or $F \leqslant \frac{2}{3}E = 6\frac{2}{3}$. But $V = 5$, $E = 10$, and $V - E + F = 2$, so that $F = 7$. This contradiction establishes the theorem. ∎

The last theorem, as well as the graphs involved in it, become much more interesting when we note the following theorem, proved in 1930 by Kuratowski, one of the founders of topology. His theorem is actually much more general, but we must omit a proof even of the one we state.

Theorem 6.2.10   *If a graph is not embeddable in the plane, then it contains a copy of either the GWE graph or K_5.*

For this reason the GWE graph and K_5 are sometimes called the *Kuratowski graphs*. We note also that this solves a problem for electrical engineers, namely, which circuits can be printed. For a circuit can be printed if its wiring diagram, a graph, can be embedded in the plane, and hence if it does not contain a copy of either the GWE graph or K_5.

The next application of Euler's Formula is to the regular solids or regular convex polytopes. For us a *convex polytope* is a bounded part of three-dimensional space whose boundary consists of portions of a finite number of planes. The parts of the planes in its boundary are called its *faces*, the common part of two faces is an *edge*, and the point common to two edges is a *vertex*. A convex polytope is *regular* if the faces are all alike, the edges are all alike, and the vertexes are all alike.

We now show five regular convex polytopes and also how they look when cut apart and flattened.

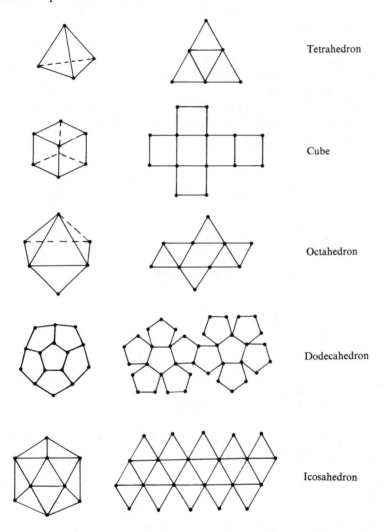

Tetrahedron

Cube

Octahedron

Dodecahedron

Icosahedron

The five regular polytopes shown above were known to Plato (427–347 B.C.). What we will show next is that there are no more. This was shown in Euclid's *Elements*, about 300 B.C., but by methods different from ours. We will again use Euler's Formula.

Now Euler's Formula applies to connected planar maps. It is easy to see that the edges and vertexes of a regular polyhedron form a connected graph on the surface of a solid object. By smoothing things out a bit (perfectly legitimate for a topologist of course) we see that we can assume

189

that the solid object is a ball, so that what we have is a graph on the surface of a ball, that is, on a sphere.

We can certainly carry over our map terminology to the case of a graph on a sphere. If we bore a small hole in one face of the resulting map, the remainder can be flattened out and placed in the plane. There is then a one-to-one correspondence between the vertexes, edges, and faces of the map on the sphere and the vertexes, edges, and faces of a planar map. Note that the face in which we bored the hole corresponds to the unbounded face of the planar map. If the graph on the sphere was connected, then it remains so upon flattening it, so that connected maps on the sphere become connected maps in the plane. It is clear, then, that we have the following result.

Theorem 6.2.11   (Euler's Formula for the Sphere)   *For any connected map on a sphere, $V - E + F = 2$.*

We can now prove the following result.

Theorem 6.2.12   (Theorem on Regular Polytopes)   *There are exactly five regular polytopes.*

PROOF.   Since we have already exhibited five, what we must do to prove the theorem is to show that only these five can exist.

Suppose we have a regular polytope in which each face has p sides and each vertex is on q edges. Since the polyhedron is formed by intersecting planes, and hence the edges are straight line segments and the faces are regular polygons, we see that both p and q must be at least 3.

We now apply Euler's Formula, since the edges, vertexes, and faces of the regular polytope are the edges, vertexes, and faces of a connected map on a sphere. If we count the edges of each face, we get pF, and we have counted each edge twice, so that $pF = 2E$. Similarly, by counting the edges at each vertex, we get $qV = 2E$. Thus $V = 2E/q$ and $F = 2E/p$, so by Euler's Formula we have

$$2 = V - E + F = \frac{2}{q}E - E + \frac{2}{p}E = \left(\frac{2}{q} - 1 + \frac{2}{p}\right)E.$$

Hence,

$$E = \frac{2pq}{2p + 2q - pq}, \qquad V = \frac{4p}{2p + 2q - pq}, \qquad F = \frac{4q}{2p + 2q - pq}.$$

For this to make sense, one must certainly have

$$2p + 2q - pq > 0,$$

hence

$$-4+2p+2q-pq > -4,$$
$$pq-2p-2q+4 < 4,$$
$$(p-2)(q-2) < 4.$$

Since p and q are both at least three, the only possibilities are

$$p=3, q=3;$$
$$p=4, q=3;$$
$$p=3, q=4;$$
$$p=5, q=3;$$
$$p=3, q=5.$$

Hence, there can be at most five regular polytopes. ∎

Exercises

1. What is the minimum number of vertexes a graph with n arcs must have?

2. What is the maximum number of vertexes a graph with n arcs must have?

3. Is the number of vertexes of a graph a topological property of graphs?

4. Give an example of a single graph which contains vertexes of orders 0, 1, 2, and 3.

5. **a.** Prove that if h is a homeomorphism from a graph G onto a graph G' and V is a vertex of G of order n, $n \neq 2$, then $h(V)$ is a vertex of G' of order n.
   b. Give an example which shows that the assertion in (a) is not true if $n=2$.

6. **a.** Prove that the union of the arcs in a path in a graph is the continuous image of $[0,1]$.
   b. Prove that for graphs the graph theory definition of connectedness given in this section is equivalent to the topological definition given in Chapter 2.

7. Prove that having an Eulerian path is a topological property of graphs.

8. State and prove a theorem characterizing those graphs having Eulerian paths. Note that a graph can have an Eulerian path and not be connected.

9. By definition a *tree* is a connected graph containing no closed path.
   a. Prove that every tree contains at least one vertex of order one. Hint: if not, then one can use the technique in the proof of Theorem 6.2.3 to construct a closed path.
   b. Prove that in a tree the number of vertexes is exactly one more than the number of edges. Hint: use (a) and erase the arc ending at a vertex of order 1. Prove that the remainder is still a tree and continue.

10. The map of Konigsberg is now as shown, with a railroad bridge and another bridge added.

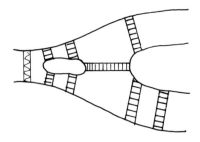

Can one now take a walk and cross each bridge exactly once? Can one do it without the railroad bridge? Justify your answers.

11. The floor plan of a house is as shown.

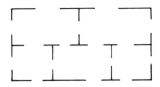

Can you walk through the house using each door exactly once?

12. **a.** Remove an arc from the *GWE* graph and draw the remainder on a sheet of paper using only straight line segments.
b. Do the same for K_5.

13. Rigorously define the *inside* and *outside* of a polygonal simple closed curve using concepts in the proof of the polygonal case of the Jordan Curve Theorem.

14. Show that the sets A and B in the proof of the polygonal case of the Jordan Curve Theorem are not empty and are disjoint.

15. Complete the proof of Theorem 6.2.9.

16. Can the *GWE* graph and K_5 be drawn on an inner tube? Justify your answers.

17. Prove that every tree can be embedded in the plane (see Exercise 9).

18. Match the regular polytopes shown earlier with the possibilities for p and q listed in the proof of the Theorem on Regular Polytopes.

6.3 Surfaces

Surfaces have already crept into our attention in the last section. For example, the sphere is crucial in our study of polytopes, and the surface of an inner tube came up in some exercises. In this chapter we will decide exactly what a surface is, we will build some surfaces, and we will prove a classification theorem for surfaces, i.e., we will make a list of all possible surfaces of a certain kind.

The first task is to decide exactly what a surface is. To do this we will make a list of some surfaces and some nonsurfaces and see whether we can write down a definition that will distinguish them properly.

EXAMPLES.

1.

Disk

2.

Sphere

3.

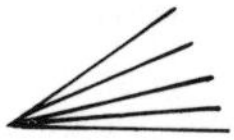

Fan

4.

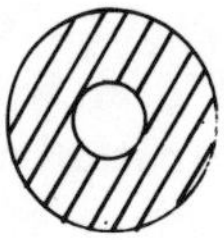

Annulus

5.

Disk with a sticker

6.

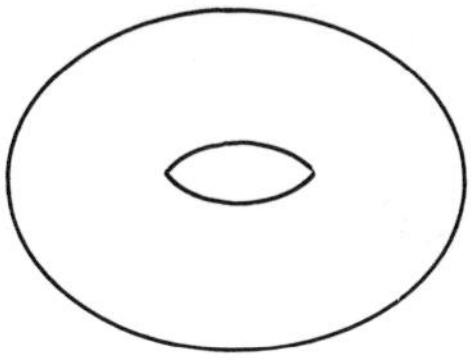

Torus = surface of a doughnut

7.

Sphere with
three handles

Probably everyone agrees that Examples 1, 2, 4, 6, 7 are surfaces, but Examples 3, 5 are not. Also the examples which are surfaces show that it is certainly not the overall structure of an object that makes it a surface. However, the surfaces shown have the property that locally, i.e., near any given point, they each look like a disk, at least topologically. What this means is that if you were a near-sighted inhabitant of a surface, the part of the surface that you could see would look like a disk. It is this fact that we seize upon and make into a definition.

Definition A *surface* is a separable metric space each point of which lies in an open set whose closure is homeomorphic to the unit disk $B^2 = \{(x,y) \in R^2 : x^2 + y^2 \leq 1\}$.

We emphasize that this definition is just the rigorous mathematical way of expressing the fact that near each point a surface looks topologically like a disk. We also note that the reader who has studied Section 4.3 has already encountered this definition in the exercises for that section and he will notice that a surface is exactly a two-dimensional manifold.

The astute reader will remark that there is a discontinuity between Sections 6.2 and 6.3. In particular, Section 6.2 dealt with finite one-dimensional simplicial complexes and the natural expectation is that Section 6.3 would deal with two-dimensional simplicial complexes. In fact this section deals with a restricted collection of two-dimensional simplicial complexes and we must now explore that restriction. As usual, the entire collection is too complicated for us to deal with.

Experimentation suggests that we can build a surface by pasting 2-simplexes together along one-dimensional faces, as long as we never have a 1-simplex which is a face of more than two 2-simplexes. Also, the pasting must always be done along one-dimensional faces in order to avoid a situation like this:

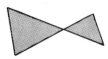

The natural guess is that surfaces are identical with two-dimensional simplicial complexes having the additional properties suggested by this discussion. The next definition is designed to express the restrictions we must place on the pasting process, even though it is a step or two away from the most direct such expression. Its justification is Theorems 6.3.1 and 6.3.2.

Definition Let p be a 0-simplex of the simplicial complex $\mathcal{K}$. The *link* of p in $\mathcal{K}$ is $\mathrm{Lk}(p) = \{s \in \mathcal{K} : s$ and p are disjoint faces of some simplex in $\mathcal{K}\}$. A *combinatorial n-manifold* is a simplicial complex $\mathcal{K}$ such that the link of each vertex of $\mathcal{K}$ is homeomorphic to either the $(n-1)$-ball B^{n-1} or the $(n-1)$-sphere S^{n-1}.

Strictly speaking, we should be more careful in our definition of combinatorial n-manifold, in that the homeomorphism should respect the simplicial structure. However, this would lead us away from the main goal of this chapter and we will use the definition only in low dimensions, where the added care is not needed.

Theorem 6.3.1 *The underlying space of a combinatorial 2-manifold $\mathcal{K}$ is a surface.*

PROOF. Let p be a vertex, that is, a 0-simplex of $\mathcal{K}$. Since $\mathrm{Lk}(p)$ is homeomorphic to either a line segment or a circle, the simplicial structure of K implies that the collection of simplexes of which p is a face looks like either

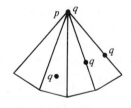

or

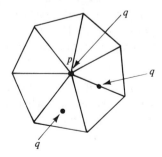

If q is any point of $|\mathcal{K}|$, then we may let p be a vertex of the lowest-dimensional simplex of $\mathcal{K}$ to which q belongs. The possibilities for the position of q are then as indicated and clearly in each case q has a neighborhood whose closure is homeomorphic to a disk. ∎

The next theorem was first proved in the 1920s. It's three-dimensional version is true but was not verified until the 1950s, and in the late 1960s the higher-dimensional versions were shown to hold in some cases but not in others. The proof of even the two-dimensional case is well beyond the aim of this book.

Theorem 6.3.2 (**Triangulation Theorem for Surfaces**) *Every surface is homeomorphic to the underlying space of a combinatorial 2-manifold.*

The Triangulation Theorem for Surfaces really says that every surface can be built by pasting 2-simplexes together along their edges with no three edges ever being pasted, and Theorem 6.3.1 says that every construction project of this sort yields a surface. There are only two remaining complications. First, the building process may require infinitely many 2-simplexes. Second, the building process may yield an object which is not connected.

The second complication is easily overcome by noticing that each connected piece (more precisely, each component) of a surface is itself a surface. Thus we need only worry about connected surfaces while keeping in mind that the disjoint union of any number of connected surfaces may be regarded as a single surface.

The necessity for infinitely many 2-simplexes is not so easy to avoid. In fact, any open subset of the plane is a 2-manifold requiring infinitely many 2-simplexes, and there are so many different ones of these that there is little hope for a reasonable theory. So we will restrict our study to surfaces built from just finitely many 2-simplexes. According to the exercises in Section 6.1, this is equivalent to restricting ourselves to compact surfaces.

For those readers who have not studied the topological ideas of connectedness and compactness, we record here definitions of these concepts which agree with the topological ones for surfaces. The rest of this section will deal exclusively with compact connected surfaces.

Definition A surface is *compact* if it is the underlying space of a finite simplicial complex and it is *connected* if whenever s and t are simplexes of its simplicial complex $\mathcal{K}$, then there are simplexes $q_0, q_1, \ldots, q_n$ of $\mathcal{K}$ such that $s = q_0$, $t = q_n$, and $q_i \cap q_{i+1}$ is not empty for $i = 0, 1, 2, \ldots, n-1$.

The techniques we will use to study compact connected surfaces are called *cut-and-paste techniques*. The reason for the name will become apparent. Such techniques retain their usefulness even in current research in topology.

Suppose we have a number of 2-simplexes to use to make a surface. We do this by pasting together at most two of these 2-simplexes at a time along an edge of each. This can be done in the two different ways illustrated here:

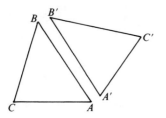 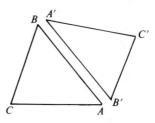

In each instance the edges AB and $A'B'$ are pasted, but by pasting different pairs of vertexes in the two cases. This can be more easily indicated by labeling the edges to be pasted with the same small letter, and putting arrows on the edges to indicate how to do the pasting. Note that sides labeled with different letters are not to be pasted. The two situations pictured above would then become

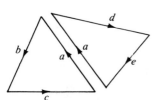 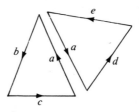

In this way any surface can be represented by a list of 2-simplexes with labeled and arrowed edges. The requirement that an arc is an edge of at most two 2-simplexes is reflected by having each label appear at most twice.

Now, triangles may be combined into polygons by pasting along the proper pairs of edges. Since the surface is connected, we will end up with a single polygon, some of whose edges still must be pasted. Conversely, a polygon with properly labeled edges can be cut apart into a collection of triangles, which by Theorem 6.2.1 will yield a surface when assembled. Hence, we may as well work with polygons of any number of sides in which we label and arrow the edges, using the same label at most twice. Examples are both instructive and fun.

EXAMPLES.

8.

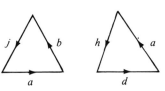

becomes

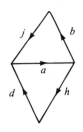

and then

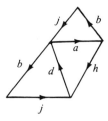

and then

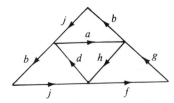

or

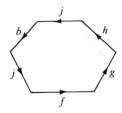

9.

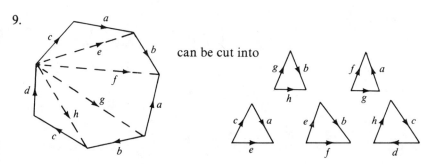

can be cut into

10.

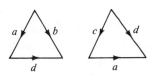

becomes

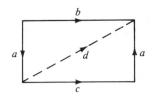

or just

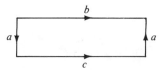

This is a very interesting surface called a *Möbius strip*. It is constructed from a strip of paper by giving one end a half-twist and then pasting the ends together. Note that if the *a* edges are pasted instead of the *d*-edges, we obtain

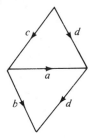

or just

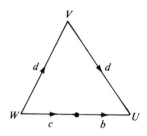

The vertex U is the end of edge d, which is also V, which is the beginning of edge d, which is also W. Hence, after pasting U, V, W all become the same point. The two edges c, b thus become a single simple closed curve. Hence, the Möbius strip has only one edge. More properties of a Möbius strip will be investigated in the exercises.

11. Since a Möbius strip has a single simple closed curve as an edge, it can be pasted to the edge of a disk. This can be represented by

Cut the disk along e and paste edges c and b together to obtain

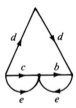

or

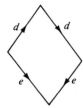

or

or

or

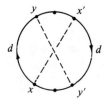

This is a disk with antipodal points identified, i.e., x with x', y with y', and so on, and this space is a surface called the *projective plane*.

Suppose we have a polygon with labeled and arrowed edges which represents a compact connected surface. Such a polygon can be represented by the string of labels, or the *word*, obtained by starting at a vertex and recording the labels met as one goes around the polygon and returns to the starting place. If one is going in the direction opposite the arrow on any given edge, the label is recorded with an exponent of -1. This can best be illustrated by some examples. The word obtained is not unique, as the examples will show, but it is a very nice bookkeeping device.

EXAMPLES.

12.

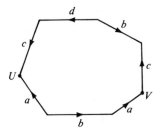

can be represented by

a. $a^{-1}bacb^{-1}dc$ by starting at U and going counterclockwise, or

b. $c^{-1}d^{-1}bc^{-1}a^{-1}b^{-1}a$ by starting at U and going clockwise, or

c. $cb^{-1}dca^{-1}ba$ by starting at V and going counterclockwise.

13. $abcda^{-1}dc^{-1}xt$ represents

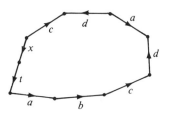

Our aim is to classify all the compact connected surfaces. We will do this by taking a word representing a surface and transform it into a word which represents the same surface and from which we can extract information about the type of surface we have. In order to get some idea of where we are heading, we look at three examples. Wavy lines represent collections of edges.

EXAMPLES.

14.

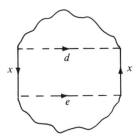

If we cut along d and e, we obtain

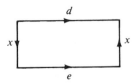

and two other pieces. Thus the surface contains a Möbius strip. A

Möbius strip attached to a surface along the edge of a hole will be called a *cross-cap*.

15.

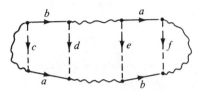

If we cut along c, d, e, and f, we obtain

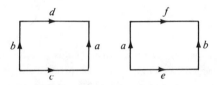

and three other pieces. If we paste along a and b, we see that we have cut a *handle* (think of a suitcase handle) out of the surface. A *handle* is obtained by attaching a tube to the edges of a pair of holes in a surface.

16.

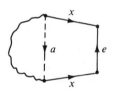

Here we assume that e does not occur elsewhere. If we cut along a, we obtain

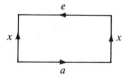

and another piece. Thus we have a handle attached at one end only, which amounts to the surface having a hole.

We need some allowable operations on words, i.e., procedures which change the word but do not change the surface it represents. We will then use these procedures to transform a given word into a standard form in which the cross-caps, handles and holes are clearly visible. In the following discussion capital letters will stand for *blocks* of letters, which may be empty. Thus $abcdefghe^{-1}$ can be represented by $XeYe^{-1}Z$. Here X represents *abcd*, Y represents *fgh*, and Z is empty. We now state the operations we need and show that they transform a given word into another word representing the same surface.

Operation I: Cyclic permutation of letters, for example, *abcde* may be changed to *cdeab*. This just amounts to starting at a different vertex when the edges are listed, so that both words clearly represent the same surface.

Operation II: Change of variables or labels, including, for example, changing *XabYabZ* to *XcYcZ*. This just renames an edge or combines several edges into one when the edges occur always as a block.

Operation III: Add or erase xx^{-1} anywhere, that is, XY is the same as $Xxx^{-1}Y$. The following figures show why this does not change the surface: we cut along x to obtain $Xxx^{-1}Y$, or paste along x to change $Xxx^{-1}Y$ to XY.

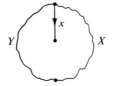 

Operation IV: Change $XAtCDt^{-1}Y$ to $XtDCt^{-1}AY$ or the reverse. The result of this is to move $\ldots t \ldots t^{-1}$ toward the front or rear of the word. We illustrate why this does not change the surface:

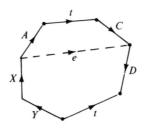

Cut along e, to obtain

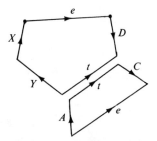

Now paste along t, to obtain

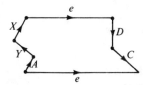

This is represented by $XeDCe^{-1}AY$, and by Operation II this is the same as $XtDCt^{-1}AY$. It is clear that the surface has not been changed, since no pasting has been disturbed.

Operation V: Change $XAbCDbY$ to $XbDA^{-1}bC^{-1}Y$ or the reverse. The result of this is to change the position of $\ldots b \ldots b \ldots$. We again cut and paste to justify this operation:

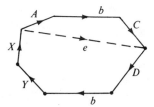

Cut along e to obtain

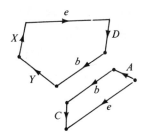

Paste along b to obtain

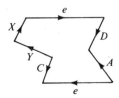

This is represented by the word $XeDA^{-1}eC^{-1}Y$, and Operation II allows us to replace e by b to obtain $XbDA^{-1}bC^{-1}Y$.

We now take a word representing a surface and put it into canonical form.

Step 1: Collect cross-caps. Suppose $\ldots x \ldots x \ldots$ occurs. Then we proceed as follows.

$$PQxRxS$$

$\parallel$

Let $X = P$, $A = Q$, $b = x$, $C = R$, $D = \varnothing$, $b = x$, $Y = S$ and use Operation V.

$$PxQ^{-1}xR^{-1}S$$

$\parallel$

Let $X = P$, $b = x$, $C = Q^{-1}$, $b = x$, $Y = R^{-1}S$, $A = D = \varnothing$ and use Operation V.

$$PxxQR^{-1}S$$

To collect the first cross-cap, we take P to be empty. To collect the second, we take P to be the first, i.e., xx. We continue by taking P to be those already collected. In all cases, $QR^{-1}S$ has no letters in common with Pxx, since each letter occurs at most twice. Since there are only finitely many letters and we create no new one, this procedure must terminate with the word $c_1 c_1 c_2 c_2 \ldots c_q c_q W$, where W contains no $\ldots x \ldots x \ldots$.

Step 2: Collect handles. Suppose $c_1 c_1 c_2 c_2 \ldots c_q c_q W$ contains an interlaced pair, that is, something of the form $\ldots a \ldots b \ldots a^{-1} \ldots b^{-1}$. Since each letter occurs at most twice, this interlaced pair must occur in W. We then proceed as follows.

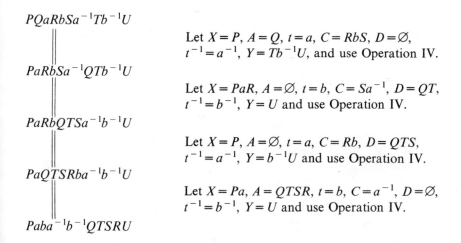

$PQaRbSa^{-1}Tb^{-1}U$

Let $X = P$, $A = Q$, $t = a$, $C = RbS$, $D = \varnothing$, $t^{-1} = a^{-1}$, $Y = Tb^{-1}U$, and use Operation IV.

$PaRbSa^{-1}QTb^{-1}U$

Let $X = PaR$, $A = \varnothing$, $t = b$, $C = Sa^{-1}$, $D = QT$, $t^{-1} = b^{-1}$, $Y = U$ and use Operation IV.

$PaRbQTSa^{-1}b^{-1}U$

Let $X = P$, $A = \varnothing$, $t = a$, $C = Rb$, $D = QTS$, $t^{-1} = a^{-1}$, $Y = b^{-1}U$ and use Operation IV.

$PaQTSRba^{-1}b^{-1}U$

Let $X = Pa$, $A = QTSR$, $t = b$, $C = a^{-1}$, $D = \varnothing$, $t^{-1} = b^{-1}$, $Y = U$ and use Operation IV.

$Paba^{-1}b^{-1}QTSRU$

In this procedure P contains the cross-caps collected in Step 1 and whichever handles have already been collected. No new cross-caps are created, since W contained no $\ldots x \ldots x \ldots$ and no new inverses have been added, that is, we start with Q, R, S, T, U and end with Q, T, S, R, U. Again, since there are only finitely many letters, we must eventually run out of interlaced pairs. This step thus concludes with a word of the form

$$c_1 c_1 c_2 c_2 \ldots c_q c_q a_1 b_1 a_1^{-1} b_1^{-1} \ldots a_p b_p a_p^{-1} b_p^{-1} W,$$

where W now contains no $\ldots x \ldots x \ldots$ and no interlaced pairs.

Step 3: Collect boundaries, or holes. If an xx^{-1} occurs, it can be erased by Operation III. Suppose that after all such erasures, W still contains recurring letters. Then since W contains no $\ldots x \ldots x \ldots$, it must contain $\ldots x \ldots x^{-1} \ldots$. If the portion $x \ldots x^{-1}$ contains a letter y which recurs in W, then both occurrences of y must be in $x \ldots x^{-1}$, since otherwise there would be an interlaced pair. Now consider $y \ldots y^{-1}$ and apply the same argument as above. Continuing this procedure we finally must obtain $\ldots dEd^{-1} \ldots$ in W such that no letter other than d in dEd^{-1} appears elsewhere in W. Also, E is not empty, since all xx^{-1}'s have been erased. E may then be replaced by a single edge e by using Operation II. Finally, by letting $X = P$, $A = Q$, $t = d$, $C = e$, $D = \varnothing$, $t^{-1} = d^{-1}$, $Y = R$ and using Operation IV we may change $PQded^{-1}R$ to $Pded^{-1}QR$. Here, of course, P contains the collected cross-caps and handles plus whatever boundaries have already been collected.

The procedure described above introduces no new cross-caps because it introduces no new inverse and no new interlaced pairs since Q and R remain in the same order. By finiteness, the procedure must terminate with the word in the form

$$(*)\ c_1c_1c_2c_2\ldots c_qc_qa_1b_1a_1^{-1}b_1^{-1}a_2b_2a_2^{-1}b_2^{-1}\ldots a_pb_pa_p^{-1}b_p^{-1}$$
$$d_1e_1d_1^{-1}d_2e_2d_2^{-1}\ldots d_re_rd_r^{-1}W,$$

where W consists only of nonrecurring letters or is empty.

Let us suppose that W is not empty. Since it consists only of nonrecurring letters, it can be replaced by a single edge which will be called e_{r+1} for reasons to be apparent later. We want to remedy the somewhat unpleasant situation of a dangling e_{r+1}, so we introduce some new tools to be used both now and a bit later.

First, if we take D to be empty in Operation IV, we see that $XAtCt^{-1}Y$ is equivalent to $XtCt^{-1}AY$, that is, a block of letters can be pulled through a tCt^{-1} in either direction. Second, if we take R, S, and T to be empty in Step 2 of the procedure above, we see that $PQaba^{-1}b^{-1}U$ is equivalent to $Paba^{-1}b^{-1}QU$, that is, a block of letters can be pulled through an interlaced pair in either direction. Finally, if we take R to be empty in Step 1, we see that $PQxxS$ is equivalent to $PxxQS$, that is, a block of letters can be pulled through a $\ldots xx\ldots$ in either direction.

Now by Operation III, we can add $d_{r+1}^{-1}d_{r+1}$ between d_r^{-1} and e_{r+1} to obtain

$$c_1c_1c_2c_2\ldots c_qc_qa_1b_1a_1^{-1}b_1^{-1}a_2b_2a_2^{-1}b_2^{-1}\ldots a_pb_pa_p^{-1}b_p^{-1}$$
$$d_1e_1d_1^{-1}d_2e_2d_2^{-1}\ldots d_re_rd_r^{-1}d_{r+1}^{-1}d_{r+1}e_{r+1}.$$

Now use the tools outlined above to pull d_{r+1}^{-1} through each $d_ie_id_i^{-1}$ in succession, then through each interlaced pair, and finally through each c_ic_i to obtain

$$d_{r+1}^{-1}c_1c_1c_2c_2\ldots c_qc_qa_1b_1a_1^{-1}b_1^{-1}a_2b_2a_2^{-1}b_2^{-1}\ldots a_pb_pa_p^{-1}b_p^{-1}$$
$$d_1e_1d_1^{-1}d_2e_2d_2^{-1}\ldots d_re_rd_r^{-1}d_{r+1}e_{r+1}.$$

By Operation I this is equivalent to

$$c_1c_1c_2c_2\ldots c_qc_qa_1b_1a_1^{-1}b_1^{-1}a_2b_2a_2^{-1}b_2^{-1}\ldots a_pb_pa_p^{-1}b_p^{-1}$$
$$d_1e_1d_1^{-1}d_2e_2d_2^{-1}\ldots d_re_rd_r^{-1}d_{r+1}e_{r+1}d_{r+1}^{-1}.$$

To sum up, a word representing a compact connected surface can be changed into a word in the canonical form

$$(*)\ c_1c_1c_2c_2\ldots c_qc_qa_1b_1a_1^{-1}b_1^{-1}a_2b_2a_2^{-1}b_2^{-1}\ldots a_pb_pa_p^{-1}b_p^{-1}d_1e_1d_1^{-1}$$
$$d_2e_2d_2^{-1}\ldots d_se_sd_s^{-1},$$

without changing the surface that the word represents. The cases A, B, C listed before Operations I–V were introduced indicate that a surface represented by (*) must be a sphere with q cross-caps, p handles and s holes. To show that this is actually the case, we will cut up a sphere with q cross-caps, p handles and s holes. We will assemble the pieces into a polygon, represent it by a word, and put the word into canonical form. This form will turn out to be (*). Since all our operations are reversible, this will complete our classification of compact connected surfaces.

The astute reader will ask why (*) represents a *sphere* with things attached rather than a disk or something else with attachments. The reason is that the word with no letters represents a sphere, and to see this note that Operation III says that xx^{-1} represents the same surface as the word with no letters, and folds and sews up into a sphere.

The following illustration shows the front part of a sphere with a number of holes drilled. A cross-cap has been removed from the hole whose edge has the labels y_i, z_i, and the removed cross-caps are shown with edges labeled $y_i c_i^{-1} z_i^{-1} c_i^{-1}$. A handle has been removed from the pair of holes with edges labeled u_i, v_i, and the removed handles are shown with edges labeled $b_i v_i^{-1} b_i^{-1} u_i^{-1}$. Finally, the holes whose edges are labeled $e_1, e_2, \ldots, e_s$ are just that—holes.

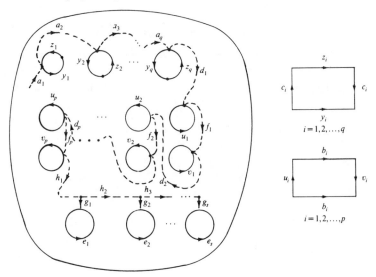

We make the cuts $a_1, a_2, \ldots, a_q$, $d_1, f_1, d_2, f_2, \ldots, d_p$, $f_p, h_1, g_1, h_2, g_2, \ldots, h_s$, g_s, which make a polygon of the sphere shown. The edges of the polygon are labeled by walking around the holes and cuts on the sphere, always keeping the area of the sphere on the right. The following polygon is obtained.

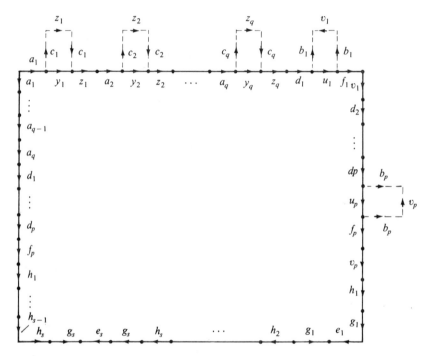

Now attach the cross-caps and handles as shown by the dotted lines. The pair of edges $c_i z_i$ can be combined into the single edge x_i by Operation II. The word representing the surface can now be read from the labeled polygon and is

$$a_1 x_1 x_1 a_2 x_2 x_2 \ldots a_q x_q x_q d_1 b_1 v_1^{-1} b_1^{-1} f_1 v_1 d_2 b_2$$
$$v_2^{-1} b_2^{-1} f_2 v_2 \ldots d_p b_p v_p^{-1} b_p^{-1} f_p v_p h_1 g_1 e_1 g_1^{-1}$$
$$h_2 g_2 e_2 g_2^{-1} \ldots h_s g_s e_s g_s^{-1} h_s^{-1} h_{s-1}^{-1} \ldots h_1^{-1} f_p^{-1}$$
$$d_p^{-1} f_{p-1}^{-1} d_{p-1}^{-1} \ldots f_1^{-1} d_1^{-1} a_q^{-1} a_{q-1}^{-1} \ldots a_1^{-1}.$$

We noted earlier that a block of letters can be pulled through a tCt^{-1} in either direction. Hence, h_1 can be pulled through $g_1 e_1 g_1^{-1}$ to get $h_1 h_2$, then $h_1 h_2$ can be pulled through $g_2 e_2 g_2^{-1}$ to get $h_1 h_2 h_3$ and so on. Finally $h_1 h_2 \ldots h_s$ can be pulled through $g_s e_s g_s^{-1}$ to obtain $h_1 h_2 \ldots h_s h_s^{-1} h_{s-1}^{-1} \ldots h_1^{-1}$. All the h_i^{-1}'s can now be cancelled by Operation III. The resulting word is

$$a_1 x_1 x_1 a_2 x_2 x_2 \ldots a_q x_q x_q d_1 b_1 v_1^{-1} b_1^{-1} f_1 v_1$$
$$d_2 b_2 v_2^{-1} b_2^{-1} f_2 v_2 \ldots d_p b_p v_p^{-1} b_p^{-1} f_p v_p g_1 e_1 g_1^{-1} g_2 e_2 g_2^{-1} \ldots g_s e_s g_s^{-1}$$
$$f_p^{-1} d_p^{-1} f_{p-1}^{-1} d_{p-1}^{-1} \ldots f_1^{-1} d_1^{-1} a_q^{-1} a_{q-1}^{-1} \ldots a_1^{-1}.$$

We again use the fact that a letter or block of letters can be pulled through tCt^{-1} in either direction to pull f_i backwards through $b_i v_i^{-1} b_i^{-1}$ to form $d_i f_i$. If we do this for $i = 1, 2, \ldots, p$, the resulting word is

$$a_1 x_1 x_1 a_2 x_2 x_2 \ldots a_q x_q x_q d_1 f_1 b_1 v_1^{-1} b_1^{-1} v_1$$
$$d_2 f_2 b_2 v_2^{-1} b_2^{-1} v_2 \ldots d_p f_p b_p v_p^{-1} b_p^{-1} v_p g_1 e_1 g_1^{-1} g_2 e_2 g_2^{-1} \ldots g_s e_s g_s^{-1}$$
$$f_p^{-1} d_p^{-1} f_{p-1}^{-1} d_{p-1}^{-1} \ldots f_1^{-1} d_1^{-1} a_q^{-1} a_{q-1}^{-1} \ldots a_1^{-1}.$$

Now recall that a block of letters can be pulled through an interlaced pair in either direction. Thus $d_1 f_1$ can be pulled through $b_1 v_1^{-1} b_1^{-1} v_1$ to form $d_1 f_1 d_2 f_2$, then $d_1 f_1 d_2 f_2$ can be pulled through $b_2 v_2^{-1} b_2^{-1} v_2$ to form $d_1 f_1 d_2 f_2 d_3 f_3$, and so on. As above, $d_1 f_1 d_2 f_2 \ldots d_p f_p$ can be pulled through $g_1 e_1 g_1^{-1}$, then through $g_2 e_2 g_2^{-1}$ and so on. Finally we obtain

$$\ldots d_1 f_1 d_2 f_2 \ldots d_p f_p f_p^{-1} d_p^{-1} f_{p-1}^{-1} d_{p-1}^{-1} \ldots f_1^{-1} d_1^{-1}$$

which cancels by Operation III. The resulting word is

$$a_1 x_1 x_1 a_2 x_2 x_2 \ldots a_q x_q x_q b_1 v_1^{-1} b_1^{-1} v_1 b_2 v_2^{-1} b_2^{-1} v_2 \ldots b_p v_p^{-1} b_p^{-1} v_p$$
$$g_1 e_1 g_1^{-1} g_2 e_2 g_2^{-1} \ldots g_s e_s g_s^{-1} a_q^{-1} a_{q-1}^{-1} \ldots a_1^{-1}.$$

Recall that a combination of letters can be pulled through a $\ldots yy \ldots$. This can be used to pull a_1 through $x_1 x_1$ to obtain $a_1 a_2$, then $a_1 a_2$ through $x_2 x_2$ to obtain $a_1 a_2 a_3$, and so on. We then use the fact that a combination of letters can be pulled through an interlaced pair to pull $a_1 a_2 \ldots a_q$ through each $b_i v_i^{-1} b_i^{-1} v_i$ in turn. Finally, $a_1 a_2 \ldots a_q$ can be pulled through each $g_i e_i g_i^{-1}$ in turn to obtain $\ldots a_1 a_2 \ldots a_q a_q^{-1} a_{q-1}^{-1} \ldots a_1^{-1}$. This cancels by Operation III, and the resulting word is

$$x_1 x_1 x_2 x_2 \ldots x_q x_q b_1 v_1^{-1} b_1^{-1} v_1 b_2 v_2^{-1} b_2^{-1} v_2 \ldots b_p v_p^{-1} b_p^{-1} v_p$$
$$g_1 e_1 g_1^{-1} g_2 e_2 g_2^{-1} \ldots g_s e_s g_s^{-1}.$$

It is easy to see that if y is an edge and y^{-1} is replaced by m, then y is replaced by m^{-1}. We can thus replace v_1^{-1} by v_1 and v_1 by v_1^{-1} to obtain

$$x_1 x_1 x_2 x_2 \ldots x_q x_q b_1 v_1 b_1^{-1} v_1^{-1} b_2 v_2 b_2^{-1} v_2^{-1} \ldots b_p v_p b_p^{-1} v_p^{-1}$$
$$g_1 e_1 g_1^{-1} g_2 e_2 g_2^{-1} \ldots g_s e_s g_s^{-1}.$$

Since this word was obtained from a surface which was a sphere with q cross-caps, p handles and s holes we have proved the following theorem.

Theorem 6.3.3 *Every compact connected surface can be represented by a word in the canonical form*

$$c_1 c_1 c_2 c_2 \ldots c_q c_q a_1 b_1 a_1^{-1} b_1^{-1} \ldots a_p b_p a_p^{-1} b_p^{-1} d_1 e_1 d_1^{-1} \ldots d_s e_s d_s^{-1}.$$

This word represents a surface which is a sphere with q cross-caps, p handles and s holes.

A question which may have occurred to the alert reader is whether two different words in canonical form might represent the same surface. Suppose, for example, that a given surface is cut up in two different ways, assembled into a single polygon with labeled edges, and then put into canonical form. Is it possible to obtain two different words?

The answer to this is yes. In fact a cross-cap and a handle is equivalent to three cross-caps. This is made plausible by an examination of the *Klein bottle* (see the exercises), which is really a sphere with two cross-caps but which also very much resembles a handle.

Recall that Operation V states that $XbDA^{-1}bC^{-1}Y$ is equivalent to $XAbCDbY$. We use this several times as follows:

$$Pccmnm^{-1}n^{-1}Q$$

$$X = P, b = c, D = A^{-1} = \phi, C^{-1} = mnm^{-1},$$
$$Y = n^{-1}Q$$

$$Pcmn^{-1}m^{-1}cn^{-1}Q$$

$$X = Pcm, b = n^{-1}, D = \varnothing, A^{-1} = m^{-1}c,$$
$$Y = Q, C = \phi$$

$$Pcmc^{-1}mn^{-1}n^{-1}Q$$

$$X = Pc, b = m, D = \varnothing, A^{-1} = c^{-1},$$
$$b = m, C = \varnothing, Y = n^{-1}n^{-1}Q$$

$$Pccmmn^{-1}n^{-1}Q$$

We have thus taken the cross-cap cc and the handle $mnm^{-1}n^{-1}$ and changed them into the cross-caps cc, mm, and $n^{-1}n^{-1}$. It is important to note that a handle alone is not equivalent to two cross-caps; the cross-cap must be there to act as a sort of catalyst.

One now easily sees that if a cross-cap is present in the canonical word, then each handle can be changed into a pair of cross-caps to obtain a word of the form

$$c_1 c_1 c_2 c_2 \ldots c_q c_q d_1 e_1 d_1^{-1} d_2 e_2 d_2^{-1} \ldots d_s e_s d_s^{-1}.$$

If no cross-cap is present, then the word has the form

$$a_1 b_1 a_1^{-1} b_1^{-1} a_2 b_2 a_2^{-1} b_2^{-1} \ldots a_p b_p a_p^{-1} b_p^{-1} d_1 e_1 d_1^{-1} d_2 e_2 d_2^{-1} \ldots d_s e_s d_s^{-1}.$$

Recall that if the word representing a surface contains $\ldots x \ldots x \ldots$, then the surface contains a Möbius strip. This motivates the following definition.

Definition A surface S which does not contain a Möbius strip is said to be *orientable*, otherwise, S is said to be *nonorientable*.

A word representing an orientable surface can always be put in the form

$$a_1 b_1 a_1^{-1} b_1^{-1} a_2 b_2 a_2^{-1} b_2^{-1} \ldots a_p b_p a_p^{-1} b_p^{-1} d_1 e_1 d_1^{-1} d_2 e_2 d_2^{-1} \ldots d_s e_s d_s^{-1},$$

and a word representing a nonorientable surface can always be put in the form

$$c_1 c_1 c_2 c_2 \ldots c_q c_q d_1 e_1 d_1^{-1} d_2 e_2 d_2^{-1} \ldots d_s e_s d_s^{-1}.$$

There is still a question of uniqueness remaining, namely, are the numbers p, q, and s unique? For example, could the same surface be represented by

$$c_1 c_1 c_2 c_2 \ldots c_{100} c_{100} d_1 e_1 d_1^{-1} d_2 e_2 d_2^{-1} \ldots d_{36} e_{36} d_{36}^{-1}$$

and by

$$c_1 c_1 c_2 c_2 \ldots c_{99} c_{99} d_1 e_1 d_1^{-1} d_2 e_2 d_2^{-1} \ldots d_{37} e_{37} d_{37}^{-1}?$$

The fact is that the answer is no, but the proof is beyond the scope of this book. The numbers p, q and s are topological properties of the surface in question and do not depend on the particular representation. We sum up the situation in the following theorem.

Theorem 6.3.4 (Classification Theorem for Surfaces) *Let S be a compact connected surface. If S is orientable, then there are unique numbers p and s depending only on S such that any word representing S can be changed into the word*

$$a_1 b_1 a_1^{-1} b_1^{-1} a_2 b_2 a_2^{-1} b_2^{-1} \ldots a_p b_p a_p^{-1} b_p^{-1} d_1 e_1 d_1^{-1} d_2 e_2 d_2^{-1} \ldots d_s e_s d_s^{-1}$$

by using Operations I–V so that S is a sphere with p handles and s holes. If S is nonorientable, then there are unique numbers q and s depending only on S such that any word representing S can be changed into the word

$$c_1 c_1 c_2 c_2 \ldots c_q c_q d_1 e_1 d_1^{-1} d_2 e_2 d_2^{-1} \ldots d_s e_s d_s^{-1}$$

by using Operations I–V so that S is a sphere with q cross-caps attached and s holes drilled.

Our next objective is to use the Classification Theorem for Surfaces to generalize Euler's Formula for the Plane. Recall that Euler's formula dealt with connected graphs in the plane or on the sphere. In the general case we must work with objects which are nearly but not quite graphs. The following example shows why.

Consider the surface represented by $aba^{-1}b^{-1}$. Its polygon is

After doing the indicated pasting, the edges a and b take the form

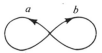

Now this object is not a graph, but only because some vertexes have been suppressed. We could just as well deal with

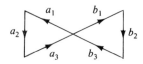

which is a graph. Note that the vertexes which have been added always separate a single edge into two new edges, so that (number of vertexes) − (number of edges) remains the same. We are led to the following definition.

Definition A *network* is the underlying space of a graph, together with the simplicial structure that remains when some or all of the vertexes of the graph have been suppressed. Each arc must begin and end at a vertex. A *map on a surface* is a network on that surface. The portions into which the network divides the surface are called the *faces of the map*, the arcs of the network are called the *edges of the map*, and the vertexes of the network are called the *vertexes of the map*. The numbers of faces, edges, and vertexes are denoted by F, E, and V respectively. Finally, a map on a surface is said to be *simple* if each face becomes a disk when the surface is cut along the network and the edges of the holes of the surface are edges of the map.

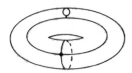

We note that $V - E + F = 1 - 1 + 1 = 1$ for the map on the left but that $V - E + F = 3 - 5 + 2 = 0$ for the map on the right. Just as Euler's Formula holds only for connected maps, its generalization holds only for simple maps. The figure on the right shows a simple map, while the figure on the left does not.

Theorem 6.3.5 *Let S be a sphere with q cross-caps, p handles, and r holes and suppose M is a simple map on S. Then*

$$V - E + F = 2 - q - 2p - r.$$

PROOF. Cut S along each edge of M. Since M is simple, this disassembles S into the faces of M, i.e., a collection of polygons with properly labeled edges in which each edge and vertex of M appears. We can thus obtain the number $V - E + F$ for M by doing our counting on the disassembled S. Before we do so, we would like to have the polygons put into canonical form.

First, assemble the polygons into a single polygon. Each time two polygons are pasted along an edge, one edge and one polygon disappear. Hence, $V - E + F$ is unchanged. Once the polygons are all assembled, operations I–V will be used to put the polygon into canonical form. Let us see what Operations I–V do to $V - E + F$.

Operation I: Cyclic permutation clearly changes none of V, E, and F.

Operation II: Changing the name of an edge clearly changes nothing. Replacing xy by a single edge deletes one edge and one vertex, leaving $V - E + F$ unchanged.

Operation III: Adding or erasing xx^{-1} adds or drops an edge and vertex, leaving $V - E + F$ unchanged.

Operations IV and V: In justifying these operations we made a cut, thus adding an edge and a face, and then pasted, thus dropping an edge and a face. Thus $V - E + F$ is left unchanged.

Operations I–V can thus be used to change the word obtained from the assembled polygon into the proper canonical word without changing $V - E + F$.

Orientable Case

In this case $q = 0$ and the canonical word is

$$a_1 b_1 a_1^{-1} b_1^{-1} a_2 b_2 a_2^{-1} b_2^{-1} \ldots a_p b_p a_p^{-1} b_p^{-1} d_1 e_1 d_1^{-1} d_2 e_2 d_2^{-1} \ldots d_r e_r d_r^{-1}$$

Since there is only one polygon, $F=1$. By counting letters it is clear that the number of edges is $E=2p+2r$. Vertexes are counted as follows, where the numbers at the tail of arrows indicate vertex numbers:

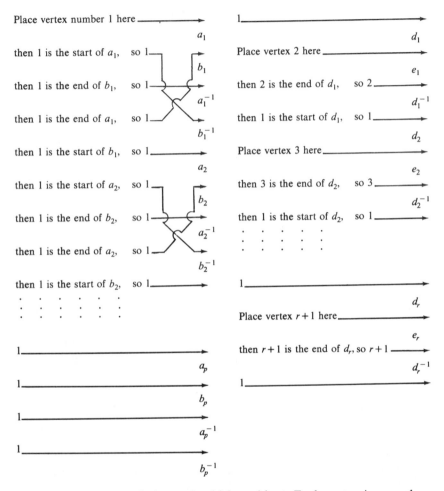

The procedure used above should be evident. Each vertex is spread as far as possible, and then a new one is placed. There are thus $r+1$ vertexes, so in this case

$$V - E + F = (r+1) - (2p+2r) + 1 = 2 - 2p - r$$
$$= 2 - q - 2p - r \quad \text{since } q = 0.$$

Nonorientable Case

Here q is not zero, but p may also not be zero. However, if $p \neq 0$, then each handle can be changed into two cross-caps, and the canonical word

216

obtained is

$$c_1c_1c_2c_2\ldots c_tc_td_1e_1d_1^{-1}d_2e_2d_2^{-1}\ldots d_re_rd_r^{-1},$$

where $t = q + 2p$. Again $F = 1$ and it is evident that $E = t + 2r = q + 2p + 2r$. The vertexes are counted by using the same procedure:

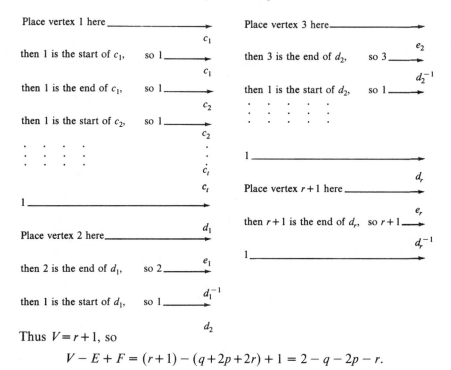

Thus $V = r + 1$, so

$$V - E + F = (r + 1) - (q + 2p + 2r) + 1 = 2 - q - 2p - r.$$

This finishes the proof. ∎

Definition If S is a sphere with q cross-caps, p handles, and r holes, then the *Euler characteristic* of S is $\mathcal{X}(S) = 2 - q - 2p - r$.

The Classification Theorem for Surfaces implies that the Euler characteristic is a topological property of a surface. Further, in order to identify a surface S, it is enough to know its orientability, its Euler characteristic, and the number of holes it has. For if S is orientable, then $q = 0$, and if not, one may assume that $p = 0$. Since $\mathcal{X}(S) = V - E + F$, one can identify S by counting V, E, and F and then determining orientability and the number of holes. S is nonorientable if and only if $\ldots x \ldots x \ldots$ occurs in a word representing S. Further, it is evident from our representation of surfaces that each loop of unrepeated letters in the word gives rise to a hole. We illustrate the identification procedure by examples.

Let us identify the surface S represented by $abcdec^{-1}da^{-1}b^{-1}e^{-1}$. Since

217

...d...d... occurs, S is nonorientable and p may be taken to be zero. There is a single polygon, so $F = 1$, and there are five different labels, so $E = 5$. The vertex-counting procedure may be used to obtain V. This is done step-by-step as before, but here we number the steps in the order they are taken:

1. Place vertex 1 here $\underrightarrow{\hspace{2cm}}$
   a

8. 1 is the start of b, so 1 $\underrightarrow{\hspace{1.5cm}}$
   b

3. 1 is the end of b, so 1 $\underrightarrow{\hspace{1.5cm}}$
   c

5. 1 is the start of d, so 1 $\underrightarrow{\hspace{1.5cm}}$
   d

10. 1 is the end of d, so 1 $\underrightarrow{\hspace{1.5cm}}$
    e

6. 1 is the end of c, so 1 $\underrightarrow{\hspace{1.5cm}}$
   c^{-1}

4. 1 is the start of c, so 1 $\underrightarrow{\hspace{2cm}}$
   d

9. 1 is the end of a, so 1 $\underrightarrow{\hspace{1.5cm}}$
   a^{-1}

2. 1 is the start of a, so 1 $\underrightarrow{\hspace{1.5cm}}$
   b^{-1}

7. 1 is the end of e, so 1 $\underrightarrow{\hspace{1.5cm}}$
   e^{-1}

11. 1 is the start of e, so 1 $\underrightarrow{\hspace{1.5cm}}$

We conclude that $V = 1$. Since there are no unrepeated labels, there are no holes, so $r = 0$. Hence $\mathcal{X}(S) = V - E + F = 1 - 5 + 1 = -3 = 2 - q$, so that $q = 5$. Thus S is a sphere with five cross-caps. One can also say that S is a sphere with one cross-cap and two handles, or three cross-caps and one handle.

Now let's identify the surface S represented by $abxcdegc^{-1}f^{-1}a^{-1}$ $yrb^{-1}e^{-1}$. No ...x...x... occurs, so S is orientable and q is zero. There is a single polygon, so $F = 1$, and there are ten different labels, so $E = 10$. The vertex-counting procedure illustrated below shows that $V = 6$:

1. Place vertex 1 here $\underrightarrow{\hspace{2cm}}$
   a

5. Place vertex 2 here $\underrightarrow{\hspace{1.5cm}}$
   b

9. Place vertex 3 here $\underrightarrow{\hspace{1.5cm}}$
   x

11. Place vertex 4 here $\underrightarrow{\hspace{1.5cm}}$
    c

13. Place vertex 5 here $\underrightarrow{\hspace{1.5cm}}$
    d

4. 1 is the start of e, so 1 $\underrightarrow{\hspace{1.5cm}}$
   e

7. 2 is the end of e, so 2 $\underrightarrow{\hspace{1.5cm}}$
   g

14. 5 is the end of c, so 5 $\underrightarrow{\hspace{1.5cm}}$
    c^{-1}

12. 4 is the start of c, so 4 $\underrightarrow{\hspace{1.5cm}}$
    f^{-1}

8. By (5), 2 is the end of a, so 2 $\underrightarrow{\hspace{1.5cm}}$
   a^{-1}

2. 1 is the start of a, so 1 $\underrightarrow{\hspace{1.5cm}}$
   y

15. Place vertex 6 here $\underrightarrow{\hspace{1.5cm}}$
    r

10. 3 is the end of b, so 3 $\underrightarrow{\hspace{1.5cm}}$
    b^{-1}

6. 2 is the start of b, so 2 $\underrightarrow{\hspace{1.5cm}}$
   e^{-1}

3. Because the word is cyclic, 1 is also $\rightarrow$

Now x, d, g, f, y, and r are the unrepeated letters. Loops are determined as follows: x runs from vertex 3 to vertex 4, then f^{-1} runs from vertex 4 to vertex 2, then g runs from vertex 2 to vertex 5, then d runs from vertex 5 to vertex 1, then y runs from vertex 1 to vertex 6, and then r runs from vertex 6 to vertex 3, completing the loop. Since all unrepeated letters have been used in this one loop, there is one hole, that is, $r = 1$. Hence $\mathfrak{X}(S) = V - E + F = 6 - 10 + 1 = -3 = 2 - 2p - 1$, so $p = 2$, and we conclude that S is a sphere with two handles and one hole.

The Euler characteristic of a surface plays an important role in the problem of map coloring. If we are given a map on a surface, then we would like to color the faces in such a way that two faces which share a common edge have different colors, otherwise they may have the same color. The problem is then to determine how many colors are both necessary and sufficient to color every map on a given surface.

This question has a long and colorful history going back at least to 1852, when DeMorgan remarked that four colors always seemed to be sufficient to color a planar map. In 1880 Kempe and Tait published proofs that four colors always sufficed for a planar map, but in 1890 Heawood pointed out errors in these proofs, proved some theorems of his own, and made some conjectures. To state these results we use the notation $[x]$ for the largest integer not larger than the number x.

Heawood's Theorem *To color any map on a surface without holes of Euler characteristic $\chi < 2$ requires at most $[\frac{1}{2}(7 + \sqrt{49 - 24\chi}\,)]$ colors.*

Heawood's Conjecture *If S is a surface without holes and having Euler characteristic χ, then there is always a map on S that requires $[\frac{1}{2}(7 + \sqrt{49 - 24\chi}\,)]$ colors.*

In 1957 P. Franklin showed that six colors always suffice for maps on the sphere with two cross-caps, also called the *Klein bottle*. Since the Euler characteristic of the Klein bottle is zero, Heawood's Conjecture is false in this case. Work on Heawood's Conjecture culminated in 1968, with the net result that it is true for all surfaces except the Klein bottle. Thus at this stage the map coloring problem had been solved for all surfaces except the sphere or plane.

This left one of the most famous problems in mathematics, namely, the *Four Color Problem*, which asked whether four colors always sufficed for a planar map. This was finally solved in 1977 by Haken and Appel, who with the help of over 1000 hours of computer time showed that four colors always do suffice for coloring a planar map.

Proofs of these coloring results would lead us too far astray. We must leave the subject of combinatorial topology here with the hope that the reader is intrigued and will pursue the subject elsewhere.

Exercises

1. Give two nonhomeomorphic examples of two-dimensional simplicial complexes whose underlying spaces are not surfaces.

2. Describe a simplicial complex whose underlying space is
   a. the 2-sphere
   b. a torus
   c. a sphere with three holes.

3. Assemble the following into a single polygon.
   a.

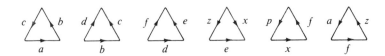

   b.

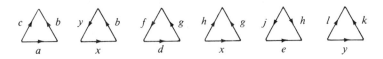

   c.

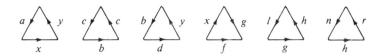

4. **a.** What happens when you cut a Möbius strip down the center?
   b. What happens when you cut a Möbius strip near its edge?
   c. Construct a labeled polygon representing the result of pasting two Möbius strips together along their edges. This surface is called the *Klein bottle*.
   d. Draw a picture of the actual Klein bottle.

e. Describe or draw a simplicial complex whose underlying space is the Möbius strip. Now try to orient each 2-simplex in such a way that edges shared by two 2-simplexes receive opposite orientations; that is, this

but not this

This phenomenon gives rise to the term *nonorientable*.

5. Prove that every graph can be embedded in a sphere with p handles for some p. Hint: put the vertexes on the sphere and then add handles as necessary.

6. Check that the surface operations IV and V are still valid when
   a. X is empty;
   b. C is empty;
   c. Y and D are empty.

7. Show that the following pairs of words represent the same surfaces:
   a. $XAbCDb^{-1}Y$ and $XAYbCDb^{-1}$
   b. $XAbCDb^{-1}Y$ and $XAbDCb^{-1}Y$.

8. Apply the cross-cap, handle, and hole-collecting procedure to the following words:
   a. $gabcdec^{-1}f^{-1}a^{-1}b^{-1}eg$
   b. $abacdbc^{-1}dxefge^{-1}y$
   c. $abca^{-1}xyb^{-1}dc^{-1}td^{-1}$.

9. Write a word that represents
   a. a sphere with six cross-caps and two holes
   b. a sphere with four handles and no holes
   c. a sphere with two cross-caps, two handles, and one hole
   d. a sphere with one cross-cap and five holes.

10. Identify the surfaces represented by
   a. $aabbccded^{-1}fgf^{-1}$
   b. $aabcb^{-1}c^{-1}ded^{-1}e^{-1}f^{-1}g^{-1}fghih^{-1}$
   c. $aabbcdc^{-1}d^{-1}efe^{-1}ghg^{-1}iji^{-1}$.

11. Identify the surfaces determined by the following words or information:
   a. $abca^{-1}xbdtyt^{-1}j$
   b. $pqrstuq$

c. $p^{-1}rtvqpsr^{-1}$

d. $mathem^{-1}a^{-1}t^{-1}ics$

e. $acba^{-1}db^{-1}ecef$

f. $\mathfrak{X}(S) = -8$, S has two holes and S is orientable

g. $\mathfrak{X}(S) = -9$ and S has no holes

h. $\mathfrak{X}(S) = -12$, S has four holes and S is nonorientable

i. the surface in Exercise 3.a

j. the surface in Exercise 3.b

k. the surface in Exercise 3.c.

12. By mimicking the proof that K_5 is not embeddable in the plane, prove that the graph with eight vertexes and all possible arcs cannot be embedded in the torus in such a way that the resulting map is simple.

13. How many colors are necessary and sufficient to color every map on
    a. a torus?
    b. a sphere with three handles?
    c. a sphere with six cross-caps?

14. Construct a map on the torus that requires seven colors.

15. What effect do holes in a surface have on map coloring?

7

The fundamental group

Although all the subject matter of this book comes under the heading of topology, there are at least three distinct themes. One is the foundational aspect of topology, studied in Chapters 2, 3 and to some extent 4. These chapters make the fundamental definitions, prove and apply the basic theorems and introduce the reader to that branch of the subject known as *general topology*. A second aspect of the subject called *geometric topology* is found in parts of Chapter 4 and in Chapter 6. Here the study shifts to more concrete objects such as spheres and surfaces.

A third major branch of topology called *algebraic topology* has been touched on in Chapter 5 and we return to it here. Recall that the main idea of Chapter 5 was the association of a number with certain curves in the plane. This is the fundamental notion in algebraic topology, namely, the association of an algebraic object with a topological object. The hope is that the algebraic objects will be simpler in some sense, so that we can obtain algebraic results which then translate back into topological ones.

In this chapter we will define and study perhaps the most important example of this transference from topology to algebra, the *fundamental group*. It would be nice if the reader had some algebraic background, but we will provide the material necessary to keep the chapter fairly self-contained. As usual, we hope the reader's appetite will be whetted and he will pursue these algebraic topological studies elsewhere.

7.1 The homotopy relation

In order to see why we need the results of this section, we give a preview of Section 7.2. There we will put an algebraic structure on a certain set of paths in a space X. The basic ingredient of an algebraic structure is a binary operation, and there is a natural binary operation on paths in which two paths f and g in X from a third path by first running along f and then along g. Unfortunately, this binary operation lacks even the most rudimentary algebraic properties. It is not associative nor does it have an identity element, so that the algebraic structure thus obtained is bad indeed.

In order to remedy this we need an equivalence relation on the set of paths in a space, and this is what we construct and investigate in this section. The basic idea is that two functions f and g are equivalent if we can slide f so as to agree with g (see the illustration). We really need a collection of "intermediate functions" $\{f_t\}$, so that $f_0 = f$ and $f_1 = g$ and the f_t's vary continuously with t. This is the heart of the definition, though it contains some added (necessary) details.

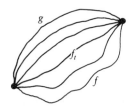

Definition Let f and g be continuous functions from a space X into a space Y such that $f(x) = g(x)$ for each x in the subset A of X. Then f is *homotopic to g relative to A*, written $f \simeq g$ rel A, if there is a continuous function F from $X \times I$ (recall that $I = [0, 1]$) into Y such that $F(x, 0) = f(x), F(x, 1) = g(x)$ for all x in X and $F(x, t) = f(x)$ for all x in A and t in I. Then F is said to be a *homotopy* from f to g relative to A. If A is empty, then we will just say that f is homotopic to g and write $f \simeq g$.

EXAMPLES.

1. A subset Y of R^n is said to be *convex* if $tp + (1 - t)q$ is in Y whenever p, q are in Y and $0 \leqslant t \leqslant 1$. Let f and g be any two continuous functions from a space X into a convex subset Y of R^n. Define $F(x, t) = tg(x) + (1 - t)f(x)$. Then F is easily seen to be a homotopy from f to g, and if f and g agree on a subset A of X, then F is a homotopy from f to g relative to A. One important example of a convex subset of R^n is the n-ball B^n.

2. Let $Y=\{0,1\}\subset R$ and let $X=\{0\}\subset R$. Define $f(0)=0$ and $g(0)=1$. If F were a homotopy from f to g, then F would take the connected space $\{0\}\times I$ onto the disconnected space Y. This cannot happen, so that f and g cannot be homotopic. This example shows that the ideas of homotopy and connectedness are thickly intertwined.

3. Recall from Chapter 5 that we denote $R^2\backslash\{(0,0)\}$ by $\tilde{R}^2$ and call it the punctured plane. Recall also that $S^1=\{(x,y)\in R^2:x^2+y^2=1\}\subset \tilde{R}^2$. Define $f:\tilde{R}^2\rightarrow S^1$ by $f(p)=p/|p|$. Since the line segment from p to $p/|p|$ always lies in $\tilde{R}^2$, we can define $F(p,t)=tf(p)+(1-t)p$. Then F is a homotopy from the identity function on $\tilde{R}^2$ to f viewed as a function into $\tilde{R}^2$. We will return to this example and generalize it later.

4. For this example we need the following definition.

Definition A *path* from x to y in a space X is a continuous function f from I into X such that $f(0)=x$ and $f(1)=y$.

Now let $\{a\}$ be any single-point space. A homotopy between two functions from $\{a\}$ into a space Y is a function $H:\{a\}\times I\rightarrow Y$ which can be identified with the function $f(t)=H(a,t)$. Thus paths are examples of homotopies between functions. In deeper studies of the subject this viewpoint is expanded.

The study of the homotopy relation rests on the construction of the homotopies, so before we begin the study proper we need a technique for checking continuity. The following result is the natural generalization of Exercise 6 of Section 4.3.

Theorem 7.1.1 **(The Pasting Lemma)** *Let $C_1,C_2,\ldots,C_r$ be closed subsets of a space X whose union is X. Let $f_1,f_2,\ldots,f_r$ be continuous functions from C_1, $C_2,\ldots,C_r$ respectively into a space Y such that $f_i(x)=f_j(x)$ whenever $x\in C_i\cap C_j$ and $1\leqslant i,j\leqslant r$. Then $f:X\rightarrow Y$ defined by $f(x)=f_i(x)$ for $x\in C_i$ is a continuous function.*

PROOF. The proof is straightforward and a good review of continuity, so we leave it as an exercise. ∎

The Pasting Lemma together with the continuity of the linear operations in R^n and the continuity of the composition of two continuous functions furnishes the basis for almost all proofs of continuity in elementary homotopy theory. Consequently we will leave many of the details as exercises and eventually will even be content with a picture, leaving it up to the reader to furnish the analytical details.

Theorem 7.1.2 *Let X and Y be spaces and A a subset of X. Then homotopy relative to A is an equivalence relation on any set $\mathcal{C}$ of continuous functions from X to Y; that is, whenever f, g and h are in $\mathcal{C}$, then*

1. $f \simeq f \operatorname{rel} A$;
2. *If $f \simeq g \operatorname{rel} A$, then $g \simeq f \operatorname{rel} A$;*
3. *If $f \simeq g \operatorname{rel} A$ and $g \simeq h \operatorname{rel} A$, then $f \simeq h \operatorname{rel} A$.*

PROOF. We will define the requisite homotopies in each case and leave all other details to the reader:

1. $F(x, t) = f(x)$
2. If G is the homotopy from f to g relative to A, then the function $F(x, t) = G(x, 1 - t)$ is a homotopy from g to f relative to A.
3. If G is a homotopy from f to g relative to A and K is a homotopy from g to h relative to A, then

$$F(x, t) = \begin{cases} G(x, 2t) & 0 \leqslant t \leqslant \frac{1}{2} \\ K(x, 2t - 1) & \frac{1}{2} \leqslant t \leqslant 1 \end{cases}$$

is a homotopy from f to h relative to A. ∎

Theorem 7.1.3 *Let f and f' be continuous functions from X to Y and let g and g' be continuous functions from Y to Z. If $f \simeq f' \operatorname{rel} A$ and $g \simeq g' \operatorname{rel} B$, where $f(A) \subset B$, then $g \circ f \simeq g' \circ f' \operatorname{rel} A$.*

PROOF. If H is a homotopy from f to f' relative to A, and K is a homotopy from g to g' relative to B, then it is easy to check that $F(x, t) = K(H(x, t), t)$ is a homotopy from $g \circ f$ to $g' \circ f'$ relative to A. ∎

It turns out that the algebraic objects which an algebraic topologist associates with topological objects do not change under homotopies. For example, essentially the same algebraic function will be associated with two homotopic continuous functions. We now introduce the terminology and results which form the beginning of the study of this classification of topological objects "up to homotopy."

Definition A continuous function f from a space X to a space Y is said to be a *homotopy equivalence* from X to Y if there is a continuous function g from Y to X such that $f \circ g \simeq \operatorname{Id}_Y$ and $g \circ f \simeq \operatorname{Id}_X$, where Id_W denotes the *identity function* on W. The space X is then said to be *homotopy equivalent* to the space Y and g is said to be a *homotopy inverse* of f.

Theorem 7.1.4

1. *A space X is homotopy equivalent to itself.*

2. *If a space X is homotopy equivalent to a space Y, then Y is homotopy equivalent to X.*

3. *If a space X is homotopy equivalent to a space Y and Y is homotopy equivalent to a space Z, then X is homotopy equivalent to Z.*

PROOF. Parts (1) and (2) are trivial. If f is a homotopy equivalence from X to Y with homotopy inverse g, and h is a homotopy equivalence from Y to Z with homotopy inverse k, then consider the functions $h \circ f$ and $g \circ k$. Applications of Theorem 7.1.3 yield $(h \circ f) \circ (g \circ k) = h \circ (f \circ g) \circ k \simeq h \circ \mathrm{Id}_Y \circ k = h \circ k \simeq \mathrm{Id}_Z$ and $(g \circ k) \circ (h \circ f) = g \circ (k \circ h) \circ f \simeq g \circ \mathrm{Id}_Y \circ f = g \circ f \simeq \mathrm{Id}_X$. Hence $h \circ f$ is a homotopy equivalence from X to Z. ∎

The last theorem says that homotopy equivalence leads to a classification of spaces just like homeomorphism does. We will see in examples that nonhomeomorphic spaces may be homotopy equivalent, so that the homotopy classification is coarser. However, it is very often just fine enough and algebraic topology in general is built on the homotopy rather than the homeomorphism classification. Before we look at examples, we introduce some more terminology.

Definition A space X is *contractible* to the point p of X if the identity function on X is homotopic to the constant function taking X to p.

Definition The subspace A of the space X is a *deformation retract* of X if there is a continuous function r from X to A such that $r(x) = x$ for each x in A and r is homotopic to Id_X when r is viewed as a map from X to itself. The function r is called a *retraction* of X onto A.

EXAMPLES.

5. Recall our earlier punctured plane and circle example. The function $f(p) = p/|p|$ certainly satisfies $f(p) = p$ for each p in S^1, and we have shown that f is homotopic to the identity function on the punctured plane $\tilde{R}^2$. Hence S^1 is a deformation retract of $\tilde{R}^2$.

6. Let X be a convex subset of R^n. As shown earlier, any two maps from any space into X are homotopic, so that in particular Id_X is homotopic to any constant map from X to a point of itself. Thus convex subsets of R^n are contractible.

The relationships among contractibility, deformation retraction, and homotopy equivalence are important and the basic ones are given in the next theorem.

Theorem 7.1.5

1. *If the subspace A of the space X is a deformation retract of X, then X is homotopy equivalent to A.*
2. *A space X is contractable if and only if X is homotopy equivalent to a single-point space.*

PROOF.

1. Let r be a retraction of X onto A which is homotopic to Id_X, and define $J: A \to X$ by $J(a) = a$. Since $r(x) = x$ for each x in A, $r \circ J = \mathrm{Id}_A$. Also, $J(r(x)) = r(x)$, so the homotopy from r to Id_X shows that $J \circ r \simeq \mathrm{Id}_X$. Hence r is a homotopy equivalence from X to A.
2. If X is contractable to the point p, then $\{p\}$ is clearly a deformation retract of X, so that (1) says that X is homotopy equivalent to the single-point space $\{p\}$. Conversely, if X is homotopy equivalent to the single-point space $\{z\}$, then there is a function $g(z) = p$ which is a homotopy inverse of the constant function $f: X \to \{z\}$. Since $g \circ f \simeq \mathrm{Id}_X$, there is ·a homotopy $H: X \times I \to X$ such that $H(x, 0) = x$ and $H(x, 1) = g(f(x)) = p$ for all $x \in X$. Thus Id_X is homotopic to the constant function taking X to p. ∎

EXAMPLE.

7. Let $S = \{(x, \sin 1/x): 0 < x \leqslant \pi\} \cup \{(x, y): (x - 2\pi)^2 + y^2 = \pi^2\} \subset R^2$, $T = \{(0, y): -1 \leqslant y \leqslant 1\} \subset R^2$ and $X = S \cup T$. Now $\mathrm{Cl}(S) = X$ and S is homeomorphic to the union of $(0, \pi]$ and a circle with center $(2\pi, 0)$ and radius π, so that X is connected. X is also compact. Finally, S is homotopy equivalent to a circle. We will show that a homotopy which starts in S or T must stay in S or T, even though X is connected.

    Let f be a continuous function from $[0, 1]$ into X such that $f([0, 1])$ meets S. Suppose that $f([0, 1])$ also meets T and that $f(z_0) \in S$. Since $f^{-1}(T)$ is closed, there is either $z_1 < z_0$ such that $f(z_1) \in T$ but $f((z_1, z_0]) \subset S$ or $z_2 > z_0$ such that $f(z_2) \in T$ but $f([z_0, z_2)) \subset S$. Consider the first case, the other being similar. Since $f([z_1, z_0])$ is connected and meets both S and T, it must contain $\{(t, \sin 1/t): 0 < t < (x\text{-coordinate of } f(z_0)\}$. Then since $f([z_1, z_0])$, is compact it must contain all of T. But $f([z_1, z_0]) \cap T = \{f(z_1)\} \neq T$. Hence any path in X that meets S must lie entirely in S.

    Suppose now that H is a homotopy from f to g, where f, g are continuous functions from a space Y into X and $f(Y) \subset S$. The function H_x defined by $H_x(t) = H(x, t)$ is a path in X from $H_x(0) = f(x)$ to $H_x(1) = g(x)$, so that $g(x)$ must also lie in S. Thus homotopies that begin in S must stay in S. A similar argument shows that homotopies that begin in T must stay in T.

This example and our previous comparison of homotopy equivalence with homeomorphism suggests that one should study properties of spaces that are homotopy invariant, and that these properties may differ from topological properties. We make the relevant definition and prove one theorem, but leave other results for the exercises.

Definition A property P of spaces is *homotopy invariant* or a *homotopy property* if Y has P whenever X has P and X is homotopy equivalent to Y.

Theorem 7.1.6 *Connectedness is a homotopy invariant but compactness is not.*

PROOF.   Any convex subset of R^n is contractible. In particular, R^n itself is contractible and so is homotopy equivalent to a point. But a single-point space is compact and R^n is not, so compactness is not a homotopy invariant.

Suppose now that f is a homotopy equivalence from X to Y with homotopy inverse g and that X is connected. Let H be a homotopy from Id_Y to $f \circ g$. If $y \in Y$, then $H(\{y\} \times I)$ is a connected subset of Y that contains $y = H(y, 0)$ and $f(g(y)) = H(y, 1)$. This connected set meets the connected set $f(X)$, so if x_0 is any point of X, then each point of Y lies together with $f(x_0)$ in a connected subset of Y, namely, $f(X) \cup H(\{y\} \times I)$. Hence Y is connected.   ∎

Exercises

1. Provide all the details for Example 3.

2. Prove Theorem 7.1.1.

3. Provide all the details of the proof of Theorem 7.1.2.

4. Provide all the details of the proof of Theorem 7.1.3.

5. A space X is *path-connected* if whenever p, q are points of X, then there is a path in X from p to q.
   a. Prove that path-connectedness is a homotopy invariant;
   b. Prove that a contractible space is path-connected.

6. Prove that if X is contractible to the point p and q is any point of X, then X is contractible to the point q. Hint: there is a path in X from p to q. Paste this path on to the end of the homotopy from Id_X to the constant map of X to p.

7. The *comb space* is the subspace of R^2 given by $X = \{(x, y) \in R^2 : (y = 0$ and $0 \leqslant x \leqslant 1)$ or $(x = 0$ and $0 \leqslant y \leqslant 1)$ or $(x = 1/n$ and $0 \leqslant y \leqslant 1$ for $n = 1, 2, \ldots)\}$.
   a. Prove that the comb space is contractible to $(0, 1)$.

b. Prove that there is no homotopy H from Id_X to the constant map from X to $(0,1)$ which satisfies $H((0,1),t)=(0,1)$ for all t. Hint: if $H((0,1),t)=(0,1)$ for all t, then there is a neighborhood U of $(0,1)$ such that $d(H(p,t),(0,1))<\frac{1}{2}$ for all $p\in U$ and all t. But $H((1/n,1),t)$ must be $(0,0)$ for some t.

8. Prove that if f and g are continuous functions from I into a space X such that $f(0)=g(0)$, then $f\simeq g\,\mathrm{rel}\{0\}$. Hint: $H(x,t)=f((1-t)x)$.

9. Prove that the following pairs of spaces are homotopy equivalent.
  a. S^1 and $\{(x,y)\in R^2:\frac{1}{2}\leqslant x^2+y^2\leqslant 4\}$.
  b. A point and the n-od$\{(x,y)\in R^2:0\leqslant x\leqslant 1$ and $y=x/j$ for $j=1,2,\ldots,n\}$.
  c. A point and the space pictured by H.
  d. S^1 and the solid torus $T=S^1\times B^2$.
  e. The space X and the space $X\times Y$, where Y is contractible.

10. a. Prove that any two continuous functions from any space Y into a contractible space X are homotopic.
  b. Prove that any two continuous functions from a contractible space X into a path-connected space Y are homotopic.
  c. Show that Y must be path-connected for (b) to be true.

11. Prove that the product of contractible spaces is contractible.

7.2 The fundamental group

In this section we use the set of paths in a space X to define an algebraic group associated with X and we also begin an investigation of these groups. As we noted earlier, there is a natural way to form a new path from two given ones f and g, namely, run first along f and then along g to get $f*g$. In order for this to make sense, we must require that $f(1)=g(0)$. We would also like to combine f and g in the other order to get $g*f$, so that we must also require that $f(0)=g(1)$. Finally, as it stands, this operation is not associative, that is, $(f*g)*h$ is not the same function as $f*(g*h)$, so we must introduce homotopies of such paths and treat two homotopic paths as if they represented the same object. Exercise 8 of the previous section then implies that homotopies $\mathrm{rel}\{0\}$ are not what we want, since eventually *any* two paths are homotopic $\mathrm{rel}\{0\}$ so that all information about the space X is lost. We are led to the following definitions.

Definition For two paths f and g in a space X, which satisfy $f(1)=g(0)$, we define $f*g$ by

$$f*g(t) = \begin{cases} f(2t) & 0\leqslant t\leqslant \frac{1}{2} \\ g(2t-1) & \frac{1}{2}\leqslant t\leqslant 1. \end{cases}$$

If x_0 is a point of the space X, then a *loop* in X based at x_0 is a path f in X such that $f(0) = f(1) = x_0$ and the set of all such loops is denoted by $\Omega(X, x_0)$. Theorem 7.1.2 says that homotopy relative to $\{0, 1\}$ is an equivalence relation in $\Omega(X, x_0)$. When f is in $\Omega(X, x_0)$ we denote its equivalence class by $[f]$, that is, $[f] = \{ g \in \Omega(X, x_0) : f \simeq g \operatorname{rel} \{0, 1\} \}$. Finally, the set of such equivalence classes is denoted by $\pi_1(X, x_0)$.

We now have the set and the operation which will form the algebraic group associated with the space X. The next theorem verifies that it has the required properties.

Theorem 7.2.1 *Let x_0 be a point of the space X and let f, g, h, f' and g' be loops in $\Omega(X, x_0)$. Then the following statements are true*:

1. $f*g$ *is in $\Omega(X, x_0)$.*
2. *If $f \simeq f' \operatorname{rel} \{0, 1\}$ and $g \simeq g' \operatorname{rel} \{0, 1\}$, then $f*g \simeq f'*g' \operatorname{rel} \{0, 1\}$.*
3. $f*(g*h) \simeq (f*g)*h \operatorname{rel} \{0, 1\}$.
4. *If e is the element of $\Omega(X, x_0)$ which takes all of I to x_0, then $e*f \simeq f \operatorname{rel} \{0, 1\}$ and $f*e \simeq f \operatorname{rel} \{0, 1\}$.*
5. *There is an element f^{-1} of $\Omega(X, x_0)$ such that $f*f^{-1} \simeq e \operatorname{rel} \{0, 1\}$ and $f^{-1}*f \simeq e \operatorname{rel} \{0, 1\}$.*

PROOF.

1. The Pasting Lemma and the continuity of linear operations in R show that $f*g$ is continuous. By definition $(f*g)(0) = f(0) = x_0$ and $(f*g)(1) = g(1) = x_0$, so that $f*g$ is indeed a loop in X based at x_0.
2. Let F be a homotopy from f to f' relative to $\{0, 1\}$ and G a homotopy from g to g' relative to $\{0, 1\}$. Define H by

$$H(s, t) = \begin{cases} F(2s, t) & 0 \leqslant s \leqslant \frac{1}{2} \\ G(2s - 1, t) & \frac{1}{2} \leqslant s \leqslant 1. \end{cases}$$

Since $F(1, t) = x_0 = G(0, t)$ for all t, H is well defined, and the Pasting Lemma shows that H is continuous. Further,

$$H(s, 0) = \begin{cases} F(2s, 0) & 0 \leqslant s \leqslant \frac{1}{2} \\ G(2s - 1, 0) & \frac{1}{2} \leqslant s \leqslant 1 \end{cases} = \begin{cases} f(2s) & 0 \leqslant s \leqslant \frac{1}{2} \\ g(2s - 1) & \frac{1}{2} \leqslant s \leqslant 1 \end{cases} = (f*g)(s)$$

and similarly $H(s, 1) = (f'*g')(s)$. Thus H is a homotopy from $f*g$ to $f'*g'$ relative to $\{0, 1\}$. The situation is easily described by the following diagram, where H is given by the entire square:

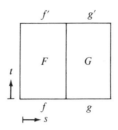

3. The required homotopy is exhibited in the following diagram, where the line

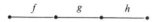

at any level means that the entire loop f is traversed in the first piece, the loop g in the middle piece, and the loop h in the last piece of the interval.

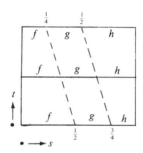

The application of some analytic geometry yields

$$
H(s,t) = \begin{cases} f\left(\dfrac{4}{2-t}s\right) & 0 \leqslant s \leqslant \dfrac{2-t}{4} \\[2ex] g\left(4\left(s - \dfrac{2-t}{4}\right)\right) & \dfrac{2-t}{4} \leqslant s \leqslant \dfrac{3-t}{4} \\[2ex] h\left(\dfrac{4}{1+t}\left(s - \dfrac{3-t}{4}\right)\right) & \dfrac{3-t}{4} \leqslant s \leqslant 1 \end{cases}.
$$

The Pasting Lemma shows that H is continuous after one checks that H is well defined. It is easy to verify that H is a homotopy from $f*(g*h)$ to $(f*g)*h$ relative to $\{0,1\}$. In the rest of the proof we will be content with drawing the diagram, leaving the analytic geometry and other details for the exercises.

4.

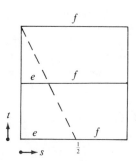
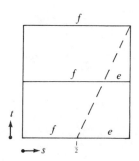

5. Define f^{-1} by $f^{-1}(s) = f(1-s)$. Then f^{-1} is a loop in X based at x_0, and the desired homotopies are given in the following diagrams:

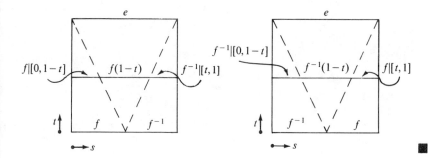

We will need the *inverse of a path* in a more general situation, so we make the following definition.

Definition If k is a path in X, then the *inverse of* k is the *path* k^{-1} defined by $k^{-1}(t) = k(1-t)$.

We need some facts from the theory of groups. The reader unsure of his background would be well advised to consult any text on modern algebra.

Definition A *group* is a set G together with a binary operation $\circ$ on G (we may write a group as $(G, \circ)$) which satisfies the following properties:

1. $g \circ (h \circ k) = (g \circ h) \circ k$ for all g, h, k in G (associativity);
2. There is an element e of G such that $e \circ g = g \circ e = g$ for each g in G (we call e the identity element of G);
3. For each element g of G there is an element g^{-1} of G such that $g \circ g^{-1} = g^{-1} \circ g = e$ (we call g^{-1} the inverse of g).

7 The fundamental group

Theorem 7.2.2 *The set $\pi_1(X,x_0)$ together with the operation $*$ defined by $[f]*[g]=[f*g]$ is a group.*

PROOF. Parts (1) and (2) of Theorem 7.2.1 show that $*$ is a well-defined binary operation on $\pi_1(X,x_0)$, that is, $[f]*[g]$ is not altered if we choose different representatives f',g' of $[f],[g]$, respectively. Part (3) shows that $[f*(g*h)]=[(f*g)*h]$, so that $[f]*([g]*[h])=([f]*[g])*[h]$. The identity element of $\pi_1(X,x_0)$ is the equivalence class of the constant loop e, and part (5) of Theorem 7.2.1 shows that inverses exist. ∎

Definition The group consisting of $\pi_1(X,x_0)$ together with the operation $*$ is called the *fundamental group* of X based at x_0. Henceforth $\pi_1(X,x_0)$ will denote this group, that is, the operation $*$ is understood to accompany the set.

Recall the space $X = S \cup T$ of Example 7 in Section 7.1. Results from this section and the next will show that $\pi_1(S,x_0)$ is isomorphic to the additive group of integers while $\pi_1(T,x_1)$ consists of a single element whenever x_0 is in S and x_1 is in T. Since any loop or homotopy in X that starts in S or T must remain in S or T, respectively, we see that $\pi_1(X,z)$ is isomorphic to the integers if z is in S but is trivial if z is in T.

The example shows that we cannot speak of *the* fundamental group of X, but instead must also state which base point we are using. This is a defect of the fundamental group which can be overcome to some extent but which tends to appear at inopportune moments. Our next project is the necessary remedy.

If x_0 and x_1 are different points of a space X, then $\pi_1(X,x_0)$ and $\pi_1(X,x_1)$ are groups consisting of different elements. We need a way of comparing such groups, just as (a long time ago) we needed a way of comparing two spaces. Just as continuous functions preserve much of the topological structure, the functions which we use to compare groups must preserve the algebraic structure. We will return to these *similarities in the large* later.

Definition Suppose $(G,\circ)$ and $(H,\cdot)$ are groups. A *homomorphism* from $(G,\circ)$ to $(H,\cdot)$ is a function ϕ from G to H which satisfies $\phi(g_1\circ g_2)=\phi(g_1)\cdot\phi(g_2)$ for all elements g_1,g_2 of G. An *isomorphism* from $(G,\circ)$ to $(H,\cdot)$ is a homomorphism from $(G,\circ)$ to $(H,\cdot)$ which is also one-to-one and onto.

There is a large body of group theory which we will not even begin to touch, even though significant parts of it are intimately connected with topology. We will introduce only the bare minimum required for our purposes. It suffices here to say that two isomorphic groups are identical to the group theorist, just as homeomorphic spaces are identical to the topologist. With this in mind, the reader will see the usefulness of the following theorem.

Theorem 7.2.3 *Let α be a path in X from x_0 to x_1. Then the function ϕ_α defined by $\phi_\alpha([f]) = [\alpha^{-1}*(f*\alpha)]$ is an isomorphism from $\pi_1(X, x_0)$ to $\pi_1(X, x_1)$.*

PROOF. The homotopies necessary in this proof are constructed very much like those in the proof of Theorem 7.2.1, so we leave many details for the reader. We note first that if f and f' are loops in X based at x_0 with $f \simeq f' \operatorname{rel}\{0,1\}$, then $\alpha^{-1}*(f*\alpha) \simeq \alpha^{-1}*(f'*\alpha)\operatorname{rel}\{0,1\}$, so that $\phi_\alpha([f])$ does not depend on the choice of f in the equivalence class. Next, $\phi_\alpha([f]*[g]) = \phi_\alpha([f*g]) = [\alpha^{-1}*((f*g)*\alpha)]$. But

$$\alpha^{-1}*((f*g)*\alpha) \simeq (\alpha^{-1}*(f*\alpha))*(\alpha^{-1}*(g*\alpha))\operatorname{rel}\{0,1\},$$

so that

$$\phi_\alpha([f]*[g]) = \left[(\alpha^{-1}*(f*\alpha))*(\alpha^{-1}*(g*\alpha))\right]$$
$$= \left[\alpha^{-1}*(f*\alpha)\right]*\left[\alpha^{-1}*(g*\alpha)\right] = \phi_\alpha([f])*\phi_\alpha([g]).$$

Hence ϕ_α is a homomorphism.

If we define Ψ from $\pi_1(X, x_1)$ to $\pi_1(X, x_0)$ by $\Psi([h]) = (\alpha*(h*\alpha^{-1})]$, then a proof analogous to that for ϕ_α shows that Ψ is a well-defined homomorphism from $\pi_1(X, x_1)$ to $\pi_1(X, x_0)$. Further, $\Psi(\phi_\alpha([f])) = \Psi([\alpha^{-1}*(f*\alpha)]) = [\alpha*((\alpha^{-1}*(f*\alpha))*\alpha^{-1})]$. The following diagram shows how to construct a homotopy between $\alpha*((\alpha^{-1}*(f*\alpha))*\alpha^{-1})$ and f, so that $\Psi(\phi_\alpha([f])) = [f]$. Similarly $\phi_\alpha(\Psi([h])) = [h]$. Hence ϕ_α and Ψ are inverse functions so that ϕ_α is one-to-one and onto and so is an isomorphism. ∎

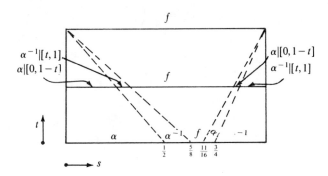

Recall that a space X is path-connected if there is a path from each point x_0 of X to every other point x_1 of X. The last theorem says that in a path-connected space the fundamental groups with different base points are all isomorphic, so we will speak with some justification of *the* fundamental group of a path-connected space, omitting reference to the base point. In more advanced work one must be more careful, since there may be lots of different isomorphisms from one such fundamental group to another, but that will not concern us here. There is a definition related to this discussion which turns out to be crucial in much of the work in algebraic topology.

Definition A space X is *simply connected* if it is path-connected and $\pi_1(X,x_0)$ consists of a single element for some point x_0 of X.

EXAMPLE.

1. Since any two continuous functions into a convex subset X of R^n are homotopic relative to any set, it is easy to show that $\pi_1(X,x_0)$ consists of a single element and that X is path-connected. Hence convex subsets of R^n are simply connected. We will generalize this example later in Corollary 7.2.8.

We now turn to the investigation of the relationship between fundamental groups of different spaces. It seems natural that the space-comparing functions, that is, the continuous functions, would give rise to group-comparing functions, that is, homomorphisms. Look at the next theorem.

Theorem 7.2.4 *Let f be a continuous function from a space X to a space Y and let x_0 be a point of X. The function $\pi_1(f)$ defined by $\pi_1(f)([g])=[f\circ g]$ is a homomorphism from $\pi_1(X,x_0)$ to $\pi_1(Y,f(x_0))$.*

PROOF. If g is a loop in X based at x_0, then $f\circ g$ is certainly a path in Y, and $f(g(0))=f(g(1))=f(x_0)$, so that $f\circ g$ is a loop in Y based at $f(x_0)$. Further, if $g\simeq h$ rel$\{0,1\}$, then Theorem 7.1.3 says that $f\circ g\simeq f\circ h$ rel$\{0,1\}$, so that $\pi_1(f)$ is a well-defined function from $\pi_1(X,x_0)$ to $\pi_1(Y,f(x_0))$. Finally, since

$$f\circ(g*h)(t) = \begin{cases} f(g(2t)) & 0\leqslant t\leqslant \frac{1}{2} \\ f(h(2t-1)) & \frac{1}{2}\leqslant t\leqslant 1 \end{cases} = (f\circ g)*(f\circ h),$$

$\pi_1(f)([g]*[h]) = \pi_1(f)([g*h]) = [f\circ(g*h)] = [(f\circ g)*(f\circ h)] = [f\circ g]*[f\circ h] = (\pi_1(f)([g]))*(\pi_1(f)([h]))$, so that $\pi_1(f)$ is a homomorphism. ∎

Theorem 7.2.5

1. *If Id_X is the identity function on X and x_0 is a point of X, then $\pi_1(Id_X)$ is the identity function on $\pi_1(X,x_0)$.*

2. *If f is a continuous function from a space X to a space Y, g is a continuous function from Y to a space Z and x_0 is a point of X, then $\pi_1(g \circ f) = \pi_1(g) \circ \pi_1(f)$ as functions from $\pi_1(X, x_0)$ to $\pi_1(Z, g(f(x_0)))$.*

PROOF.
1. $\pi_1(\mathrm{Id}_X)([f]) = [\mathrm{Id}_X \circ f] = [f]$.
2. $\pi_1(g \circ f)([k]) = [(g \circ f) \circ k] = [g \circ (f \circ k)] = \pi_1(g)([f \circ k]) = \pi_1(g)(\pi_1(f)([k]))$. ∎

We can now view π_1 as a transformation from topology to algebra which takes spaces with base points to groups and continuous functions to homomorphisms. There is a large body of sophisticated mathematics called *category theory* which deals with such transformations called *functors*. Category theory investigates many of the *similarities in the large* which exist between various bodies of mathematics, but we will not pursue this topic here.

Since homotopy has played a crucial role in the definition of the fundamental groups, one would expect it to play a role in the definition of the homomorphism induced by continuous functions. It does: its role is important; our next goal is to clarify it. The base point hinders us here in that results cannot be simply stated. One would like to say that homotopic functions induce the same homomorphism, but instead must be content with the next theorem.

Theorem 7.2.6 *Let f and g be homotopic continuous functions from a space X to a space Y. Let x_0 be a point of X. Then there is a path α in Y from $f(x_0)$ to $g(x_0)$ such that $\pi_1(g) = \phi_\alpha \circ \pi_1(f)$, where ϕ_α is the isomorphism defined in Theorem 7.2.3.*

PROOF. Let $H : X \times I \to Y$ be a homotopy from f to g. Define a path α by $\alpha(t) = H(x_0, t)$. Then $(\phi_\alpha \circ \pi_1(f))([k]) = \phi_\alpha([f \circ k]) = [\alpha^{-1} * ((f \circ k) * \alpha)]$. The following diagram shows how to construct a homotopy between $\alpha^{-1} * ((f \circ k) * \alpha)$ and $g \circ k$. Note that $\alpha^{-1}(1 - t) = \alpha(t) = H(x_0, t) = H(k(0), t) = H(k(1), t)$, so the homotopy is well defined. Other details are left as exercises. Note also that we use the notation H_t for the function from X to Y defined by $H_t(x) = H(x, t)$. ∎

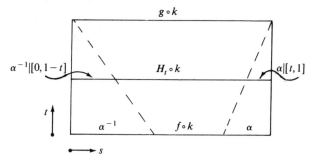

We now show that as nearly as possible, the fundamental group is a homotopy property. The *nearly as possible* arises again because of the base point.

Theorem 7.2.7 *Let f be a homotopy equivalence from the space X to the space Y and let x_0 be a point of X. Then $\pi_1(f)$ is an isomorphism from $\pi_1(X, x_0)$ to $\pi_1(Y, f(x_0))$.*

PROOF. Let g be a function from Y to X which is a homotopy inverse of f. Since $g \circ f \simeq \mathrm{Id}_X$, there is a path α in X from $x_0 = \mathrm{Id}_X(x_0)$ to $g(f(x_0))$ such that $\pi_1(g \circ f) = \phi_\alpha \circ (\pi_1(\mathrm{Id}_X))$ where ϕ_α is the isomorphism defined in Theorem 7.2.3. By Theorem 7.2.5 we have $\pi_1(g) \circ \pi_1(f) = \phi_\alpha$. Similarly there is a path β in Y from $f(x_0)$ to $fgf(x_0)$ such that $\pi_1(f) \circ \pi_1(g) = \phi_\beta$. We thus have the following diagram of groups and homomorphism which commutes, that is, following any two paths from one group to another yields the same result. Note that the two $\pi_1(f)$'s are really different functions.

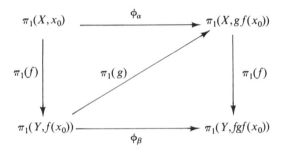

Since ϕ_α is an isomorphism and hence is onto, $\pi_1(g)$ must be onto. Since ϕ_β is an isomorphism and hence is one-to-one, $\pi_1(g)$ must also be one-to-one. Then we can write $\pi_1(f) = (\pi_1(g))^{-1} \circ \phi_\alpha$, so that $\pi_1(f)$ must be an isomorphism. □

Corollary 7.2.8 *A contractable space is simply connected.*

PROOF. If X is a contractable space, then there is a homotopy equivalence from X to a single-point space. This homotopy equivalence induces an isomorphism between the fundamental groups, and the fundamental group of a single-point space certainly consists of a single element. ■

We now have a lot of information about the fundamental group and there is more in the exercises. Unfortunately, we have not produced a single example of a nontrivial fundamental group. This is the concern of the next section.

Exercises

1. Furnish the missing analytical details in the proof of Theorem 7.2.1.

2. Furnish the missing details in the proof of Theorem 7.2.3.

3. Furnish the missing details in the proof of Theorem 7.2.6.

4. Prove that a space X is simply connected if and only if it is path-connected and every continuous function from the circle S^1 into X extends to a continuous function from the disk B^2 into X. Hint: loops may be identified with functions with domain S^1. Also $K(s,t)=((1-t)\cos 2\pi s, (1-t)\sin 2\pi s)$ is a very interesting function from $I \times I$ onto B^2.

5. Use Exercise 4 and the results from Chapter 5 to prove that the fundamental group of the punctured plane consists of more than one element.

6. Let α and β be two paths in X from x_0 to x_1, and suppose that $\alpha \simeq \beta$ rel$\{0,1\}$. Prove that $\phi_\alpha = \phi_\beta$, where ϕ_α, ϕ_β are defined in Theorem 7.2.3.

7. Let $(G, \circ)$ and $(H, \cdot)$ be groups. The direct sum $G \oplus H$ of G and H is defined to be the set $G \times H$ together with the operation $\times$ defined by $(g,h)\times(g',h')=(g\circ g',h\cdot h')$.
a. Prove that $(G \times H, \times)$ is a group.
b. Prove that if X and Y are spaces containing points x_0 and y_0, then $\pi_1(X \times Y, (x_0,y_0))$ is isomorphic to the direct sum of $\pi_1(X,x_0)$ and $\pi_1(Y,y_0)$.

8. The reader may be curious about the use of the subscript 1 in $\pi_1(X,x_0)$. This exercise explains it. We let $I^n=\{(t_1,t_2,\cdots t_n) \in R^n: 0 \leqslant t_i \leqslant 1$ for each $i=1,2,\cdots n\}$ and Bd $I^n=\{(t_1,t_2,\ldots,t_n) \in I^n: t_i=0$ or $t_i=1$ for some $i=1,2,\cdots n\}$. We define an n-*loop* in X based at x_0 to be a continuous function f from I^n into X such that $f(\text{Bd}\,I^n)=x_0$. Homotopy relative to Bd I^n is an equivalence relation in the set of n-loops in X based at x_0, and we define $[f]=\{g:g$ is an n-loop in X based at x_0 and $f\simeq g$ rel Bd $I^n\}$ for any n-loop f based at x_0. Finally, for two n-loops f and g in X based at x_0, we define

$$f*g = \begin{cases} f(2t_1,t_2,\ldots,t_n) & 0 \leqslant t_1 \leqslant \tfrac{1}{2} \\ g(2t_1-1,t_2,\ldots,t_n) & \tfrac{1}{2} \leqslant t_1 \leqslant 1. \end{cases}$$

a. Prove that $\{[f]: f$ is an n-loop in X based at $x_0\}$ together with the operation $[f]*[g]=[f*g]$ is a group. This group is the nth *homotopy group* of X based at x_0 and is denoted by $\pi_n(X,x_0)$.
b. Prove the analogue of Theorem 7.2.3 for $\pi_n(X,x_0)$.
c. Prove the analogue of Theorems 7.2.4 and 7.2.5 for $\pi_n(X,x_0)$.
d. Prove the analogue of Theorem 7.2.6 for $\pi_n(X,x_0)$.
e. Prove the analogue of Theorem 7.2.7 for $\pi_n(X,x_0)$.
f. The following arrows show the results of three homotopies between 2-loops rel Bd I^2. The boxes represent the 2-loops themselves: the middle boxes in each case show the t-level of the homotopy. Give the analytical details and generalize to the case $n \geqslant 2$.

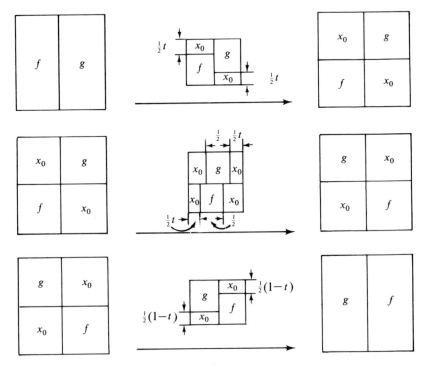

g. Use (f) to prove that when $n \geqslant 2$, $\pi_n(X, x_0)$ is abelian, that is, $[f]*[g] = [g]*[f]$. This is not true in general for $\pi_1(X, x_0)$, but we do not have the tools to prove it.

7.3 Covering spaces and $\pi_1(S^1, x_0)$

The last section developed the basic theory of the fundamental group but stopped short of computing any nontrivial such groups. There is a good reason for this: it is hard. In this section we develop some machinery which will enable us to compute some fundamental groups, and then will give an illustration of how the algebraic theory is used to solve a topological problem.

Our first definition generalizes the properties of the function taking the real number t to the point $(\cos 2\pi t, \sin 2\pi t)$ of the unit circle. Such functions play a large role in some advanced work in topology and will be quite useful in our own computations of fundamental groups.

Definition A continuous function p from a space $\tilde{X}$ onto a space X is a *covering map* if each point x of X lies in an open set $U(x)$ such that

$p^{-1}(U(x)) = \cup\{\tilde{U}(z) : z \in p^{-1}(x)\}$, where the $\tilde{U}(z)$'s are open sets such that $\tilde{U}(z) \cap \tilde{U}(z') = \varnothing$ when $z \neq z'$ and $p | \tilde{U}(x)$ is a homeomorphism onto $U(x)$ for each z in $p^{-1}(x)$. We will call the $U(x)$'s and $\tilde{U}(z)$'s *canonical neighborhoods*. Also, if there is a covering map p from $\tilde{X}$ onto X, then we say that $\tilde{X}$ is a *covering space* of X with covering map p.

EXAMPLES.

2. Consider the function $p: R \to S^1$ defined by $p(t) = (\cos 2\pi t, \sin 2\pi t)$. It is clearly continuous and onto. If x is a point of S^1, then for some number t_0, $p^{-1}(x) = \{t_0 + n : n \text{ is an integer}\}$. Further, the restriction of p to the compact set $[t_0 + n - \frac{1}{4}, t_0 + n + \frac{1}{4}]$ is one-to-one and so is a homeomorphism (see Exercise 7 of Section 2.7, Part A]. Thus if $U(x)$ is the open semicircle with center x and $\tilde{U}(t_0 + n) = (t_0 + n - \frac{1}{4}, t_0 + n + \frac{1}{4})$, then $U(x)$ and the $\tilde{U}(t_0 + n)$'s satisfy the requirements in the definition of covering map. The function p is thus a covering map for which $p^{-1}(x)$ is countably infinite for each x.

3. Recall from Chapter 6 that the projective plane P^2 is the surface obtained from the unit disk B^2 by identifying antipodal points on the boundary of B^2, that is, there is a continuous function f from B^2 onto P^2 such that $f(x) = f(y)$ only if $x = -y$ and x, y lie on S^1. (Our results on quotient spaces in Chapter 3 show that this property of P^2 essentially defines the space P^2.) Define a function p from the 2-sphere S^2 to P^2 by

$$p((x, y, z)) = \begin{cases} f((x, y)) & z \geq 0 \\ f((-x, -y)) & z \leq 0. \end{cases}$$

Note that p is well defined since $f((x, y)) = f((-x, -y))$ when (x, y) lies on S^1. Further, p is continuous since $p | \{(x, y, z) \in S^2 : z \geq 0\}$ and $p | \{(x, y, z) \in S^2 : z \leq 0\}$ both are. Finally, $p(u) = p(u')$ if and only if $u = -u'$, so that p is exactly two-to-one. Given a point z of P^2, the fact that p identifies antipodal points of S^2 allows us to find two disjoint open sets U and V in S^2 containing the two points of $p^{-1}(z)$ respectively such that p takes each of U and V homeomorphically onto an open set in P^2 containing z. Hence p is a covering map for which $p^{-1}(z)$ contains exactly two points for each z in P^2.

Suppose that p is a covering map from $\tilde{X}$ onto X. Our next project is to determine the relationships between homotopies in $\tilde{X}$ and homotopies in X. The first result is a *uniqueness theorem* which will aid in the proof of the main fact regarding these homotopies.

Theorem 7.3.1 *Let p be a covering map from a space $\tilde{X}$ onto a space X. Let α and β be paths in $\tilde{X}$ such that $\alpha(0) = \beta(0)$ and $p \circ \alpha = p \circ \beta$. Then $\alpha = \beta$.*

PROOF. Let $u = \text{lub}\{t : \alpha\|[0,t] = \beta\|[0,t]\}$. Since $[0,0] = \{0\}$ and $\alpha(0) = \beta(0)$, this least upper bound is defined. Further, $\alpha(u) = \beta(u)$. For suppose not. Then $u > 0$, and since $p(\alpha(u)) = p(\beta(u))$, there are disjoint canonical neighborhoods $\tilde{U}(\alpha(u))$ and $\tilde{U}(\beta(u))$. But there are t's arbitrarily close to and less than u for which $\alpha(t) = \beta(t)$, and since α and β are continuous, these points $\alpha(t)$, $\beta(t)$ must lie in $\tilde{U}(\alpha(u))$ and $\tilde{U}(\beta(u))$, respectively, when t is sufficiently near u. This contradiction shows that $\alpha(u) = \beta(u)$.

Suppose now that $u \neq 1$. For some canonical neighborhood $\tilde{U}(\alpha(u))$, $p|\tilde{U}(\alpha(u))$ is a homeomorphism. Further, since α and β are continuous, there is a positive number δ such that $\alpha([u, u + \delta])$ and $\beta([u, u + \delta])$ lie in $\tilde{U}(\alpha(u))$. Since p is one-to-one on $\tilde{U}(\alpha(u))$ and $p \circ \alpha = p \circ \beta$, it must be the case that $\alpha\|[u, u + \delta] = \beta\|[u, u + \delta]$. This contradicts the fact that $u = \text{lub}\{t : \alpha\|[0,t] = \beta\|[0,t]\}$, so that u must equal 1. Hence $\alpha = \beta$. ∎

Corollary 7.3.2 *Let p be a covering map from $\tilde{X}$ onto X. If Z is a path-connected space and h and k are continuous functions from Z into $\tilde{X}$ such that $p \circ h = p \circ k$ and $h(z_0) = k(z_0)$ for some point z_0, then $h = k$.*

PROOF. Let z be any point in Z. There is a path α in Z such that $\alpha(0) = z_0$ and $\alpha(1) = z$. Then $h \circ \alpha$ and $k \circ \alpha$ are paths in $\tilde{X}$ such that $p \circ (h \circ \alpha) = (p \circ h) \circ \alpha = (p \circ k) \circ \alpha = p \circ (k \circ \alpha)$, and $p(h(\alpha(0))) = p(z_0) = p(k(\alpha(0)))$. Theorem 7.3.1 says that $h \circ \alpha = k \circ \alpha$ and in particular $h(z) = h(\alpha(1)) = k(\alpha(1)) = k(z)$. ∎

The situation in Corollary 7.3.2 occurs so often that it warrants some terminology.

Definition If p is a covering map from $\tilde{X}$ onto X and h and $\tilde{h}$ are continuous functions from a space W into X and $\tilde{X}$ respectively such that $p \circ \tilde{h} = h$, then we say that $\tilde{h}$ *lifts* h or h *may be lifted* to $\tilde{h}$.

The next theorem is the crucial fact regarding covering maps. We give it the name which properly belongs to its generalization, but the result as stated will be sufficient for our purposes. Though its generalization is no harder to prove conceptually, it requires some tools we do not have. We defer other comments until the reader has seen the proof.

Theorem 7.3.3 (Covering Homotopy Theorem) *Let p be a covering map from $\tilde{X}$ onto X. The set A may be either $\varnothing$, $\{0\}$, or $\{0,1\}$ but is fixed* *throughout a given discussion. Let $\tilde{G}$ be a continuous function from the set $(I \times \{0\}) \cup (A \times I)$ into $\tilde{X}$ and F a continuous function from $I \times I$ into X such that $p \circ \tilde{G} = F|(I \times \{0\}) \cup (A \times I)$. Then there is a unique function $\tilde{F}$ from $I \times I$ into $\tilde{X}$ which lifts F and satisfies $\tilde{F}|(I \times \{0\}) \cup (A \times I) = \tilde{G}$.*

PROOF. Note first that Corollary 7.3.2 says that any two functions which lift F and agree at $(0,0)$ must be equal, so that $\tilde{F}$ is unique if it exists. The rest of the proof is devoted to constructing $\tilde{F}$.

The basic idea is that when suitably restricted to canonical neighborhoods, p^{-1} becomes a continuous function. This function can then be used to lift F to a function $\tilde{F}$. The details are a bit nasty.

For each point z of $I \times I$ there is an open set $V(z)$ containing z which F takes into a canonical neighborhood of $F(z)$. $\{V(z) : z \in I \times I\}$ is an open cover of the compact set $I \times I$, so there is a positive number δ such that any subset of $I \times I$ of diameter less than δ lies in some $V(z)$ (see Exercise 8 of Section 2.7, Part A). There is a positive integer n such that the diameter of $[k/n, (k+1)/n] \times [j/n, (j+1)/n]$ is less than δ for any integers k and j. Let S_{ij} be the square $[(i-1)/n, i/n] \times [(j-1)/n, j/n]$ for $i, j = 1, 2, \ldots, n$.

Suppose $\tilde{F}$ has already been defined and is continuous on a connected subset L of S_{ij} and satisfies $p \circ \tilde{F} = F$ on L. Now $F(S_{ij})$ lies in a canonical neighborhood $U(x)$, so $\tilde{F}(L)$ lies in $p^{-1}(U(x))$. But $\tilde{F}(L)$ is connected and $p^{-1}(U(x))$ is the union of pairwise disjoint open canonical neighborhoods, so there is a single canonical neighborhood $\tilde{U}(\tilde{x})$ which contains $\tilde{F}(L)$. The function $p|\tilde{U}(\tilde{x})$ is a homeomorphism onto $U(x)$, so its inverse is a continuous function $q_{\tilde{x}}$ from $U(x)$ onto $\tilde{U}(\tilde{x})$. If we define $\tilde{F}(z) = q_{\tilde{x}}(F(z))$ for z in S_{ij}, then $\tilde{F}$ is defined and continuous on S_{ij}, satisfies $p \circ \tilde{F} = F$ on S_{ij} and has not been changed on L.

$\tilde{F}$ is now constructed inductively. Define $\tilde{F}$ to be equal to $\tilde{G}$ on $(I \times \{0\}) \cup (A \times I)$. It is then defined and continuous on a connected subset of S_{11} and satisfies $p \circ \tilde{F} = F$ there, so $\tilde{F}$ may be extended continuously to all of S_{11} and satisfies $p \circ \tilde{F} = F$ on S_{11}. This procedure may be continued inductively from square to square in the sequence $S_{11}, S_{12}, \ldots, S_{1n}, S_{21}, S_{22}, \ldots, S_{nn}$ and we finally obtain the desired function $\tilde{F}$ from $I \times I$ into $\tilde{X}$. ∎

The technique used in the proof of the Covering Homotopy Theorem would work on $X \times I$ as long as X could be subdivided into sufficiently small pieces which fit together nicely. In particular, polyhedra are such spaces, and this is the generalization of the theorem to which we referred earlier. The present result is enough to prove the following corollaries, which is all we will need.

Corollary 7.3.4 *Let p be a covering map from $\tilde{X}$ onto X with $p(\tilde{x}) = x$. If α is any path in X with $\alpha(0) = x$, then there is a unique path $\tilde{\alpha}$ in $\tilde{X}$ which lifts α and satisfies $\tilde{\alpha}(0) = \tilde{x}$.*

PROOF. Define $\tilde{G}$ from $(I \times \{0\}) \cup (\{0\} \times I)$ into $\tilde{X}$ by $\tilde{G}(x,t) = \tilde{x}$. Define F from $I \times I$ into X by $F(s,t) = \alpha(st)$. Then $F(0,t) = F(t,0) = \alpha(0) = x = p(\tilde{x})$, so that $F|(I \times \{0\}) \cup (\{0\} \times I) = p \circ \tilde{G}$. The Covering Homotopy Theorem delivers a continuous function $\tilde{F}$ from $I \times I$ into $\tilde{X}$ such that $p \circ \tilde{F} = F$ and $\tilde{F} = \tilde{G}$ where $\tilde{G}$ is defined. Define a path $\tilde{\alpha}$ by $\tilde{\alpha}(s) = \tilde{F}(s,1)$. Then $(p \circ \tilde{\alpha})(s) = p(\tilde{F}(s,1)) = F(s,1) = \alpha(s)$ and $\tilde{\alpha}(0) = \tilde{F}(0,1) = \tilde{G}(0,1) = \tilde{x}$. Uniqueness follows from Corollary 7.3.2. ∎

Corollary 7.3.5 *Let p be a covering map from $\tilde{X}$ onto X. Let α and β be paths in X which are homotopic relative to $\{0,1\}$. Let α lift to $\tilde{\alpha}$ and β lift to $\tilde{\beta}$ where $\tilde{\alpha}(0) = \tilde{\beta}(0)$. Then $\tilde{\alpha} \simeq \tilde{\beta}$ rel $\{0,1\}$ and in particular $\tilde{\alpha}(1) = \tilde{\beta}(1)$.*

PROOF. Define $\tilde{G}$ from $(I \times \{0\}) \cup (\{0,1\} \times I)$ into $\tilde{X}$ by

$$\tilde{G}(s,t) = \begin{cases} \tilde{\alpha}(s) & t = 0 \\ \tilde{\alpha}(0) & s = 0 \\ \tilde{\alpha}(1) & s = 1. \end{cases}$$

Let F be the homotopy in X from α to β relative to $\{0,1\}$. Then F agrees with $p \circ \tilde{G}$ where $\tilde{G}$ is defined. The Covering Homotopy Theorem delivers a continuous function $\tilde{F}$ from $I \times I$ into $\tilde{X}$ such that $p \circ \tilde{F} = F$ and $\tilde{F}$ agrees with $\tilde{G}$ where $\tilde{G}$ is defined. Then $\tilde{F}(s,0) = \tilde{G}(s,0) = \tilde{\alpha}(s)$. Further, if $\tilde{\beta}'(s)$ is defined to be $\tilde{F}(s,1)$, then $\tilde{\beta}'$ is a path in $\tilde{X}$ satisfying $\tilde{\beta}'(0) = \tilde{F}(0,1) = \tilde{\alpha}(0) = \tilde{\beta}(0)$ and $(p \circ \tilde{\beta}')(s) = p(\tilde{F}(s,1)) = F(s,1) = \beta(s)$. By the uniqueness part of Corollary 7.3.4 we must have $\tilde{\beta}' = \tilde{\beta}$, so that $\tilde{F}$ is a homotopy from $\tilde{\alpha}$ to $\tilde{\beta}$ relative to $\{0,1\}$. ∎

These corollaries have important implications regarding the fundamental groups of a space and a covering space. We first state one of these implications and then make some remarks which begin to show how algebra can be applied to topology.

Theorem 7.3.6 *Let p be a covering map from $\tilde{X}$ onto X and $\tilde{x}$ be a point of $\tilde{X}$. Then the homomorphism $\pi_1(p)$ from $\pi_1(\tilde{X}, x)$ to $\pi_1(X, p(\tilde{x}))$ is one-to-one.*

PROOF. Suppose $[\alpha]$ and $[\beta]$ are elements of $\pi_1(\tilde{X}, x)$ with $\pi_1(p)([\alpha]) = \pi_1(p)([\beta])$. Then $p \circ \alpha$ and $p \circ \beta$ are paths in X which are homotopic relative to $\{0,1\}$. Further, they lift to the paths α and β, respectively, and

$\alpha(0) = \tilde{x} = \beta(0)$. Corollary 7.3.5 then says that $\alpha \simeq \beta$ rel$\{0, 1\}$, so that $[\alpha] = [\beta]$. Thus $\pi_1(p)$ is one-to-one. ∎

We can use Theorem 7.3.6 in some instances to determine whether a given space Y could be a covering space of a given space X. For example, if the fundamental group of X is trivial whereas that of Y is not, then there cannot be a one-to-one function from $\pi_1(Y, y)$ to $\pi_1(X, x)$, so Theorem 7.3.6 says there cannot be a covering map from Y onto X. Unfortunately, we know no space whose fundamental group is not trivial. We correct this situation by using Example 1 and our theory of covering maps.

Theorem 7.3.7 *The fundamental group of the circle is isomorphic to the additive group of integers.*

PROOF. Since S^1 is path-connected we can choose any base point for computing its fundamental group. For convenience we choose $x_0 = (1, 0)$. Recall that the function $p(t) = (\cos 2\pi t, \sin 2\pi t)$ is a covering map from R onto S^1. We choose $\tilde{x}_0$ to be 0.

If α is a loop in S^1 based at x_0, then α lifts to a unique path in R starting at 0 and ending at a point of $p^{-1}(x_0)$, that is, at an integer which we will denote by $\psi(\alpha)$. If α and β are loops in S^1 based at x_0 which are homotopic relative to $\{0, 1\}$, then Corollary 7.3.5 says that $\psi(\alpha) = \psi(\beta)$. Thus we may define a function which we also call ψ from $\pi_1(S^1, x_0)$ to the integers by $\psi([\alpha]) = \psi(\alpha)$.

Suppose that $\psi([\alpha]) = \psi([\beta])$. Then the paths $\tilde{\alpha}$, $\tilde{\beta}$ in R, to which α, β lift, both start at 0 and end at the same integer. Example 1 of Section 7.1 applies here to show that $\tilde{\alpha} \simeq \tilde{\beta}$ rel$\{0, 1\}$. If we compose p with this homotopy we get a homotopy in S^1 from α to β relative to $\{0, 1\}$, so that $[\alpha] = [\beta]$. Hence ψ is one-to-one.

If n is any integer, then we can define a path $\tilde{\alpha}$ in R by $\tilde{\alpha}(s) = ns$. We obtain the loop $p \circ \tilde{\alpha}$ in S^1 based at x_0 which lifts to $\tilde{\alpha}$, so that $\psi([p \circ \tilde{\alpha}]) = n$. Hence ψ is onto.

It remains to show that ψ is a homomorphism. Let α and β be two loops in S^1 based at x_0 which lift to paths $\tilde{\alpha}$ and $\tilde{\beta}$ in R starting at 0. The function $\tilde{\gamma}$ defined by

$$\tilde{\gamma}(s) = \begin{cases} \tilde{\alpha}(2s) & 0 \leqslant s \leqslant \frac{1}{2} \\ \tilde{\alpha}(1) + \tilde{\beta}(2s - 1) & \frac{1}{2} \leqslant s \leqslant 1 \end{cases}$$

is a path in R starting at 0. Further,

$$p(\tilde{\gamma}(s)) = \begin{cases} p(\tilde{\alpha}(2s)) & 0 \leqslant s \leqslant \frac{1}{2} \\ p(\tilde{\alpha}(1) + \tilde{\beta}(2s - 1)) & \frac{1}{2} \leqslant s \leqslant 1 \end{cases} = \begin{cases} \alpha(2s) & 0 \leqslant s \leqslant \frac{1}{2} \\ \beta(2s - 1) & \frac{1}{2} \leqslant s \leqslant 1 \end{cases}$$

245

since $\tilde{\alpha}(1)$ is an integer. Hence $\tilde{\gamma}$ is the unique path which lifts $\alpha*\beta$ and starts at 0, so that $\psi([\alpha*\beta]) = \tilde{\gamma}(1) = \tilde{\alpha}(1) + \tilde{\beta}(1) = \gamma([\alpha]) + \gamma([\beta])$. ■

The application we wish to make of the fact that $\pi_1(S^1, x_0)$ is not trivial requires a little bit of group theory. We make a definition and state a result, the easy proof of which we leave as an exercise.

Definition   Let $(G, \circ)$ be a group and H a subset of G. If H together with the operation $\circ$ restricted to H (which we also denote by $\circ$) forms a group, then we call H or $(H, \circ)$ a *subgroup* of $(G, \circ)$.

Theorem 7.3.8   *Let ψ be a homomorphism from a group $(K, \cdot)$ to a group $(G, \circ)$. Then $\psi(K)$ is a subgroup of $(G, \circ)$.*

Theorem 7.3.9   *Let A be a subspace of a space X and r a retraction from X onto A, that is, a continuous function from X to A that satisfies $r(a) = a$ for each point a of A. Let $a_0 \in A$. Then $\pi_1(X, a_0)$ contains a subgroup isomorphic to $\pi_1(A, a_0)$.*

PROOF.   Define the function j from A into X by $j(a) = a$. Then $r \circ j = \mathrm{Id}_A$, so that $\pi_1(r) \circ \pi_1(j) = \pi_1(r \circ j) = \pi_1(\mathrm{Id}_A)$, which is the identity function on $\pi_1(A, a_0)$. We conclude that $\pi_1(j)$ must be one-to-one. Theorem 7.3.8 guarantees that $\pi_1(j)(\pi_1(A, a_0))$ is a subgroup of $\pi_1(X, a_0)$, and $\pi_1(j)$ is an isomorphism from $\pi_1(A, a_0)$ to $\pi_1(j)(\pi_1(A, a_0))$. ■

Theorem 7.3.10   *There is no retraction from the disk B^2 to the circle S^1.*

PROOF. B^2 is contractible, so that its fundamental group consists of a single element. The fundamental group of S^1 is isomorphic to the integers and so cannot be isomorphic to a subgroup of $\pi_1(B^2, x_0)$. Theorem 7.3.9 then implies that no retraction from B^2 to S^1 exists. ■

Note how π_1 transforms a difficult topological problem, namely, the question of the existence of a certain kind of continuous function, into an easy algebraic problem, namely, the question of the existence of a certain kind of subgroup. Herein lies the power of algebraic topology. We leave further investigations to the reader.

Exercises

1. Prove Theorem 7.3.8.

2. Suppose that X is a path-connected space whose fundamental group is finite,

and that J is a subspace of X homeomorphic to S^1. Prove that there is no retraction from X onto J.

3. In this exercise we compute the fundamental group of the projective plane P^2 by using the covering map p from S^2 onto P^2 given in Example 2.

  a. Prove that if α and β are two paths in the 2-sphere S^2 such that $\alpha(0) = \beta(0)$ and $\alpha(1) = \beta(1)$, then $\alpha \simeq \beta$ rel$\{0, 1\}$. Hint: choose a point p of S^2 not equal to $\alpha(0)$ or $\alpha(1)$. By using homotopies in a small disk on S^2 with center p, we can find paths α^1 and β^1 in S^2 which miss p and satisfy $\alpha^1 \simeq \alpha$ rel$\{0, 1\}$ and $\beta^1 \simeq \beta$ rel$\{0, 1\}$. But $S^2 \setminus \{p\}$ is homeomorphic to R^2 and any two maps in R^2 are homotopic.

  b. Define $\tilde{\alpha}$ by $\tilde{\alpha}(t) = (\cos \pi t, \sin \pi t, 0)$. Prove that $\alpha = p \circ \tilde{\alpha}$ is a loop in P^2 based at $x_0 = p((1, 0, 0))$. We use these paths throughout this exercise.

  c. Let β be any loop in P^2 based at x_0. Prove that β lifts to a loop $\tilde{\beta}$ in S^2 such that $\tilde{\beta}(0) = (1, 0, 0)$ and either $\tilde{\beta}(1) = (1, 0, 0)$ or $\tilde{\beta}(1) = (-1, 0, 0)$.

  d. Continuing (c), prove that if $\tilde{\beta}(1) = (1, 0, 0)$, then $[\beta]$ is the identity element of $\pi_1(P^2, x_0)$ and if $\tilde{\beta}(1) = (-1, 0, 0)$, then $[\beta] = [\alpha]$. Hint: use (a).

  e. Prove that $[\alpha]$ is not the identity element of $\pi_1(P^2, x_0)$. Hint: use Corollary 7.3.5.

  f. Prove that $\pi_1(P^2, x_0)$ consists exactly of the identity element $[e]$ and $[\alpha]$. Conclude that $[\alpha]^*[\alpha] = [e]$. This group is usually denoted by Z_2.

4. Prove that the fundamental group of the torus is isomorphic to $Z \oplus Z$, where Z is the group of integers under addition.

5. Prove that no two of the torus, the 2-sphere and the projective plane are homeomorphic. Hint: Exercises 4 and 3.

Appendix

We have gathered in this Appendix those facts of set theory and the theory of n-dimensional Euclidean spaces necessary for this book. It is to serve as a reference and refresher section only, so we have departed from our usual custom and do not provide explicit exercises or many proofs. The reader can check his competency by furnishing proofs of the theorems and facts stated. Definitions will not be noted as such, but the terms will be set in different type. Finally, Kelly's *General Topology* and Dugundji's *Topology* as well as many other texts provide much more detail on these matters.

A.1 Basic set theory

We take a very naive approach to set theory and ignore the paradoxes that thus arise. A *set* is any well-defined collection of objects, called the *members* or *elements* of the set. We write the fact that the object x is an element of the set A as $x \in A$, and $x \notin A$ means that x is not an element of the set A. If A is a set and P a property of objects, then $\{x \in A : x \text{ has } P\}$ denotes the set of objects which belong to A and have property P. Also, $\{x_1, x_2, \ldots, x_r\}$ denotes the set whose elements are $x_1, x_2, \ldots, x_r$.

A set B is a *subset* of the set A (written $B \subset A$) if every element of B is also an element of A. Two sets A and B are equal (written $A = B$) if $A \subset B$ and $B \subset A$, that is, if A and B have exactly the same elements. The set with no elements is called the *empty set* and is denoted by $\varnothing$. Clearly $\varnothing \subset A$ for any set A.

If A is a set and for each $\alpha \in A$ there is a set X_α, then $\{X_\alpha : \alpha \in A\}$ is called a *family of sets*. The *union* of this family of sets is $\cup \{X_\alpha : \alpha \in A\} = \{x : x \in X_\alpha$ for some $\alpha \in A\}$ and the *intersection* of this family is $\cap \{X_\alpha : \alpha \in A\} = \{x : x \in X_\alpha$ for each $\alpha \in A\}$. If $A = \{1, 2, \ldots, n\}$ then we may denote this union and intersection by $X_1 \cup X_2 \cup \ldots \cup X_n$ and $X_1 \cap X_2 \cap \ldots \cap X_n$ respectively. If A and B are any two sets, then the *complement* of B in A is $A \setminus B = \{x \in A : x \notin B\}$. Further, A and B are *disjoint* if $A \cap B = \varnothing$; otherwise, A and B are said to *meet*. A family $\{X_\alpha : \alpha \in A\}$ of sets is *pairwise disjoint* if either $X_\alpha = X_\beta$ or $X_\alpha \cap X_\beta = \varnothing$ for all $\alpha, \beta \in A$.

There are numerous facts concerning the concepts introduced so far. We list a few in the next theorem and leave the discovery of others to the reader.

Theorem A.1.1 *If $\{X_\alpha : \alpha \in A\}$ is a family of sets and Y is a set, then*

1. $Y \setminus (\cup \{X_\alpha : \alpha \in A\}) = \cap \{Y \setminus X_\alpha : \alpha \in A\};$ ⎫
2. $Y \setminus (\cap \{X_\alpha : \alpha \in A\}) = \cup \{Y \setminus X_\alpha : \alpha \in A\};$ ⎬ De Morgan's laws
3. $Y \cup (\cap \{X_\alpha : \alpha \in A\}) = \cap \{Y \cup X_\alpha : \alpha \in A\};$
4. $Y \cap (\cup \{X_\alpha : \alpha \in A\}) = \cup \{Y \cap X_\alpha : \alpha \in A\};$
5. $Y \setminus (Y \setminus X_\alpha) = Y \cap X_\alpha.$

Since $\{a, b\} = \{b, a\}$, sets do not keep track of order. To do this we need the idea of an *ordered pair* (a, b). By definition two ordered pairs (a, b) and (c, d) are equal if and only if $a = c$ and $b = d$. One can then inductively define an ordered n-tuple, but it is easier (though not as rigorous) to start from scratch. Thus an *ordered n-tuple* is the object $(a_1, a_2, \ldots, a_n)$; two ordered n-tuples $(a_1, a_2, \ldots, a_n)$ and $(b_1, b_2, \ldots, b_n)$ are equal if and only if $a_1 = b_1, a_2 = b_2, \ldots$, and $a_n = b_n$.

If A and B are sets, then the *Cartesian product* of A and B is the set $A \times B = \{(x, y) : (x, y)$ is an ordered pair with $x \in A$ and $y \in B\}$. Just as ordered pairs generalize to ordered n-tuples, the Cartesian product of two sets generalizes to the Cartesian product of n sets. Thus, the Cartesian product of the sets $A_1, A_2, \ldots, A_n$ is $A_1 \times A_2 \times \ldots \times A_n = \{(x_1, x_2, \ldots, x_n) : (x_1, x_2, \ldots, x_n)$ is an ordered n-tuple with $x_i \in A_i$ for $i = 1, 2, \ldots, n\}$.

A *relation* R on a set A is a subset of the Cartesian product $A \times A$. If $(a, b) \in R$, then we write aRb and think of this as saying that b is one of the (possibly many) elements of A which are R-related to a. A relation R on A is *reflexive* if aRa for each $a \in A$, *symmetric* if bRa whenever aRb for all $a, b \in A$, *antisymmetric* if aRb and bRa imply that $a = b$ for all $a, b \in A$, and *transitive* if aRc whenever aRb and bRc for any a, b, c in A.

A relation R on a set A is an *equivalence relation* on A if R is reflexive, symmetric and transitive. If R is an equivalence relation on A, then the *equivalence class* of the element a of A is the set $[a]=\{b\in A:aRb\}$. The properties of an equivalence relation imply that two equivalence classes are either equal or disjoint and that A is the union of the equivalence classes of its elements. Thus an equivalence relation partitions a set A into a collection of pairwise disjoint sets whose union is A. An example worth thinking about is the relation R on the set of ordered pairs of integers defined by $(m,n)R(p,q)$ if $mq=np$.

A relation L on a set A is a *partial order* if L is reflexive, antisymmetric and transitive. The basic example is "less than or equal to" on the real numbers. A partial order L is a *linear order* on a set A if either aLb or bLa whenever $a,b\in A$. If L is a partial order on a set A, then the element b of A is a *maximal element* if bLa implies that $b=a$ for any $a\in A$. *Minimal element* is similarly defined. Note that a maximal element b need not have the property that aLb for every $a\in A$, since there may be an element x of A for which neither xLb nor bLx. An *upper bound* of a subset B of a set A partially ordered by L is an element v of A such that bLv for each $b\in B$. The *least upper bound* of a subset B of a set A partially ordered by L is an element u of A which is an upper bound of B and which satisfies uLv for any upper bound v of B. One can easily define *lower bound* and *greatest lower bound*. We use the notation lub B for the least upper bound of a set B and glb B for the greatest lower bound of B, when they exist.

Closely related to and more important than relations are functions. A good way to think of a function from a set A to a set B is as a black box into which one puts an element of A and which then produces an element of B. The formal definition is a bit less picturesque. A *function f* from a set A to a set B (written $f:A\rightarrow B$) is a subset of the Cartesian product $A\times B$ such that for each $a\in A$ there is a unique $b\in B$ with $(a,b)\in f$. We then call A the *domain* of f and B the *range*. If $(a,b)\in f$, then we write $f(a)=b$. The uniqueness part of the definition distinguishes a function from a relation, in that $a\in A$ may be related to many b's in B, but there is just one $f(a)$ when f is a function. If P is a subset of A then the *image* of P is $f(P)=\{f(a):a\in P\}$ and if Q is a subset of B then the *inverse image* of Q is $f^{-1}(Q)=\{a\in A:f(a)\in Q\}$. We regularly identify $f(x)$ with $f(\{x\})$ and $f^{-1}(\{b\})$ with $f^{-1}(b)$.

If f is a function from A to B and the image of A is B, then we say that f is *onto*. If $f(x)=f(y)$ implies that $x=y$, then we say that f is *one-to-one*. A one-to-one and onto function is called a *bijection*. For a bijection f the set $f^{-1}(b)$ consists of a single element for each $b\in B$, so that f^{-1} becomes a function.

There are two common ways of forming new functions from old ones. If $f:A\rightarrow B$ and $P\subset A$, then the *restriction* of f to P is $f|P=\{(a,b)\in f:a\in P\}$. Thus $f|P$ does the same thing that f does, but only to elements of P. If

$f:A\to B$ and $g:B\to C$, then the *composition* of g and f is $g\circ f=\{(a,c):$ for some $b, f(a)=b$ and $g(b)=c\}$. Thus $(g\circ f)(a)=g(f(a))$.

It is useful to rephrase some of these concepts in terms of black boxes. Thus, $f(P)$ is the set of all things that come out of the black box when elements of P are put in and $f^{-1}(Q)$ is the set of all things which when put in yield an element of Q. The composition of g and f is the result of putting the black boxes end-to-end. The reader should rephrase other concepts himself, and also know and be able to prove the facts to follow.

Theorem A.1.2 *Let* $f:A\to B$, $g:B\to C$, $\{X_\delta:\delta\in D\}$ *be a family of subsets of* A *and* $\{Y_\gamma:\gamma\in G\}$ *be a family of subsets of* B. *Then*:

1. $f(\cup\{X_\delta:\delta\in D\})=\cup\{f(X_\delta):\delta\in D\}$.
2. $f(\cap\{X_\delta:\delta\in D\})\subset\cap\{f(X_\delta):\delta\in D\}$ *but equality need not hold.*
3. $f^{-1}(\cup\{Y_\gamma:\gamma\in G\})=\cup\{f^{-1}(Y_\gamma):\gamma\in G\}$.
4. $f^{-1}(\cap\{Y_\gamma:\gamma\in G\})=\cap\{f^{-1}(Y_\gamma):\gamma\in G\}$.
5. $f^{-1}(B\setminus Y_\gamma)=A\setminus f^{-1}(Y_\gamma)$ *for any* $\gamma\in G$.
6. *If* f *is one-to-one and onto, then* $f\circ f^{-1}(x)=x$ *for each* $x\in B$ *and* $f^{-1}\circ f(y)=y$ *for each* $y\in A$;
7. *If* $g\circ f$ *is one-to-one, then* f *must be one-to-one but* g *need not be.*
8. *If* $g\circ f$ *is onto, then* g *must be onto but* f *need not be.*
9. *If* $h:C\to E$, *then* $h\circ(g\circ f)=(h\circ g)\circ f$.
10. *If* $F\subset A$, *then* $(f|F)^{-1}(Y_\gamma)=f^{-1}(Y_\gamma)\cap F$.

There are several special functions which we take note of here. If X is any set, then the *identity function* on X is $\mathrm{Id}_X=\{(x,x):x\in X\}$, so that $\mathrm{Id}_X(x)=x$ for each $x\in X$. A *binary operation* on a set X is a function from $X\times X$ to X (see Section 7.2). If $*$ is a binary operation on X, then $*((x,y))$ is usually denoted by $x*y$. Finally, a *sequence* in a set X is a function f from the set N of positive integers into X. In this case we often denote $f(n)$ by x_n.

Throughout this text we assume as given the real numbers and their properties. We will return to the real field a bit later, but now want to pay special attention to the set N of positive integers. We assume the *Principle of Mathematical Induction* stated as follows: If for each positive integer n, $P(n)$ is a statement, if $P(1)$ is true and if $P(n+1)$ is true whenever $P(n)$ is true, then $P(n)$ is true for each positive integer n. We have used this principle in various ways in the body of the text and leave its further investigation to the reader.

Now that we have the idea of a function we can use it to compare two sets. Two sets A and B are said to have the same *cardinality* if there is a bijection from A to B. It is easy to check that having the same cardinality is an equivalence relation on any collection of sets. There is an entire arithmetic of cardinality, but we need just the following: a set is said to be *finite* if it has the same cardinality as $\varnothing$ or $\{1,2,\ldots,n\}$ for some positive integer n. A set is said to be *countably infinite* if it has the same cardinality as the set N of positive integers. A set is *countable* if it is either finite or countably infinite, otherwise it is *uncountable*.

Theorem A.1.3

1. *Any subset of a countable set is countable.*
2. *If A is countable and X_α is a countable set for each $\alpha \in A$, then $\cup\{X_\alpha : \alpha \in A\}$ is countable.*
3. *If X and Y are countable, then so is $X \times Y$.*
4. *The set of rationals is countable.*
5. *The set of real numbers is uncountable.*

PROOF. For any countable set X there is a bijection f from $\varnothing$ or $\{1,2,\ldots,n\}$ or N to X. We will use x_i to denote $f(i)$ so that X is either $\varnothing$ or $\{x_1,x_2,\ldots,x_n\}$ or $\{x_1,x_2,\ldots\}$. To prove (1), let B be a subset of X. Let $g(1)$ be the least integer r such that $x_r \in B$ and if $g(1),g(2),\ldots,g(n)$ have been defined, then let $g(n+1)$ be the least integer r such that $x_r \in B \setminus \{x_{g(1)},x_{g(2)},\ldots x_{g(n)}\}$. Clearly $f \circ g$ is a bijection from $\varnothing$ or $\{1,2,\ldots,m\}$ or N onto B, depending on when this inductive procedure must stop.

To prove (2), we list the elements of A as $\alpha_1,\alpha_2,\ldots$ and then list the elements of X_{α_i} as shown:

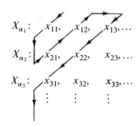

The arrows show how to define a function from N onto $\cup\{X_\alpha : \alpha \in A\}$. If we skip elements we have already hit, then the function will be a bijection which will show that $\cup\{X_\alpha : \alpha \in A\}$ is countable.

To prove (3), we note that $\{x\} \times Y$ is countable since it has the same cardinality as Y. Then $X \times Y = \cup\{\{x\} \times Y : x \in X\}$ is a countable union of countable sets and so is countable.

Let Q be the set of rational numbers and Q^+ the set of positive rational numbers. If we define $f : Q^+ \to N \times N$ by $f(m/n) = (m,n)$ when m/n is in lowest terms, then f is a bijection from Q^+ onto a subset of $N \times N$. By (1) and (3), Q^+ is countable and then clearly the set Q^- of negative rational numbers is also. By (2), $Q = Q^+ \cup Q^- \cup \{0\}$ is countable.

If the set R of real numbers were countable, then the interval $(0, 1)$ would also be countable so we could make the following list of the decimal expansions of the numbers in $(0, 1)$:

$$0.x_{11}x_{12}x_{13}x_{14}\cdots$$
$$0.x_{21}x_{22}x_{23}x_{24}\cdots$$
$$0.x_{31}x_{32}x_{33}x_{34}\cdots$$
$$\cdot$$
$$\cdot$$
$$\cdot$$

Define a number $0.y_1y_2y_3y_4\cdots$ by letting $y_i = 3$ if $x_{ii} = 5$ and $y_i = 5$ if $x_{ii} \neq 5$. Then $0.y_1y_2y_3\cdots$ differs from $0.x_{i1}x_{i2}x_{i3}\cdots$ in the ith place and so does not appear in the list. Hence R is not countable. ∎

The axiom of set theory we wish to consider next is at a deeper level than those so far discussed but plays a role in several of the results in Chapter 3. We state it in the form most directly used in the study of product spaces and then give a short discussion and an equivalent formulation.

Axiom of Choice *Let $\{X_\alpha : \alpha \in A\}$ be a family of sets such that $X_\alpha \neq \varnothing$ for each $\alpha \in A$. Then there is a function f from A into $\cup \{X_\alpha : \alpha \in A\}$ such that $f(\alpha) \in X_\alpha$ for each $\alpha \in A$.*

The point here is that A may be a set of any size and the Axiom of Choice says that we can simultaneously choose an element from each of the sets X_α. The axiom asserts the existence of something which is difficult if not impossible to actually construct and consequently some mathematicians are uncomfortable when it is used. It is a good idea to avoid it whenever possible. In particular, choosing an element from a non-empty set does not involve the Axiom of Choice. We have followed the common practice of using it without regret when necessary but always noting its appearance. The first use of the Axiom of Choice is in the study of product sets. The following definition is also made in Chapter 3, but we repeat it here for convenience. Let $\{X_\alpha : \alpha \in A\}$ be a collection of sets. The Cartesian product of this collection is $\times \{X_\alpha : \alpha \in A\} = \{f : f$ is a function with domain A and such that $f(\alpha) \in X_\alpha$ for each $\alpha \in A\}$. The Axiom of Choice says exactly that if $X \neq \varnothing$ for each $\alpha \in A$, then $\times \{X_\alpha : \alpha \in A\} \neq \varnothing$.

There are many equivalent formulations of the Axiom of Choice. We present just the one used in Section 3.6, but provide no proofs.

Zorn's Lemma *Let X be a set partially ordered by the relation L. If every subset of X which is linearly ordered by L has an upper bound, then X has a maximal element.*

Theorem A.1.4 *Zorn's Lemma and the Axiom of Choice are equivalent.*

A.2 Euclidean spaces

In this section we give a bare outline of the axioms for the field of real numbers and the properties of the inner product space R^n. There are texts which develop the theory of numbers in detail and linear algebra texts give more thorough treatments of inner products and vector spaces. See them for more information.

A *field* is a set F together with two binary operations $+$ and $\cdot$ (sometimes written $(F, +, \cdot)$) that satisfy the following axioms:

1. $a+(b+c)=(a+b)+c$ for all $a,b,c \in F$.
2. There is an element 0 in F such that $a+0=0+a=a$ for all $a \in F$.
3. For each $a \in F$ there is a $(^-a) \in F$ such that $a+(^-a)=(^-a)+a=0$.
4. $a+b=b+a$ for all $a,b \in F$.
5. There is an element $1 \neq 0$ in F such that $1 \cdot a = a \cdot 1 = a$ for all $a \in F$.
6. $a \cdot (b \cdot c)=(a \cdot b) \cdot c$ for all $a,b,c \in F$.
7. $a \cdot b = b \cdot a$ for all $a,b \in F$.
8. For each $a \in F$ such that $a \neq 0$ there is an $a^{-1} \in F$ such that $a \cdot a^{-1} = a^{-1} \cdot a = 1$.
9. $a \cdot (b+c)=(a \cdot b)+(a \cdot c)$ for all $a,b,c \in F$.

All the algebraic properties of a field and in particular of the real numbers follow from these axioms. In addition, however, the real numbers are equipped with an order structure. There are several equivalent ways to formulate the order structure of a field; we give the one that fits the set theory preparation we have made.

An *ordered field* is a field $(F, +, \cdot)$ together with a partial order $\leqslant$ on F (we sometimes write this as $(F, +, \cdot, \leqslant)$, and we use "$<$" for "$\leqslant$ but not $=$") that satisfies the following conditions:

1. Either $a \leqslant b$ or $b \leqslant a$ for all $a,b \in F$.
2. If $a,b \in F$ and $a \leqslant b$ then $a+c \leqslant b+c$ for all $c \in F$.
3. If a,b and c are elements of F with $a \leqslant b$ and $0 < c$, then $a \cdot c \leqslant b \cdot c$.

One can prove many of the order-algebraic properties of the real field from these axioms. In particular, the *absolute value* function defined by

$$|a| = \begin{cases} a & 0 \leqslant a \\ -a & a \leqslant 0 \end{cases}$$

can be proved to have the usual properties, and $d(a,b) = |a-b|$ can be shown to be a metric (see Section 2.1) on the ordered field $(R, +, \cdot, \leqslant)$. We leave details for the ambitious reader.

Both the rational numbers and the real numbers are ordered fields, so that we need another property to characterize the reals. An ordered field $(F, +, \cdot, \leqslant)$ is said to be *complete* if every non-empty subset of F which has an upper bound has a least upper bound. We now have the following theorem, which we do not prove. We can understand *isomorphic* to mean "exactly the same as with respect to $+$, $\cdot$ and $\leqslant$".

Theorem A.2.1 *Any complete ordered field is isomorphic to the field of real numbers.*

Finally, we note that a complete ordered field F is *Archimedean*, that is, given any element $x \in F$ there is an integer $n (= 1 + 1 + \ldots + 1)$ such that $x < n$. The basic idea of the proof is that otherwise the set of integers has an upper bound, hence a least upper bound, which leads to a contradiction. Again, we omit the details.

We use R^n to denote the Cartesian product of n copies of R, that is, R^n is the set of ordered n-tuples $(x_1, x_2, \ldots, x_n)$ for which $x_i \in R$ for $i = 1, 2, \ldots, n$. If $\bar{x} = (x_1, x_2, \ldots, x_n)$ and $\bar{y} = (y_1, y_2, \ldots, y_n)$ are elements of R^n, then we define $\bar{x} + \bar{y} = (x_1 + y_1, x_2 + y_2, \ldots, x_n + y_n)$ and $r\bar{x} = (rx_1, rx_2, \ldots, rx_n)$ whenever $r \in R$. Further, the *inner product* of $\bar{x}$ and $\bar{y}$ is $\bar{x} \cdot \bar{y} = x_1 y_1 + x_2 y_2 + \ldots + x_n y_n$ and the *norm* of $\bar{x}$ is $\|\bar{x}\| = \sqrt{\bar{x} \cdot \bar{x}}$.

Theorem A.2.2

1. $\bar{x} + (\bar{y} + \bar{z}) = (\bar{x} + \bar{y}) + \bar{z}$ for all $\bar{x}, \bar{y}, \bar{z} \in R^n$.
2. $\bar{x} + \bar{y} = \bar{y} + \bar{x}$ for all $\bar{x}, \bar{y} \in R^n$.
3. If $\bar{0} = (0, 0, \ldots, 0)$, then $\bar{0} + \bar{x} = \bar{x}$ for each $\bar{x} \in R^n$.
4. If $\bar{x} = (x_1, x_2, \ldots, x_n)$ and $^-\bar{x} = (^-x_1, ^-x_2, \ldots, ^-x_n)$, then $\bar{x} + (^-\bar{x}) = \bar{0}$.
5. $r(\bar{x} + \bar{y}) = r\bar{x} + r\bar{y}$ and $(r + s)\bar{x} = r\bar{x} + s\bar{x}$ for all $\bar{x}, \bar{y} \in R^n$ and $r, s \in R$.
6. $(rs)\bar{x} = r(s\bar{x})$ and $1 \cdot \bar{x} = \bar{x}$ for all $r, s \in R$ and $\bar{x} \in R^n$.
7. $\bar{x} \cdot \bar{y} = \bar{y} \cdot \bar{x}$ for all $\bar{x}, \bar{y} \in R^n$.
8. $\bar{x} \cdot (\bar{y} + \bar{z}) = \bar{x} \cdot \bar{y} + \bar{x} \cdot \bar{z}$ for all $\bar{x}, \bar{y}, \bar{z} \in R^n$.
9. $\bar{x} \cdot \bar{x} \geqslant 0$ for each $\bar{x} \in R^n$ and $\bar{x} \cdot \bar{x} = 0$ implies that $\bar{x} = \bar{0}$.
10. $(r\bar{x}) \cdot \bar{y} = r(\bar{x} \cdot \bar{y}) = \bar{x} \cdot (r\bar{y})$ for all $\bar{x}, \bar{y} \in R^n$ and each $r \in R$.

11. $|\bar{x}\cdot\bar{y}| \leqslant \|\bar{x}\|\,\|\bar{y}\|$ for all $\bar{x},\bar{y} \in R^n$ (*Cauchy–Schwartz inequality*)

12. $\|\bar{x}+\bar{y}\| \leqslant \|\bar{x}\| + \|\bar{y}\|$ for all $\bar{x},\bar{y} \in R^n$ (*triangle inequality*).

PROOF. We have listed all these properties only because they show that R^n satisfies the axioms for a vector space with an inner product and thus all vector space and inner product properties follow from the ones listed. We will, however, prove properties (11) and (12) since they directly affect the introduction of a metric in R^n. First note that if a and b are any real numbers, then $0 \leqslant (|a| - |b|)^2 = |a|^2 - 2|a||b| + |b|^2 = a^2 - 2|a||b| + b^2$, so that $2|a||b| \leqslant a^2 + b^2$. Suppose that $\bar{x} = (x_1, x_2, \ldots, x_n)$ and $\bar{y} = (y_1, y_2, \ldots, y_n)$. If either $\|\bar{x}\| = 0$ or $\|\bar{y}\| = 0$, then the Cauchy–Schwartz inequality is trivial. Otherwise, taking $a = |x_i|/\|\bar{x}\|$ and $b = |y_i|/\|\bar{y}\|$ we see that

$$\frac{2|x_i||y_i|}{\|\bar{x}\|\,\|\bar{y}\|} \leqslant \frac{x_i^2}{\|\bar{x}\|^2} + \frac{y_i^2}{\|\bar{y}\|^2}.$$

Summing these terms for $i = 1, 2, \ldots, n$ yields

$$\frac{2(|x_1||y_1| + |x_2||y_2| + \cdots + |x_n||y_n|)}{\|\bar{x}\|\,\|\bar{y}\|} \leqslant \frac{x_1^2 + x_2^2 + \cdots + x_n^2}{\|\bar{x}\|^2} + \frac{y_1^2 + y_2^2 + \cdots + y_n^2}{\|\bar{y}\|^2}.$$

Now properties of absolute value imply that

$$|x_1 y_1 + x_2 y_2 + \cdots + x_n y_n| \leqslant |x_1||y_1| + |x_2||y_2| + \cdots + |x_n||y_n|,$$

so

$$\frac{2|\bar{x}\cdot\bar{y}|}{\|\bar{x}\|\,\|\bar{y}\|} \leqslant \frac{\|\bar{x}\|^2}{\|\bar{x}\|^2} + \frac{\|\bar{y}\|^2}{\|\bar{y}\|^2} = 1 + 1 = 2,$$

and hence $|\bar{x}\cdot\bar{y}| \leqslant \|\bar{x}\|\,\|\bar{y}\|$.

We use (11) and properties of inner product to prove (12). We have $\|\bar{x}+\bar{y}\|^2 = (\bar{x}+\bar{y})\cdot(\bar{x}+\bar{y}) = \bar{x}\cdot\bar{x} + 2\bar{x}\cdot\bar{y} + \bar{y}\cdot\bar{y} = \|x\|^2 + 2\bar{x}\cdot\bar{y} + \|\bar{y}\|^2$. By the Cauchy–Schwartz inequality we have $2\bar{x}\cdot\bar{y} \leqslant 2|\bar{x}\cdot\bar{y}| \leqslant 2\|\bar{x}\|\,\|\bar{y}\|$, so that $\|\bar{x}+\bar{y}\|^2 \leqslant \|\bar{x}\|^2 + 2\|\bar{x}\|\,\|\bar{y}\| + \|y\|^2 = (\|\bar{x}\| + \|\bar{y}\|)^2$. Since the norm of a vector is nonnegative, we obtain $\|\bar{x}+\bar{y}\| \leqslant \|\bar{x}\| + \|\bar{y}\|$. ∎

We now define $d(\bar{x},\bar{y}) = \|\bar{x}-\bar{y}\|$ for elements $\bar{x},\bar{y}$ of R^n. It is then easy to use the properties listed in the above theorem to show that d is a metric on R^n.

Epilogue

One of the aims of this book has been to incite the reader to pursue further study in some aspect of topology. Some of the topics have been chosen with this in mind and the author hopes that the glimpses thus provided of various subjects have been tantalizing. To aid the reader who is interested in a deeper or more detailed treatment of these subjects, we provide here a short discussion of some other texts. We have not attempted to give a complete list of the books available; an expert may very well provide other and better references.

Chapters 2 and 3 are an introduction to the topology that everyone should know. A classic in this area is Kelley's *General Topology*, which according to its author contains the topology that every young analyst should know. Hocking's and Young's *Topology* is slanted toward geometric and algebraic topology. Dugundji's *Topology* is a good reference, especially for the topics necessary to pursue algebraic topology. The author's personal preference for a book along these lines is Willard's *General Topology*, which blends both the analyst's and the geometer's topology. There are many more at all levels, just check your mathematics library.

The subject matter in Chapter 4 dealing with Cantor sets and curves is presented with more detail in Hocking's and Young's book mentioned above. Whyburn's *Analytic Topology* treats curves, compact connected metric spaces and the plane in a great deal of depth. Newman's *Elements of the Topology of Plane Sets of Points* does a nice job of handling some curve theory and also thoroughly explores the theory of embeddings in the plane.

Moise's *Geometric Topology in Dimensions 2 and 3* does just what its name suggests, that is, it presents the geometric topology of the plane and three-dimensional space. Rushing's *Topological Embeddings* is a good place to begin a serious study of embedding problems in all dimensions. The last section of Chapter 4 as well as the material on completeness in Chapter 3 is as much analysis as topology, so see Kelley's *General Topology* or Wilansky's *Topology for Analysis* or your favorite analyst. Singer's and Thorpe's *Lecture Notes on Elementary Topology and Geometry* nicely integrates some of the topics of topology, analysis, and geometry.

Chapter 6 is an introduction to combinatorial or piecewise linear topology. Good starting places are Hudson's *Piecewise Linear Topology* or Glaser's *Geometrical Combinatorial Topology*. Some of the books mentioned above, for example, Rushing's book, have summaries of piecewise linear topology which give a good idea of its usefulness. Some of the books mentioned below also do some combinatorial topology in order to develop algebraic tools.

There is little more to the theory of winding numbers than what has been presented in Chapter 5. Other books dealing with them are Steenrod's and Chinn's *First Concepts of Topology* and Arnold's *Intuitive Concepts in Elementary Topology*.

We turn now to algebraic topology. For presentations at a beginning level see Keesee's *An Introduction to Algebraic Topology* and Massey's *Algebraic Topology: An Introduction*. Good middle-level texts are Greenberg's *Lectures on Algebraic Topology* and Maunder's *Algebraic Topology*. Very thorough modern treatments are given in Spanier's *Algebraic Topology* and Switzer's *Algebraic Topology—Homotopy and Homology*. Eilenberg's and Steenrod's *Foundations of Algebraic Topology* is a classic and well worth studying. If you read German, then Seifert's and Threlfall's *Lehrbuch der Topologie* has a very geometric though somewhat old-fashioned approach to the subject which the author likes.

Go to the library and enjoy the subject!

Bibliography

Some of the books listed here were first printed by other publishers. We give the current information as often as possible.

Arnold, B. H., *Intuitive Concepts in Elementary Topology*, Prentice-Hall, Inc., Englewood Cliffs, N.J., 1962.

Dugundji, J., *Topology*, Allyn and Bacon Series in Advanced Mathematics, Allyn and Bacon, Boston, 1966.

Eilenberg, S. and Steenrod, N., *Foundations of Algebraic Topology*, Princeton Mathematical Series, No. 15, Princeton University Press, Princeton, N.J., 1952.

Glaser, Leslie C., *Geometrical Combinatorial Topology, Vol. 1*, Van Nostrand Reinhold Mathematical Studies, No. 27, Van Nostrand Reinhold Co., New York, 1970.

Greenberg, M., *Lectures on Algebraic Topology*, Mathematics Lecture Notes, No. 9, W. A. Benjamin, Inc., New York, 1966.

Hocking, J. and Young, G., *Topology*, Addison-Wesley Series in Mathematics, Addison-Wesley Publishing Company, Reading, Mass., 1961.

Hudson, J. F. P., *Piecewise Linear Topology*, Mathematics Lecture Note Series, W. A. Benjamin, New York, 1969.

Keesee, J., *An Introduction to Algebraic Topology*, Contemporary Undergraduate Mathematics Series, Brooks/Cole Publishing Company, Belmont, California, 1970.

Kelley, J. L., *General Topology*, Graduate Texts in Mathematics, Vol. 27, Springer-Verlag, New York, 1975.

259

Bibliography

Massey, W. S., *Algebraic Topology: An Introduction*, Harbrace College Mathematics Series, Harcourt, Brace and World, New York, 1967.

Maunder, C. R. F., *Algebraic Topology*, The New University Mathematics Series, Van Nostrand Reinhold Co., London, 1970.

Moise, E. E., *Geometric Topology in Dimensions 2 and 3*, Graduate Texts in Mathematics, Vol. 47, Springer-Verlag, New York, 1977.

Newman, M. H. A., *Elements of the Topology of Plane Sets of Points*, 2nd ed., Cambridge University Press, London, 1964.

Rushing, T. Benny, *Topological Embeddings*, Pure and Applied Mathematics Series, Vol. 52, Academic Press, New York, 1973.

Seifert, H. and Threlfall, W., *Lehrbuch der Topologie*, Chelsea Publishing Company, New York, 1945.

Singer, I. M. and Thorpe, J. A., *Lecture Notes on Elementary Topology and Geometry*, Scott, Foresman and Company, Glenview, Ill., 1967.

Spanier, E. H., *Algebraic Topology*, McGraw-Hill Series in Higher Mathematics, McGraw-Hill, Inc., New York, 1966.

Steenrod, N. and Chinn, W. G., *First Concepts of Topology*, New Mathematical Library, No. 18, The Mathematical Association of America, Washington, D.C., 1966.

Switzer, R. M., *Algebraic Topology—Homotopy and Homology*, Die Grundlehren der Mathematischen Wissenschaften, Vol. 212, Springer-Verlag, New York, 1975

Whyburn, G. T., *Analytic Topology*, 1963 Ed., Colloquium Publications, Vol. 28, American Mathematical Society, Providence, R.I., 1963.

Wilansky, A., *Topology for Analysis*, Ginn and Co., Waltham, Mass., 1970.

Willard, S., *General Topology*, Addison-Wesley Series in Mathematics, Addison-Wesley Publishing Company, Reading, Mass., 1970.

Index

A

Absolute extensor, 90
Absolute retract, 90
Absolute value, 255
Affine independence, 170
Alexandroff compactification, 95
Algebraic topology, 223
Arc
  definition, 124
  polygonal, 182
  of positive area, 133
Archimedean ordered field, 255
Archimedean property, 28
Arcwise connected, uniformly locally, 128
Arcwise Connectedness Theorem, 125
Area, properties of, 134
Axiom of Choice, 253

B

Baire Category Theorem, 76
Banach Fixed-Point Theorem, 141
Basic neighborhood, 10
Bijection, 250
Binary operation, 251
Bolzano−Weierstrass property, 68
Borsuk Nonretraction theorem, 154, 246
Borsuk−Ulam Theorem, 159
Bounded set, in metric space, 62
Brouwer Fixed-Point Theorem, 155

C

$C([0,1])$
  completeness of, 75
  definition, 17
  separability of, 55
Canonical neighborhoods, 240
Cantor middle-third set, 116ff
Cardinality, 251
Cartesian product,
  definition
  general, 98, 253
  for two sets, 249
Category theory, 237
Cauchy−Schwartz Inequality, 256
Cauchy sequence, 73
Chain of sets, 124ff
Classification Theorem for Surfaces, 213
Closed function
  definition, 105
  vs quotient map, 107
Closed set
  filters, relation with, 110
  in a metric space, 10
  sequences, relation with, 28, 30
  in a topological space, 15
Closure
  in metric space, 13
  in topological space, 15
Cocountable topology, 30
Cofinite topology, 16

Index

Comb space, 229 (Ex. 7)
Combinatorial manifold, 195
Compass space, 61ff
  and Bolzano−Weierstrass property, 69
  and complete space, 73, 77 (Ex. 6)
  countably, 68ff
  and filters, 113
  and finite intersection property, 112
  general products of, 114
  and Hilbert cube, 70
  homeomorphism on, 68 (Ex. 7), 85 (Ex. 11)
  locally, 69
  sequentially, 65ff
  and uniform continuity, 67
Compactification, 94ff
  Alexandroff, 95
  one-point, 95
  Stone−Cech, 115 (Ex. 7)
Complement of a set, 249
Complete metric space, 73ff
  and spaces of continuous functions, 75
Complete ordered field, 255
Completely regular space, 81, 109 (Ex. 12)
Completeness property, of real numbers, 43, 255
Completion, of a metric space, 92ff
Component, 48ff
Composition, of functions, 36, 251
Condensation point, 58 (Ex. 5)
Cone, over a space, 108
Connected space, 42ff
  intuitive definition, 4
  products of, 53 (Ex. 9)
Continuity, 33ff
  of algebraic operations, 38 (Ex. 5, 6)
  filters, relation with, 111
  in topological spaces, 39ff
  uniform, 66
Continuous nowhere differentiable function, 144
Continuous vector field, 156
Contractible space, 227
  fundamental group of, 238
  products of, 230 (Ex. 11)
Contraction mapping, 141
Convergent sequence, 27ff
Convex set, 224, 227
Countable base, 56
Countable set, 252
Countably compact space, 68ff
Countably infinite set, 252
Cover
  closed ϵ-, 118
  open, 57, 118
Covering Homotopy Theorem, 242
Covering map, 240ff
Covering space, 240ff
Cross-cap, 203

Crumpled Map Theorem, 155
Cubing-the-Blob Theorem, 167
Curve, 122
Cut point, 46
  intuitive definition, 6 (Ex. 3)
Cutting, 46

D

Decomposition, upper semicontinuous, 105
Decomposition space, 103ff
  of B^n is S^n, 107
  of R^3 containing Hilbert cube, 121
  vs quotient space, 106
Deformation retract, 227ff
De Morgan's Laws, 249
Dense set, 54
Diameter of a set, 68 (Ex. 8)
Different equations, existence of solutions, 142
Discrete metric, 9
Discrete topology, 16
Disjoint sets, 249

E

Edges of a graph, 175
Element of a set, 248
Embedding, 129ff
  flat, 130
  of graphs, 181ff
  nonflat, examples, 137
  of simplicial complex, 174 (Ex. 9)
  tame, 138ff
  wild, 138
Empty set, 248
Equivalence class, 250
Equivalence relation, 249
Euler characteristic, 217
Eulerian path, 177
Euler's Formula for the Plane, 187
Existence of maximum value theorem, 62

F

Face
  of a map, 186
  of a simplex, 171
Field, 254ff
Filter, 109ff
  ultra-, 112
Finite intersection property, 112
Finite set, 252
First countable space, 30ff, 40
Fixed point, 141, 154
  property, 154

Fixed-Point Theorem
  Banach, 141
  Brouwer, 155
Flat embedding, 130
Four Color Problem, 220
Function
  closed, 105
  continuous, 33ff
  continuous nowhere differentiable, 144
  definitions and properties, 250ff
  extension of, 88, 93
  homotopic, 224
Functor, 237
Fundamental group, 234ff
  of circle, 245
  of contractible spaces, 238
  and covering maps, 244
  of projective plane, 247 (Ex. 3)
  and retractions, 246
  of torus, 247 (Ex. 4)
Fundamental Theorem of Algebra, 168 (Ex. 7)
Fundamental Winding Number Theorem, 152

G

General topology, 2, 223
Geometric topology, 2, 223
Graph, 175ff
  embedding of, 181ff
  nonplanar, 188
  path in, 176
Group, 233
  direct sum of, 239 (Ex. 7)
  homomorphism of, 234
  isomorphism of, 234
  subgroup of, 246
GWE graph, 181
  nonplanarity of, 188

H

Hahn−Mazurkiewicz Theorem, 123
Hairy coconut theorem, 158
Half-open interval topology, 16
Ham Sandwich Theorem, 161
Handle, 203
Hausdorff space, 79
Heawood's Conjecture, 219
Heawood's Theorem, 219
Hilbert cube, 25
  compactness of, 70
  decomposition of R^3 containing, 121
  subspaces of, 88
Hole, in a surface, 203
Homeomorphism
  intuitive definition, 2

rigorous definition, 37
Homomorphism
  of groups, 234
  induced by continuous function, 236
Homotopic functions, 224
Homotopy, 224ff
  equivalence, 226
  groups, nth, 239 (Ex. 8)
  invariant, 229
  inverse, 226
  property, 229
  relative, 224

I

Identity function, 251
Implicit Function Theorem, 147 (Ex. 5, 6)
Indiscrete topology, 16
Induction, Principle of Mathematical, 251
Inner product, 255
Intermediate Value Theorem, 44
Intersection of sets, 249
Interval, closed, of real members
  compactness of, 63
  connectedness of, 43
  continuous image of, 123
Invariance of Domain Theorem, 130
Isometry, 91
Isomorphism of fundamental groups, 234ff

J

Jordan−Brouwer Separation Theorem, 138
Jordan Curve Theorem, 184

K

K_5 graph, 181
  nonplanarity of, 188
Kakutani's Theorem, 164
Knot, 139
Königsberg Bridge Problem, 177

L

Least upper bound, 250
Lift, of a function, 242ff
Limit point, 13
  filters, relation with, 110
  in a topological space, 15
Lindelof Covering Theorem, 57
Lindelof space, 58ff
Linear order, 250
Link, of a vertex, 195
Localization of properties, 50
Locally compact space, 69ff
Locally connected space, 51ff

Locally connected space [cont.]
  and quotient maps, 52
Loop, 231

M

Manifold, 140 (Ex. 13)
  combinatorial, 195
Map
  coloring of, 219
  in the plane, 186ff
  on a surface, 214
Metric
  definition, 8
  discrete, 9
  euclidean, 9
Metric space, definition, 8
Metrizable space, 87
Minimal element, 250
Möbius strip, 199

N

N-ball, 130
N-od, 156 (Ex. 9)
N-sphere, 46, 130
Neighborhood
  basic, 10
  canonical, 240
  of a subset, 78
  in topological space, 15
Neighborhood filter, 110
Network, 214
Noncut point, 46
Nonretraction Theorem, 154, 246
Norm, 255
Normal space, 82ff
Nowhere dense set, 76
Nth homotopy group, 239 (Ex. 8)

O

One-point compactification, 95
One-to-one function, 250
Onto function, 250
Open-and-closed sets, 118
Open cover, 57
Open set
  in a metric space, 10
  in a topological space, 15
Open subcover, 57
Order
  linear, 250
  partial, 250
Ordered field, 254

Ordered n-tuple, 249
Ordered pair, 249

P

Partial order, 250
Pasting Lemma, 225
Path-connected, definition, 229 (Ex. 5)
Path
  binary operation on, 230
  definition, in a space, 225
  Eulerian, 177
  in a graph, 176ff
  inverse of, 233
Peano space, 123
  is continuous image of interval, 128
Perfect space, 117
  vs countable space, 122 (Ex. 10)
Picard's Existence Theorem for Differential
    Equations, 142
Planar map, 186ff
Polygonal arc, 182 '
Polygonal simple closed curve, 183
Polyhedron, 172
Polytope, 188
Principle of Mathematical Induction, 251
Product space
  continuous functions on, 98
  definition in general, 98
  of n metric spaces, 19ff
  of n topological spaces, 23ff
  preservation of properties, 100
Product topology, 23, 98
Projective plane, 201, 241
  fundamental group of, 247 (Ex. 3)
Punctured plane, 150

Q

Quotient map, 52, 106
  and closed map, 107
  and locally connected spaces, 52
Quotient space, 106

R

Regular polytope, 188
Regular space, 80
Relations, and their properties, 249ff
Restriction, of a function, 250
Retract, 90, 154, 246
Retraction, 90, 154, 246

S

Schoenflies' Theorem, 136
Second countable space, 56

Separable space, 54ff
$C([0,1])$, 55
sequentially compact metric, 65
Separated sets, 44
Separation axioms, 78ff
and compact spaces, 84
completely regular, 81
and metric spaces, 83
normal, 82
regular, 80
T_1, 78
T_2, 79
T_3, 80
T_4, 82
Tychonoff, 81
Sequence in a space, 26ff
Sequentially compact space, 65
vs countably compact, 69
Sets and their properties, 248ff
Simple closed curve, 183
Simplex, 171
Simplicial complex, 172ff
connected, 174 (Ex. 4)
embedding of, 174 (Ex. 9)
isomorphic, 174 (Ex. 8)
r-skeleton of, 174 (Ex. 5)
Simply connected space, 236
S^n, 46, 130
Sorgenfrey line, 16, 40, 52, 59, 69
Sorgenfrey plane, 23, 59
Space
metric, 8
of bounded real functions, 9
of continuous functions, 74ff
of continuous functions on [0,1], 17, 55, 75
topological, 15
Stone−Cech compactification, 115 (Ex. 7)
Sub-Cantor set, 117
Subdivision of [0,1], 150
Subgroup, 246
Subsequence, 64
Subset, 248
Subspace
of a metric space, 17
of a topological space, 22
Subspace topology, 22
Surface, 194ff
classification of, 213
compact, 196
connected, 196
cross-cap in, 203
handle in, 203
hole in, 203
nonorientable, 213
orientable, 213

triangulation theorem for, 196
Suspension of a space, 108

T

T_1 space, 78
T_2 space, 79
T_3 space, 80
T_4 space, 82
Tame embedding, 138
Theorem on Regular Polytopes, 190
Tietze's Extension Theorem, 88
Topological property
intuitive definition, 3
rigorous definition, 37
Topological space, 15
Topologist's sine curve, 51
Topology
cocountable, 30
cofinite, 16
discrete, 16
half-open interval, 16
indiscrete, 16
of a metric space, 12
product, 23, 98
on a set, 15
subspace, 22
Torus, 20, 247
fundamental group of, 247 (Ex. 4)
Totally bounded metric space, 77 (Ex. 6)
Totally disconnected space, 117
vs Cantor middle-third set, 122 (Ex. 9)
Tree, 191 (Ex. 9)
Triangle inequality, 8, 256
Triangulable space, 172
Triangulation, 172
Triangulation Theorem for Surfaces, 196
Tychonoff space, 81
locally compact T_2, 97
vs subsets of products of intervals, 109 (Ex. 12)
Tychonoff's Theorem, 114

U

Uncountable set, 252
Uniform Boundedness Theorem, 146 (Ex. 3)
Uniformly continuous function, 66ff
extension of, 93
Uniformly locally arcwise connected, 128
Union, of sets, 249
Ultrafilter, 112ff
Upper bound, 250
Upper semicontinuous decomposition, 105
Urysohn's Lemma, 86

Index

Urysohn's Metrization Theorem, 87
Utilities Problem, 181

V

Vector field, 156
Vector Field Theorem for S^2, 157
Vectors, 255
Vertex, 171
  link of, 195
  order of, in a graph, 176
Volume, properties of, 161

W

Weather Theorem, 161
Width, of a set, 166
Wild embedding, 138
Winding number, 150
  fundamental theorem, 152

Z

Zorn's Lemma, 113, 254